periodic table of the elements

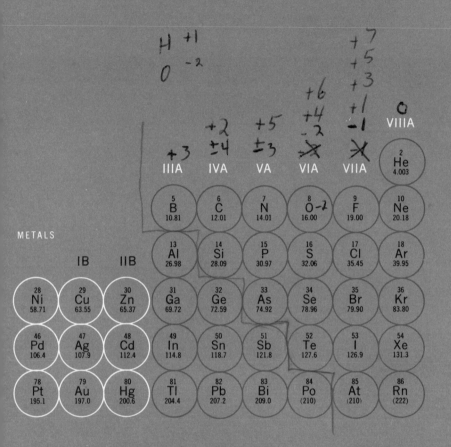

College Chemistry

SCOTT, FORESMAN AND COMPANY

College Chemistry

Leo H. Spinar   *South Dakota State University*

acknowledgments

ALUMINUM COMPANY OF AMERICA.
(*Fig. 17.2, p. 309*) Sample of gallium metal.

AMERICAN CHEMICAL SOCIETY AND DR. LINUS PAULING.
(*Fig. 4.5, p. 68; Fig. 18.1, p. 320*) Data reprinted from
Journal of the American Chemical Society, 69 (*1947*), p. 544.
Copyright 1947 by the American Chemical Society.
Reprinted by permission of the author and the American Chemical Society.

AMERICAN PETROLEUM INSTITUTE.
(*Table 19.3, p. 352; Table 19.4, p. 353*) Data reprinted from
"*Selected Values of Properties of Hydrocarbons and Related Compounds,*"
American Petroleum Institute Research Project 44,
Thermodynamics Research Center, Texas A & M University,
College Station, Texas (*Loose-leaf data sheets, extant, 1968*).

ARGONNE NATIONAL LABORATORY.
(*Fig. 9.2, p. 180*) Crystals of xenon tetrafluoride.

BLAISDELL PUBLISHING COMPANY.
(*Fig. 7.19, p. 144*) Reprinted by permission of
the publisher from Bodie E. Douglas and Darl H. McDaniel,
Concepts and Models of Inorganic Chemistry
(*Waltham, Massachusetts: Blaisdell Publishing Company,
A Division of Ginn and Company, 1965*), p. 288.

BLAISDELL PUBLISHING COMPANY AND AMERICAN INSTITUTE OF PHYSICS.
(*Table 13.2, p. 261*) Based on data from
Bodie E. Douglas and Darl H. McDaniel,
Concepts and Models of Inorganic Chemistry
(*Waltham, Massachusetts: Blaisdell Publishing Company,
A Division of Ginn and Company, 1965*), p. 116.
Originally published in D. J. Cubicciotti,
Journal of Chemical Physics, 31:1646 (*1959*); 34:2189 (*1961*),
used by permission of the author and
the American Institute of Physics. Data on electron affinities originally published
in R. S. Berry and C. W. Riemann,
Journal of Chemical Physics, 38:1540 (*1963*),
used by permission of the authors and the American Institute of Physics.

THE BETTMANN ARCHIVE.
  (*Fig. 2.10, p. 29*) *Henry Cavendish.*

CHEMICAL AND ENGINEERING NEWS.
  (*Fig. 8.12, p. 168*) *Based on data from* L. B. Asprey and
  R. A. Penneman, Chemical and Engineering News, *July 31, 1967,*
  pp. 75–90. Reproduced by permission.

THE CHEMICAL RUBBER COMPANY.
  (*Melting points, boiling points, densities, ionization potentials,*
  oxidation potentials, solubility values for selected substances)
  Reproduced by permission from
  CRC Handbook of Physics and Chemistry, *47th edition,*
  section source B-149ff, D-84ff, B-149ff, D-101, E-65.

CORNELL UNIVERSITY PRESS.
  (*Table 10.2, p. 189; Table 10.3, p. 190; Table 10.4, p. 190;*
  Table 13.2, p. 261; Table 18.1, p. 320; Fig. 4.5, p. 68;
  Fig. 7.2, p. 131; Fig. 7.6, p. 135)
  Data from Linus Pauling, The Nature of the Chemical Bond, *3rd ed.,*
  (Ithaca: Cornell University Press, 1960), pp. 93, 405, 514.
  Copyright 1939 and 1940 by Cornell University Press.
  Third edition © *1960 by Cornell University.*
  Used by permission of Cornell University Press.

CULVER PICTURES, INC.
  (*Fig. 2.9, p. 29*) *Robert Boyle;* (*Fig. 4.2, p. 65*) *Dmitri Mendeleev;*
  (*Fig. 8.1, p. 148*) *Antoine Henri Becquerel.*

DANISH INFORMATION OFFICE.
  (*Fig. 6.11, p. 111*) *Niels Bohr.*

DOW CHEMICAL COMPANY.
  (*Fig. 10.2, p. 188*) *Settling basins;*
  (*Fig. 10.3, p. 189*) *Sample of cesium metal.*

E. I. DUPONT DE NEMOURS & CO., INC.
  (*Table 13.3, p. 265*) *Reproduced by permission from*
  Freon Technical Bulletin. *Copyright 1966 by*
  E. I. duPont de Nemours & Co., Inc.

ELSEVIER PUBLISHING COMPANY.
  (*Fig. 18.6, p. 334; inside back cover*) *Relative abundance data*
  reproduced with permission from H. Remy,
  Treatise on Inorganic Chemistry, *Vol. II*
  (*Amsterdam: Elsevier Publishing Company, 1956.*)

THE FORD MOTOR COMPANY.
  (*Fig. 12.9, p. 250*) *From* Chemical and Engineering News,
  October 24, 1965, p. 55. Redrawn by permission of the Ford Motor Company.

GENERAL ELECTRIC COMPANY.
  (*Table 8.1, p. 153; Table 8.2, p. 154, Table 8.4, p. 166*)
  Data reprinted from D. T. Goldman and R. J. Roesser,
  G.E. Chart of Nuclides, *by permission of Knolls Atomic Power Laboratory,*
  Schenectady, New York. Operated by the General Electric Company
  for the United States Atomic Energy Commission.

GENERAL ELECTRIC RESEARCH AND DEVELOPMENT CENTER.
  (*Fig. 17.4, p. 313*) *Cubic boron nitride crystals.*

HISTORICAL PICTURE SERVICE-CHICAGO.

(Fig. 2.6, p. 25) Joseph Priestley; (Fig. 2.7, p. 25) Antoine Lavoisier;
(Fig. 6.2, p. 105) Aristotle.

HOLT, RINEHART & WINSTON, INC.

(Table 11.2, p. 216; Table 11.3, p. 223)
Adapted from T. R. Hogness and W. C. Johnson,
Qualitative Analysis and Chemical Equilibrium, *4th ed.,*
Tables 50 and 51. Copyright 1937, 1940,
1946, 1954, © 1965 by T. R. Hogness
and W. C. Johnson. Adapted and reproduced
by permission of Holt, Rinehart & Winston, Inc.
(Fig. 18.1, p. 320) Data on ionic radii
from Edwin S. Gould, Inorganic Reactions and Structures,
Appendix II, p. 492. Copyright © 1955, 1962 by
Holt, Rinehart & Winston, Inc.
Reproduced by permission of Holt, Rinehart & Winston, Inc.

A. LEITNER, MICHIGAN STATE UNIVERSITY.

(Fig. 9.1, p. 179) Behavior of liquid helium.

THE MACMILLAN COMPANY.

(Table 10.6, p. 198; Table 13.4, p. 267)
Data reproduced by permission from W. Latimer and J. Hildebrand,
Reference Book of Chemistry, *Third Edition.*
Copyright © 1951 by The Macmillan Company.

THE MATHESON COMPANY, INC.

(Table 9.1, p. 178; Table 13.2, p. 261; Table 15.4, p. 289)
Data on physical properties of ammonia and density values
for halogens and noble gases reproduced by permission from
Matheson Gas Data Book *(East Rutherford, New Jersey:*
The Matheson Company, Inc., 1961), pp. 11, 19.

PRINCETON UNIVERSITY.

(Fig. 9.4, p. 181) Neil Bartlett.
Reproduced courtesy of Princeton University.

REINHOLD PUBLISHING CORPORATION.

(Fig. 4.3, p. 66; Fig. 7.2, p. 131) Selected data
reproduced from R. T. Sanderson, Chemical Periodicity
(New York: Reinhold Publishing Corporation, 1960), p. 2.

THE ROYAL SOCIETY OF LONDON.

(Fig. 6.3, p. 105) John Dalton;
(Fig. 6.10, p. 111) Lord Ernest Rutherford;
(Fig. 10.1, p. 186) Sir Humphry Davy.
Copyright by The Royal Society of London.

SPENCER COLLECTION OF THE NEW YORK PUBLIC LIBRARY;
Astor, Lenox, and Tilden Foundations.
(p. 2) The alchemist. Reproduced courtesy of
Spencer Collection of the New York Public Library;
Astor, Lenox, and Tilden Foundations.

U.S. DEPARTMENT OF THE INTERIOR, GEOLOGICAL SURVEY.

(Fig. 16.2, right, p. 302) Quartz crystal.

JOHN H. WILEY & SONS, INC.

(Fig. 18.1, p. 320) Data on metallic radii from R. W. G. Wyckoff,
Crystals Structures *(New York: John H. Wiley & Sons, Inc., 1948),*
Table II-10, p. II-14. Copyright © 1948, Wiley Interscience, Vol. I.

*to my parents,
Jerry and Emma Spinar,
who have always
encouraged me*

preface

My goal in this text is to develop an understanding of chemistry on the part of the undergraduate who does not plan to major in chemistry. Such an understanding requires some acquaintance with factual material, an insight into the methods of the chemist, and comprehension of some basic concepts.

I have been guided by three premises in writing this text. First, chemistry is not an isolated study; rather it is a dynamic discipline, one that can be set into a historical perspective. Thus many references are made to historical events and dates. Secondly, the mathematical preparation of the student is high-school algebra. A brief review of the principles needed for the text is given in Appendix I. The third premise is that the student has had no previous experience in high-school chemistry or physics. For this reason, chemistry is introduced by a study of water after an introductory chapter on measurements. The concepts of molecules, atoms, and atomic structure are then developed from the behavior of gases. These concepts serve as the foundation for the material in the succeeding chapters.

Because of space limitations, the topics and the extent of their development have been subjectively selected on the basis of their contribution to my goal. A student whose interest in a particular topic goes beyond the discussion in the text will find many paperbound monographs available. Instructors have a large degree of flexibility as to the topics they choose to develop. The topics are put into a perspective by the text material. Many instructors may want to supplement the text framework with selected monographs.

I have tried to intersperse descriptive material with the more theoretical to provide an opportunity for the student to assimilate one set of concepts before being faced with another. I have limited the discussion of descriptive chemistry to the more important compounds of the elements with the emphasis upon the trends in properties. Chapter XIX provides a brief introduction to organic chemistry, involving recognition of structures, basic nomenclature, and a few of the more important type reactions. Chapter XX is a concise introduction to the very important, but complex, area of biochemistry.

Since the material in each chapter builds upon that in the earlier chapters, the student should develop habits of daily study to assimilate topics as they are presented. The worked examples should be followed to gain an understanding of the principles involved. The comprehension of the principles presented in each chapter is tested and strengthened by the list of significant terms and concepts, the review questions, and the problems. The index is a useful tool to review forgotten terms and concepts; most terms are defined the first time they are used.

This text represents the results of over ten years of teaching general chemistry and reflects the reactions of approximately three hundred students who used a trial edition at the University of Missouri as well as the suggestions of reviewers and friends.

While only one name appears as the author, there are many who have aided in transforming an idea into a finished product. Space does not permit adequate recognition of everyone who has helped. However, the contributions of Dr. Richard Fenske, University of Wisconsin, and Susan Hastings to this final product must receive a special note of recognition and gratitude.

LEO H. SPINAR
Brookings, South Dakota

contents

introduction to the study of chemistry

one

Introduction

This old woodcut of an alchemist holding his nose is too often the stereotype of the chemist. If foul odors were all there is to chemistry, the science would never have grown to its present importance. There is much more in chemistry—an understanding of the physical world about us. No longer does the chemist simply boil and mix at random, he uses sophisticated instruments to seek new knowledge. With this knowledge he is able to fabricate the plastics, the synthetic fibers, the rocket fuels, the nose cones, and the hundred and one other items that make up today's civilization.

These items are end products of the chemist's efforts. Behind all of them is a set of laws and theories without which it would not be possible to produce these embellishments of modern life. Within the limits of this book, we will introduce some of the basic principles of chemistry as well as the methodology of the scientist.

Chemistry is the sum total of knowledge that has accumulated from a systematic study of the composition and interactions of matter. It is a dynamic science, constantly changing as new information is discovered. This does not mean that the behavior of matter is changing. Rather, the techniques of measurement are constantly being improved. As more accurate data become available, interpretations change. During our studies facts, which do not change, should be distinguished from their meaning, which is subject to change.

For some people, the facts of chemistry and their interpretation is a vital part of their vocation. For everyone, the world in which we live takes on a new and richer significance from a study of chemistry. The topics discussed in the following pages serve as a foundation for a lifelong education process in an era of intense scientific development.

The development of chemistry

Man's first attempts to manipulate and experiment with the materials around him are lost in prehistory. It is known that ancient people extracted copper from its ores as far back as 5000 b.c. Iron weapons were forged by peoples living in Asia Minor during the fourteenth century b.c. Gold, silver, tin, and lead were in use more than 4000 years ago. The ancient peoples knew how to prepare dyes and inks, salts, and crude sugars. They also fabricated bricks, ceramics, and glass.

During the medieval period, the study of materials continued with the work of the alchemists. Little progress took place, as the alchemists put most of their efforts into fruitless searches for ways to turn metal into gold. Much of their work was done in secrecy to avoid persecution and also to maintain a monopoly of any process they developed. Many of the alchemists may have learned a great deal about the nature of the materials they studied.

However, their records were written in codes, and most of the few which remain are indecipherable.

Gradually, as the Renaissance and the new learning spread, the study and manipulation of materials developed on a more systematic basis. Men began to apply scientific principles of observation and experimentation. Despite such advances, chemistry lagged behind biology, physics, and astronomy. Much more progress was made in technology. It was not until the eighteenth century that the study of materials, their composition and interactions, became established firmly as the science of chemistry. Several fundamental concepts of modern chemistry were developed during this time.

Progress since then has been rapid. Chemists have branched into a number of different specialties—inorganic chemistry, organic chemistry, analytic chemistry, biochemistry, and physical chemistry, to name the major areas of research. In technological fields chemists have made numerous contributions such as synthetic fibers, plastics, drugs, and thousands of products essential to modern life. Today, chemistry is joined to a great extent with biology and physics as scientists probe the nature of the atom and the fundamental processes of life.

Matter

The chemist is concerned with matter and its behavior. Although matter can be recognized intuitively, it is difficult to formulate a meaningful basic definition. Matter is anything that has mass and occupies space. Matter usually is described in terms of its properties or characteristic qualities. In one mode of classification, these properties may be divided into two categories. Properties may be *intensive* or *extensive*. Intensive properties are independent of the amount of matter and are the same for every sample of a single substance. Extensive properties vary from sample to sample and are dependent upon the amount of matter in the sample. Both mass and volume are extensive properties. Thus, the mass of a gallon of water is four times that of a quart. Experimentally determined values of extensive properties may be combined for conversion to intensive property values which are useful for the comparison of different samples and for the development of theories. For example, the ratio of mass to volume (pounds per gallon) is an intensive property. Color is an example of an intensive property which is not related to any extensive property.

Measurements in chemistry

Unbiased observation and recording of events are crucial to the development of any science. Usually the chemist makes his observations in the course of an experiment carried out in the laboratory. Once several observations of a phenomenon have been made, the researcher sets forth a *hypothesis* to explain them. The

see P.417

hypothesis is tested further in a series of specially designed experiments, modified as dictated by the results of these tests, and developed into a *theory*. If it is possible to state the theory mathematically or prove it to be true beyond doubt, the theory becomes a *law*. At all times, the scientist must keep an open mind and be ready to modify or drop any theory or hypothesis in light of new data. It is also necessary to recognize the limitations placed upon the theory or law by the way in which the data were obtained.

Careful, quantitative measurements are needed for the formulation of theories and laws as well as the description of the properties of a substance. The metric system of measurement is used in most scientific work.

The metric system

The metric system was developed in France during the latter part of the eighteenth century to bring order out of chaos. At the time, almost every village and town had its own system. The French government decided upon a scientific basis for the new system whereby the standards could be reproduced whenever desired and could be rechecked easily. Rapid adoption of the metric system took place throughout most of Europe. One feature of the metric system is the use of multiples and submultiples of ten as prefixes to the basic unit of measurement, which simplifies the mathematical manipulation of the units and their multiples.

Table 1.1
Decimal Prefixes and Decimal Relationships

Prefix	Abbreviation	Factor by which each unit is multiplied		
pico	p	1×10^{-12}	OR	0.000 000 000 001
nano	n	1×10^{-9}		0.000 000 001
micro	μ	1×10^{-6}		0.000 001
milli	m	1×10^{-3}		0.001
centi	c	1×10^{-2}		0.01
deci	d	1×10^{-1}		0.1
deka	da	1×10^{1}		10.
kilo	k	1×10^{3}		1000.
mega	M	1×10^{6}		1 000 000.

Common Decimal Relationships in the Metric System of Measurement

1 meter (m) = 100 centimeters (cm) = 1000 millimeters (mm)
1 kilometer (km) = 1000 meters (m)
1 liter (l) = 1000 milliliters (ml) = 1000 cubic centimeters (cm^3 or cc)
1 gram (g) = 1000 milligrams (mg) = 1×10^{6} micrograms (μg)
1 kilogram (kg) = 1000 grams (g)

The primary standard of length in the metric system is the *meter* which originally was defined as 1/10,000,000 of the quadrant of the earth's meridian that passes through Paris and the North and South Poles. Later, refinements of the measuring technique showed the original work to be in error. The meter then was defined as the distance between two lines on a platinum-iridium

Fig. 1.1

Comparative Sizes of Units of Weights and Measures in the Metric and U.S. Systems. (See Appendix Table II for extensive list of equivalents.)

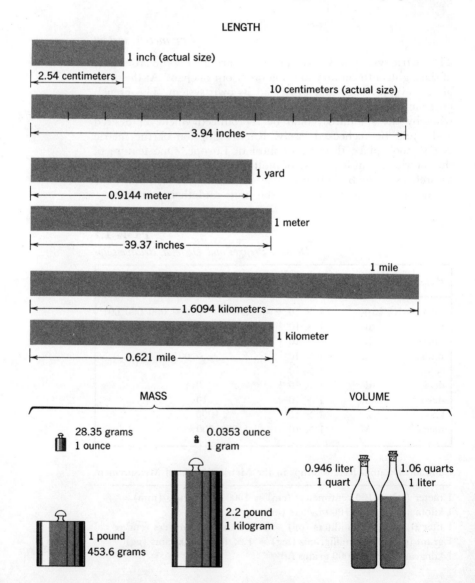

LENGTH

1 inch (actual size)

2.54 centimeters

10 centimeters (actual size)

3.94 inches

1 yard

0.9144 meter

1 meter

39.37 inches

1 mile

1.6094 kilometers

1 kilometer

0.621 mile

MASS

28.35 grams
1 ounce

0.0353 ounce
1 gram

2.2 pound
1 kilogram

1 pound
453.6 grams

VOLUME

0.946 liter
1 quart

1.06 quarts
1 liter

bar kept at 0°C in the International Bureau of Weights and Measures in Paris. Many countries keep secondary standards of length that are compared to the International Prototype Meter.

Several problems arise from the use of a single bar as an international definition of a primary standard. The bar could not be duplicated exactly, if it were lost in some disaster. It is subject to change as its environment changes, although every attempt is made to keep the surroundings constant. It is not available for use in a laboratory, where accurate length measurement is essential. For these reasons the International Meter was redefined as being 1,650,763.73 times the orange-red wavelength of light emitted by a unique type of krypton atom known as krypton-86. This is no significant change in the length of the meter, but the new definition makes it possible to reproduce the International Meter in any laboratory with appropriate equipment. However, the Prototype Meter still is used as an important reference.

The centimeter (cm), 1/100 of a meter, is a useful unit of measurement in the chemistry laboratory, since many length measurements are in this range. Two subdivisions of length measurement have been given unique names. These are the angstrom (Å) which is 10^{-8} cm and the micron (μ) which is 10^{-6} m.

MEASUREMENT OF MASS

The metric unit of mass is the *gram* which is 1/1000 of the mass of a particular cylinder of platinum-iridium alloy, called the International Prototype Kilogram, preserved by the International Bureau of Weights and Measures. There is an important distinction to be made between mass and weight. Mass is a measure of the quantity of matter. Weight is a measure of the gravitational attraction of the mass. Thus, the weight of a given mass varies with gravitational attraction. Since gravity does not vary greatly from place to place on the earth, it is convenient to make weight measurements in terms of mass units. In other words, a weight given as one gram is really the gravitational attraction of a mass of one gram.

MEASUREMENT OF VOLUME

Volume in the metric system is measured in *liters.* The liter now is defined as being exactly 1000 cubic centimeters (cc or cm³). The milliliter (ml) is a convenient unit of volume in chemistry. The liter may be approximated as the volume occupied by 1000 grams of water.

MEASUREMENT OF TIME

The basic unit of time in both the metric and the U.S. System is the *second,* the 1/86,400 part of the mean solar day.

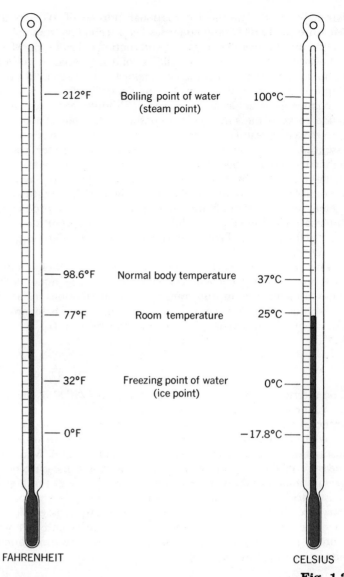

212°F   Boiling point of water   100°C
         (steam point)

98.6°F   Normal body temperature   37°C

77°F   Room temperature   25°C

32°F   Freezing point of water   0°C
         (ice point)

0°F   −17.8°C

FAHRENHEIT   CELSIUS

Fig. 1.2

*Comparison of Celsius and Fahrenheit Temperature Scales. The points
on each thermometer represent the same temperature.*

Energy measurement

Energy is defined as the ability to do work. There are several
varieties of energy. Electrical energy, kinetic energy, potential
energy, chemical energy, and heat energy are among the common types. It is possible to convert one type of energy into
another. For example, electrical energy is converted to heat

energy when an electric current passes through a resistance wire such as that found in a toaster.

Heat energy and temperature are closely related. Temperature is a quantitative measure of how hot an object is with respect to some other object which has a known, assigned value. The values on a scale of temperatures depend upon the numbers assigned to the base or reference points. Any process that occurs at a constant temperature may be used as a reference point for a temperature scale. Two easily reproduced processes that are used to determine several of the temperature scales are the ice point and steam point. The ice point is the temperature at which water begins to freeze or ice begins to melt. The steam point is the temperature at which water boils under standard atmospheric pressure. Once numbers are assigned to these two points, the size of a degree is fixed and the scale may be continued to temperatures above and below these reference points.

The Fahrenheit scale of temperatures, designated by °F, is in common usage in the United States. The ice point is fixed at 32°F and the steam point at 212°F. Thus, there are 180 Fahrenheit degrees between the boiling and freezing points of water.

The Celsius temperature scale, designated by °C, is used in most scientific work. The ice point is set at 0°C and the steam point at 100°C. The Celsius degree is larger than the Fahrenheit degree, since there are 180 Fahrenheit degrees compared to only 100 Celsius degrees between the ice point and steam point. The Celsius degree is 180/100 or 9/5 larger than the Fahrenheit degree. Thus, there are 5/9 as many Celsius degrees as Fahrenheit degrees in a given temperature range.

This fact is used to convert temperatures measured on one scale to equivalent temperatures on the other. For example, the number of Fahrenheit degrees above (or below) the ice point (32°F) is multiplied by 5/9 to obtain the number of Celsius degrees above (or below) the ice point (0°C).

Number of Celsius degrees above 0°C = 5/9 (number of Fahrenheit degrees above 32°F)

$$t°C - 0°C = 5/9 \ (t°F - 32°F)$$
$$t°C = 5/9 \ (t°F - 32°F)$$

Any two equivalent temperatures could be used as the starting point. The use of 0°C simplifies the left-hand side of the above equation.

Example 1.1 One of the coldest temperatures reported is that of $-93°F$. What would be the reading on a Celsius thermometer?

$$t°C = 5/9 \ (-93 - 32) = 5/9 \ (-125)$$
$$= -69.4°C$$

Example 1.2 The melting point of zinc is 409.5°C. What is the corresponding Fahrenheit reading?

$$409.5°C = 5/9 \ (t°F - 32)$$

Multiplying both sides of the equation by 9/5, we have

$$9/5(409.5) = (9/5)(5/9)(t°F - 32)$$
$$(9/5)(409.5) = t°F - 32$$
$$t°F = 9/5(409.5) + 32 = 737.1 + 32$$
$$= 769°F$$

The amount of heat required to change the temperature of an object by one degree is an extensive property. The related intensive property is the *specific heat* which is the heat energy required to raise the temperature of a unit mass of a substance by one degree.

Heat energy is measured in terms of *calories* or *British Thermal Units* (BTU). The calorie is the usual choice of the chemist. It may be defined in many ways. The most understandable definition at this point is that one calorie is the heat required to raise the temperature of one gram of water from 14.5° to 15.5°C. This is called the fifteen-degree calorie. For most purposes in this text it is permissible to use the approximation that the specific heat of water is one calorie per gram per degree throughout its liquid range. The specific heat of water is relatively large as seen from Table 1.2.

Example 1.3 How much heat would be required to heat 600 grams of water from 23°C to the boiling point?

Heat required = (specific heat)(weight)(temperature change)
= (1 cal/g-deg)(600 g)(100° − 23°)
= 46,200 cal
= 46.2 kcal

Density

Two of the easily measured extensive properties of matter are mass and volume. These are converted to an intensive property, density, by taking the ratio of mass to volume. In equation form,

Table 1.2

Specific Heat of Selected Materials at Room Temperatures

Substance	Specific heat (cal/g-deg)	Substance	Specific heat (cal/g-deg)
water	1.00	common salt	0.21
alcohol	0.58	glass	0.20
wood	0.42	granite	0.19
naphthalene	0.31	iron	0.11
sodium	0.29	copper	0.092
magnesium	0.24	mercury	0.033
clay	0.22	lead	0.031
aluminum	0.22		

$$D = \frac{M}{V},$$

where M is the mass expressed in grams, V is the volume expressed in liters, milliliters, or cubic centimeters, and D is the density. The usual density units are g/cc for solids, g/ml for liquids, and g/l for gases. The densities of several substances chosen to illustrate the wide range of density values are given in Table 1.3.

Table 1.3

Densities of Selected Substances Near Room Temperatures

Liquids		Solids		Gases	
mercury	13.53 g/ml	gold	19.3 g/cc	carbon dioxide	1.80 g/l
bromine	3.12 g/ml	uranium	19.0 g/cc	oxygen	1.43 g/l
water	1.00 g/ml	lead	11.3 g/cc	air	1.17 g/l
olive oil	0.92 g/ml	iron	7.86 g/cc	methane	0.66 g/l
turpentine	0.87 g/ml	granite	2.6–2.8 g/cc	helium	0.16 g/l
alcohol	0.79 g/ml	glass	2.2–2.5 g/cc	hydrogen	0.082 g/l
ether	0.74 g/ml	rock salt	2.2 g/cc		
gasoline	0.7 g/ml	bone	1.7–2.0 g/cc		
		sugar	1.59 g/cc		
		wood, oak	0.60–0.90 g/cc		
		wood, pine	0.35–0.50 g/cc		
		wood, balsa	0.11–0.14 g/cc		

Example 1.4 What is the volume of 1.00 kg of iron?

$$D = \frac{M}{V}$$

From Table 1.3, $D = 7.86$ g/cc for iron

$$7.86 \text{ g/cc} = \frac{1000 \text{ g}}{V}$$

$$V = (1000 \text{ g}) \frac{(1 \text{ cc})}{(7.86 \text{ g})}$$

$$= 127 \text{ cc}$$

Example 1.5 What is the mass of a cube of uranium measuring 1.00 inch on a side?

$$D = \frac{M}{V}$$

From Table 1.3, $D = 19.0$ g/cc. It is necessary to calculate the volume which is not given directly in the problem.

Volume of cube = (length of a side)³

$$V = (1.00 \text{ inch})\left(\frac{2.54 \text{ cm}}{1 \text{ inch}}\right)^3$$

$$= (2.54 \text{ cm})^3$$

$$= 16.4 \text{ cm}^3 = 16.4 \text{ cc}$$

$$19.05 \text{ g/cc} = \frac{M}{16.4 \text{ cc}}$$

$$M = \frac{(19.05 \text{ g})}{1 \text{ cc}}(16.4 \text{ cc})$$

$$= 312 \text{ g}$$

Atmospheric pressure

The fact that the atmosphere has mass is illustrated by an experiment first performed by Evangelista Torricelli in the early part of the seventeenth century. If a tube closed on one end is filled with mercury, and the open end is placed below the surface of a mercury pool, the level of the mercury in the tube falls to about 30 inches above the pool surface. This effect is observed with all tubes, except those with extremely small diameters and of lengths less than 30 inches.

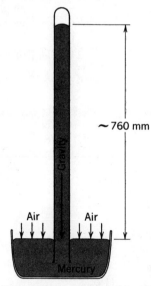

Fig. 1.3

Torricellian Barometer. The force of air pushing down on the pool of mercury outside the tube causes the mercury within to rise until the force on the liquid column is equal to the force exerted by the atmosphere. The height of the column fluctuates around 760 mm (30 in.) near sea level. A pressure of one standard atmosphere supports a mercury column 760 mm high.

The explanation of this phenomenon is aided by reference to the diagram in Fig. 1.3. Since the atmosphere has mass, it is pulled down by the earth's gravitational force. Atmospheric weight is a force exerted uniformly over the surface of the mercury pool. When the tube is inserted into the pool, the weight of the atmosphere is exerted against the closed end of the glass tube rather than against that portion of the pool surface. The mercury inside the tube also is attracted by gravity and exerts a force on the pool under the tube. If the force per unit-cross-sectional area exerted by the mercury column is greater than the force per unit area exerted by the atmosphere on the pool surface outside the tube, the column height drops until the two forces are equal. If the force per unit area exerted by the atmosphere is greater than that exerted by the mercury column, the column height rises until the forces are equal. Thus, the height of the mercury column above the pool surface is a measure of the force per unit area exerted by the atmosphere. This force per unit area is called the *atmospheric pressure.*

Torricelli unknowingly invented the first device, a barometer, to measure atmospheric pressure. Barometers based on other properties, such as the deformation of a metal diaphragm, electrical resistance changes, or electrical current changes, have been developed and often are calibrated to give readings in terms of the height of a mercury column.

Any gas exerts a force against the walls of its container. This force per unit area (e.g., pounds per square inch or g/cm^2) is the pressure exerted by the gas. Gas pressures as well as atmospheric pressures are expressed not only in terms of force per unit area but often in terms of the height of a column of mercury supported by the gas pressure. In the metric system, this expression commonly has been in terms of millimeters of mercury (mm Hg).

Recently the *torr*, named in honor of Torricelli, was adopted as the preferred unit of pressure measurement. The torr is defined as the pressure of a gas that supports a column of mercury one millimeter in height. Since the torr and mm Hg are essentially equal, one standard atmosphere (atm) is equal to 760 torr.

Notes on problem solving

Quantitative calculations aid in the understanding of many chemical principles. There should be little reliance upon memorized formulas in the solution of a problem. Rather, the problem should be read carefully to determine what information is asked for and what data are given. This should be followed by a logical stepwise procedure from data to answer. Each step should be expressed in terms of an equation. The factor-unit method is useful in this process. In this method the equation is set up using units as well as numbers in each factor. The mathematical operations first are carried out with the units. If the final answer has the desired units, numerical operations are carried out. An orderly arrangement of work aids in the problem-solving process.

The use of exponential numbers and significant figures reduces the complexity of the arithmetical operations, thereby aiding in the understanding of the problem. Exponential numbers and significant figures, along with some other basic mathematical operations, are reviewed in Appendix I.

SIGNIFICANT TERMS AND CONCEPTS IN CHAPTER I:

Extensive and intensive properties, theory and law, metric system of weights and measures, meter, micron, Angstrom, gram, liter, cubic centimeter, mass, weight, energy, Celsius and Fahrenheit temperature scales, specific heat, calorie, density, barometer, atmospheric pressure, torr, standard atmosphere, factor-unit method.

Review questions

1.1. List 4 intensive and 4 extensive properties of matter that are not discussed in the section on Matter.

1.2. List two advantages of the U.S. system of weights and measures and two advantages of the metric system.

1.3. Distinguish between the terms: temperature, heat, and specific heat.

1.4. Give one advantage of the Celsius temperature scale over the Fahrenheit scale.

1.5. Give the basic unit of the U.S. and metric systems for the measurement of: (a) length, (b) mass, (c) volume, (d) time, (e) heat energy, (f) density, (g) gas pressure.

Problems

1.6. Make the indicated conversions:
   (a) 10 cm = _____ m = _____ mm = _____ km
   (b) 25 cm = _____ Å = _____ m = _____ mm
   (c) 50 mm = _____ cm = _____ m = _____ Å
   (d) 5200 Å = _____ m = _____ mm = _____ cm
   (e) 5000 cm³ = _____ cc = _____ ml = _____ l
   (f) 250 mg = _____ g = _____ kg
   (g) 4000 g = _____ kg = _____ mg
   (h) 7.0×10^{-2} kg = _____ g = _____ mg
   (i) 0.250 l = _____ ml = _____ cc
   (j) 0.10 ml = _____ l = _____ cm³

   answers: (a) 0.10 m, 100 mm; (h) 70 g; (i) 250 ml.

1.7. Make the following conversions:
   (a) 1.0×10^{-3} l = _____ qt   (h) 25 in = _____ cm
   (b) 5.2 qt = _____ ml   (i) 116 cm = _____ in
   (c) 4.0 gal = _____ l   (j) 2.5 ft = _____ mm
   (d) 12 lbs = _____ g   (k) 100 miles = _____ km
   (e) 65 kg = _____ lb   (l) 4 km = _____ ft
   (f) 4.2 tons = _____ kg   (m) 6 in = _____ mm
   (g) 80 mg = _____ lb

   answers: (a) 1.1×10^{-3} qt, (e) 1.4×10^{2} lbs, (j) 7.6×10^{2} mm

1.8. Make the following conversions between the Fahrenheit and Celsius temperature scales.
   (a) 122°F = _____°C   (f) −180°C = _____°F
   (b) −132°F = _____°C   (g) 444°C = _____°F
   (c) 15°F = _____°C   (h) 2000°C = _____°F
   (d) 5600°F = _____°C   (i) −10°C = _____°F
   (e) 65°C = _____°F

1.9. At what temperature do the Fahrenheit and Celsius scales coincide?

1.10. If a temperature drop of 45 degrees Fahrenheit takes place, how many degrees change would be observed on the Celsius scale?

1.11. If a temperature increase of 25 degrees is observed on a Celsius scale thermometer, what would be the observed increase on a Fahrenheit thermometer?

1.12. A 400 mg film of metal measuring 3.52 cm by 9.25 cm has a thickness of 5×10^{-3} mm.
(a) What is the volume of the film in cubic centimeters?
(b) What is the density of the metal?
(The answers should include only the digits that are significant.)

1.13. A column of bromine 12.5 cm high with a cross-sectional area of 1.00 cm² weighs 38.6 g. What is the density of the bromine in units of kg/ml?
answer: 3.09×10^{-3} kg/ml

1.14. What volume is occupied by 1.00 mg of gallium if the density of the metal is 5.91 g/ml?

1.15. What is the density of a metal if 5.53 g of it can be formed into a cube 0.85 cm on a side?

1.16. What volume is occupied by 1.00 kg of mercury?
answer: 73.9 ml

1.17. How many grams of sugar are in 0.120 liters of a solution containing 0.345 mg sugar per ml of solution?
answer: 4.14×10^{-2} g

1.18. How many liters of a sugar solution which contains 2.12 mg sugar per ml of solution can be prepared from 0.50 lbs of sugar?

1.19. What are the units in which one must express the value of R in the expression, $PV = nRT$, if P is expressed in dynes per cm², V in cm³, n in moles, and T in degrees Celsius?

1.20. What are units for the value of the kinetic energy, $KE = \frac{1}{2}mv^2$, if m is expressed in g and v in cm per sec?
answer: $g/cm^2/sec^2$

1.21. How much heat is required to raise the temperature of 40 ml of water from 20°C to 35°C?   answer: 600 cal

1.22. One kilocalorie of heat raised the temperature of a sample of water from 10°C to 15°C. What is the weight of the water?

1.23. What is the temperature of a 250 g block of copper after 1.00 kilocalorie of heat has been added, if the initial temperature is 20°C?

1.24. A 2000 g block of aluminum at 25°C is placed into 500 ml of water that is at a temperature of 60°C. What is the temperature of the aluminum, if it is removed when the water has cooled to 50°C? (Assume that all of heat lost by the water is used to heat the aluminum.)

water and its components   two

Our discussion of chemistry proper begins with a study of water, one of the most familiar chemical substances. As we have seen, water serves as the basis of several units of measurement such as the Celsius degree and the calorie. Since water and its components are involved in a great many chemical reactions, the properties are not discussed fully in this chapter. They are introduced in later chapters when the chemistry of other materials is discussed.

Water

Physical properties of water

Physical properties are those characteristics which are not involved in reactions between substances to form a new substance. Such properties include density, color, taste, odor, the phases in which substances exist, and the temperature and pressure at which transitions from one phase to another occur.

Pure water is a colorless, odorless, tasteless, transparent liquid at room temperature. The density of water increases as it is cooled, until the temperature reaches 3.98°C. Below this temperature, the density decreases until the freezing point (0°C) is reached. As indicated in Chapter I, the maximum density of 1.000 g per ml is used as a secondary definition of volume in the metric system. The density of water is only 0.997 g per ml at 25°C. For most of the work in this text it is within the limits of accuracy to assume the density of water to be 1.00 g/ml at room temperature.

The specific heat of liquid water is approximately one calorie per gram per degree. This is much greater than the specific heat of most liquids. The heat required for melting (80 cal) and the heat required for vaporizing (540 cal) one gram of water are also very large. The explanation for these large values and for other unusual properties of water is discussed in Chapter VII.

Phase behavior

A *phase* is a portion of matter that exhibits distinct, uniform physical properties. Substances can exist in one gas phase, one liquid phase,* and one or more solid phases.

Three of the phases of water are well known from common experience. The liquid phase is stable at room temperatures and ordinary pressures. Above 100°C, at a pressure of one atmosphere, water exists as a gas commonly known as steam. Ice is the stable phase below 0°C at a pressure of one atmosphere. The solid phase is unique in being less dense (0.917 g/cm³) than the liquid phase (1.00 g/cm³). At considerably higher pressures ordinary ice is transformed into solids with different properties.

When a solid is heated under a constant pressure, the temperature increases until there is a transition from the solid to the liquid

* Helium is the only substance known to exist in two liquid forms.

phase. This transition is called *melting*; the reverse transition is called *freezing*. The *melting point*, the temperature at which the solid-to-liquid transition takes place, is dependent on pressure and is the same temperature as the *freezing point*.

Since energy is required to melt ice, additional heat is used for this process rather than for increasing the temperature above the melting point. The heat required to melt one gram of ice is known as the *heat of fusion* of water. The heat of fusion of water is 80 calories per gram, a high value compared to those of other substances. This high heat of fusion makes ice a good cooling agent. If a sample of water were cooled, 80 calories per gram of water would have to be removed from the sample at the freezing point to convert the water into ice at 0°C.

Typical of substances for which the solid phase is less dense than the liquid phase, ice melts when subjected to an increase in pressure. An ice skater, for example, glides across the surface of the ice on a thin film of water which immediately refreezes when the pressure of the skate blade is removed. If the density of the solid phase is greater than that of the liquid phase, as is the case for most substances, the liquid freezes when pressure is applied.

VAPORIZATION

Material escapes into the gas phase from the surface of a solid or liquid. *Sublimation* is the transition of matter directly from the solid to the gas state, while *evaporation*, or *vaporization*, is the transition from liquid to gas. *Condensation* is the gas-to-liquid transition. The rate at which matter is transferred to the gas state is constant at a given temperature and increases with increasing temperature. If a solid or liquid is placed in a closed container, the amount of material in the gaseous state at a given temperature is limited by the rate at which material returns to the solid or liquid. The rate of return increases with an increase in the amount of material in the gas phase. After a short time, the rate of return from the gaseous state becomes equal to the rate of escape from the solid and the amount of material in the gas phase becomes constant. This gaseous material exerts a pressure, known as the *vapor pressure*, on its container. As the temperature increases, the vapor pressure of the solid or liquid increases. This is true even if the container is not closed. The rate of return in an open container never equals the rate of escape, however, and there is a continual loss of gaseous material from the container.

When the vapor pressure of the solid or liquid in an open container becomes equal to the pressure of the surrounding atmosphere, the temperature has reached the *boiling point*. At the boiling point there is no further increase in the temperature of the liquid as more heat is added. The additional energy converts the liquid to steam. Rapid addition of heat results only in a more rapid transfer of material from the liquid to the gas phase. The temperature of a boiling liquid can be raised only by increasing the pressure upon the liquid. This can be done using a sealed container which prevents the escape of the pressurized vapor. The heat required to vaporize one gram of liquid is called the *heat of vaporization*. It is 540 calories per gram for water at 100°C. The same amount of heat must be removed to condense one gram of steam at 100°C.

Since the boiling point and melting point depend upon pressure, it is necessary to specify the pressure at which the measurements are made. If the pressure is not given, it is assumed that the measurement was made at, or was corrected to, a standard pressure of one atmosphere. Boiling points and melting points at one atmosphere of pressure usually are designated as *normal boiling points* and *normal melting points.* The melting point correction for pressure is small; except for very large pressure changes or very precise work, the correction can be ignored. The boiling point correction is much larger and must be considered in almost every case.

The normal melting point of water is 0°C, and the normal boiling point is 100°C. These temperatures are reference points on the Celsius temperature scale discussed in Chapter I. Tables showing the variation of the boiling point of water with pressure are readily available. Corrections of the boiling point must take into account not only the day-to-day changes in the atmospheric pressure, but also the variation of atmospheric pressure due to changes in altitude. For water, this correction is about one degree for every 1000 feet of altitude. (See Fig. 2.1.)

Fig. 2.1

Variation of the Boiling Point of Water with Altitude. Since pressure decreases with altitude, the boiling point of water increases. The relationship is linear to about 4000 ft.

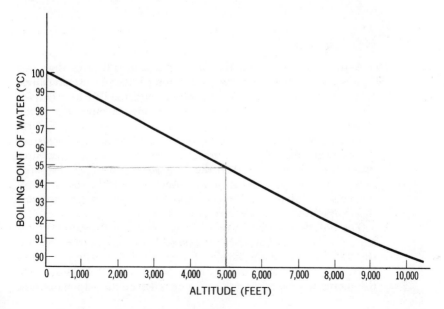

Much information about the phase behavior of materials can be summarized in a phase diagram which shows the phases present over a range of temperature and pressure values. The phase diagram of water is shown in Fig. 2.2 and summarizes much of the above discussion. The low density gas phase exists at low pressures and high temperatures, while the high density solid phase is found at high pressures and low temperatures.

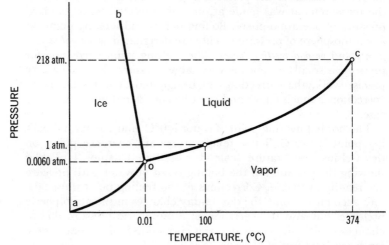

Fig. 2.2

Schematic Phase Diagram for Water. Line ao—variation of vapor pressure of ice with temperature; line oc—vapor pressure of water; line ob—variation of melting point of ice with pressure. At high pressures ob curves to the right indicating other solid phases which are more dense than the liquid. Normal boiling point—1 atm, 100°C; triple point—0.0060 atm, 0.01°C; critical point—218 atm, 374°C. (Axes expanded for clarity in low pressure region.)

A point on a line on the phase diagram indicates that two phases coexist at the corresponding temperatures and pressures. If it is specified that liquid and vapor coexist stably at a certain temperature, the pressure can be determined. Conversely, if the pressure is specified, the system can be at only one temperature.

When three lines intersect at a point, three phases coexist at the corresponding temperature and pressure. This temperature-pressure combination, called the *triple point,* is unique: the three phases cannot exist together at any other temperature or pressure. By specifying that three given phases of a substance are present, the temperature and pressure of the system are fixed.

The liquid-vapor curve does not terminate at the normal boiling point of the liquid, since it is possible to increase the pressure the temperature of the liquid by increasing the vapor pressure. With increasing temperature the liquid density decreases, while the increasing pressure causes an increase in the vapor density.

Thus the vapor pressure-temperature curve, i.e., the liquid-vapor curve, continues until the critical point is reached. The *critical point* for any substance is the temperature and pressure at which the properties of the liquid and vapor phases become identical, and it is no longer possible to distinguish between the two phases. At temperatures above the critical point it is not possible to observe the formation of a liquid as the pressure on the gas is increased. The temperature of the critical point is called the *critical temperature*; the pressure required to liquefy a vapor at the critical temperature is called the *critical pressure*.

Chemical properties of water

Chemical properties describe the manner in which one substance reacts with another to form a new substance with different properties. Since water reacts chemically with many other substances, such reactions are considered to be chemical properties of the other substances. However, one should remember that they pertain also to the chemistry of water.

Water dissolves many substances without a chemical reaction taking place. The chemical and physical properties of water are modified by the dissolved materials, which may be removed by distillation. Storage is usually in special noncontaminating plastic containers. Since water dissolves air, the properties of distilled water soon change when it is exposed to the atmosphere. Our discussion of properties refers to those of pure water which contains no dissolved material, not to those of water occurring in nature which contains minerals and air.

Fig. 2.3

Distillation of Water in the Laboratory.

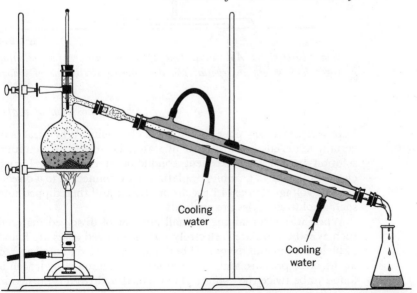

Cooling water

Cooling water

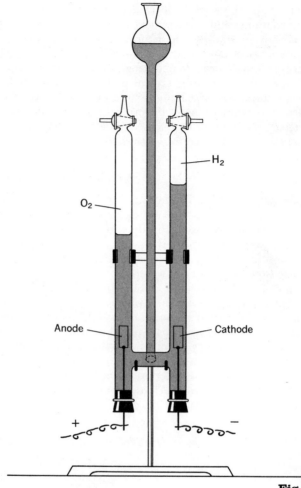

Fig. 2.4

Hoffman Electrolysis Apparatus. One of several devices for collecting hydrogen and oxygen in separate chambers during electrolysis of water.

The composition of water

Pure water is a very poor conductor of electricity. When traces of certain materials are dissolved in water, however, the resulting solution becomes an excellent conductor of electricity. If two electrodes made of graphite or platinum are connected to a direct-current voltage source of 1.8 volts or greater and then dipped into such a solution, gases are evolved.

When water containing a small amount of dissolved material such as sodium sulfate is electrolyzed, the evolved gases are found to be hydrogen and oxygen. If both gases are dried and measured at the same pressure and temperature, the volume of hydrogen is found to be twice the volume of oxygen. If hydrogen is burned in oxygen, two volumes of hydrogen react with one volume of oxygen to form two volumes of water vapor. Again, all volumes are measured at the same temperature and pressure.

Water thus appears to be made up of two parts of hydrogen and one part of oxygen; that is, water is a compound. Hydrogen and oxygen, however, are both substances that cannot be broken down into simpler substances by an ordinary chemical reaction. Substances of this type are called *elements*. Hydrogen and oxygen are two of the 103 known elements. A *compound* is the chemical combination of two or more elements.

Symbols and formulas

Each of the elements is represented by a symbol consisting of one or two letters usually derived from the English or Latin name of the element. Thus the symbol for hydrogen is H; for oxygen, O; and for chlorine, Cl. Only the first letter of the symbol is capitalized.

Chemical symbols are combined in formulas to represent the composition of chemical compounds. The formula for water is H_2O. This denotes that water is made up of two parts of hydrogen and one part of oxygen. Note that the formula refers to parts by number, not by weight. An assumption is involved here, namely, that equal volumes of gases at the same temperature and pressure contain equal numbers of particles. (The validity of this assumption is discussed in Chapter III.) In chemical formulas such as the one for water, subscripts placed after a symbol indicate the ratio of the number of particles of each element in the compound. No subscript is used to indicate a ratio of one.

Detailed rules for writing chemical formulas and naming chemical compounds are given in Chapter IV. A list of thirty-six common elements and their symbols is given in Table 2.1.

Table 2.1

*Chemical Symbols for Selected Elements**

Antimony	Sb	Copper	Cu	Neon	Ne
Argon	Ar	Fluorine	F	Nickel	Ni
Arsenic	As	Gold	Au	Nitrogen	N
Aluminum	Al	Helium	He	Oxygen	O
Barium	Ba	Hydrogen	H	Phosphorus	P
Beryllium	Be	Iodine	I	Potassium	K
Boron	B	Iron	Fe	Silicon	Si
Bromine	Br	Lead	Pb	Silver	Ag
Calcium	Ca	Lithium	Li	Sodium	Na
Carbon	C	Magnesium	Mg	Sulfur	S
Chlorine	Cl	Manganese	Mn	Tin	Sn
Chromium	Cr	Mercury	Hg	Zinc	Zn

* A complete list of the elements is found on the inside back cover.

The discovery and occurrence of oxygen

The elemental nature of hydrogen and oxygen was not recognized until the latter part of the eighteenth century. Prior to the discovery of oxygen, air was thought to be an element, although "airs" with different properties were recognized. Relatively pure samples of these airs were obtained by the use of the pneumatic trough (Fig. 2.5). This simple device, which was not invented until late in the seventeenth century, made possible the collection of gases given off in the chemical reaction.

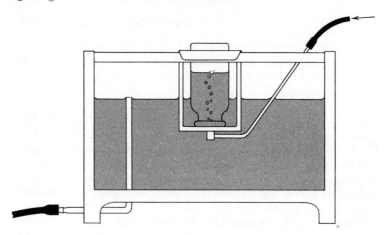

Fig. 2.5

Sketch of a Pneumatic Trough. Technique is used today to collect gases for study in the laboratory.

One of the processes studied was the burning of various substances in these gases. The *phlogiston-calx theory* was introduced in the early part of the eighteenth century to explain burning. This theory held that phlogiston was contained in anything that burned. In the process of burning, phlogiston was driven off, leaving behind the calx. The more rapidly the phlogiston was given off, the hotter the substance became. For example, when zinc was heated in air, phlogiston was given off and the calx of zinc remained. Calx could be mixed with soot or charcoal, which was almost pure phlogiston, to obtain pure zinc.

From 1770 to 1775, Carl Wilhelm Scheele in Scandinavia and Joseph Priestley in England independently studied the "airs" obtained in various reactions involving phlogiston. Both men heated the calx of mercury to obtain metallic mercury and an air in which materials burned very brightly. Since Priestley published his work in 1775, he is given credit for the discovery of oxygen. Scheele, who first characterized oxygen in his laboratory, did not publish until 1777. Neither Scheele nor Priestley understood the true nature of the gas they had isolated.

Fig. 2.6
Joseph Priestley

Antoine Lavoisier in France developed the concept of an element when he repeated many of the studies on this air. By consistent use of the analytical balance, Lavoisier showed that substances gained weight when phlogiston was supposedly lost. After extensive experimentation, Lavoisier postulated that when the calx of mercury is heated, the element oxygen is given off. In the burning process oxygen combines with the elements being burned to form chemical compounds. As more data were obtained, the phlogiston theory was replaced by Lavoisier's concept of oxygen.

Oxygen is the most common element in the earth's crust (49.2% by weight), occurring chemically unbound as about 21 per cent by volume of the atmosphere, and existing in widespread chemical combination. For example, it comprises 88.9% by weight of water, and 53% by weight of sand. In addition, combined oxygen is found in clays, most mineral ores, and in all living matter.

Fig. 2.7
Antoine Lavoisier

Laboratory preparation of oxygen

For the laboratory preparation of any material the equipment must be relatively inexpensive and commonly available. The cost of the materials used in the reaction is not an important factor.

Oxygen is usually prepared in the laboratory in one of the following ways.

(1) Release of oxygen from oxides by heating

Most compounds of oxygen, oxides, are stable when heated. However, there are a few that decompose upon heating. One of the most commonly used is what Priestley, Scheele, and others called the calx of mercury, mercuric oxide.

$$\text{mercuric oxide (HgO)} \xrightarrow{\text{heat}} \text{mercury (Hg)} + \text{oxygen (O}_2\text{)}$$

The dioxide of lead (PbO_2) and the peroxide of barium (BaO_2) also are unstable when heated, although their normal oxides (PbO and BaO) are stable.

(2) Release of oxygen from salts by heating

The common examples are the chlorates, perchlorates and nitrates of certain metals such as potassium. Thus,

$$\text{potassium nitrate (KNO}_3\text{)} \xrightarrow{\text{heat}}$$
$$\text{potassium nitrite (KNO}_2\text{)} + \text{oxygen (O}_2\text{)}$$

The nitrite still contains oxygen but is relatively stable when heated.

The decomposition of potassium chlorate is the most commonly used method of preparing oxygen in the laboratory. The compound must be heated (700–800°C) in order to drive off the oxygen at a reasonable rate. If some manganese dioxide is added, the rate of evolution is increased greatly, making the reaction feasible at somewhat lower temperatures. The manganese dioxide is not changed during the reaction.

$$\text{potassium chlorate (KClO}_3\text{)} \xrightarrow{\text{heat}}$$
$$\text{potassium chloride (KCl)} + \text{oxygen (O}_2\text{)}$$
$$\text{potassium perchlorate (KClO}_4\text{)} \xrightarrow{\text{heat}}$$
$$\text{potassium chloride (KCl)} + \text{oxygen (O}_2\text{)}$$

(3) The action of water on certain peroxides

If sodium peroxide (Na_2O_2) is added to water, oxygen is evolved, leaving behind a solution of sodium hydroxide. Gentle heating is required for the evolution of all the available oxygen. The heating of a hydrogen peroxide (H_2O_2) solution causes decomposition to water and oxygen.

Commercial preparation of oxygen

For the commercial preparation of any substance, the raw materials must be relatively cheap and readily available. The cost and complexity of the equipment is a secondary factor, since this cost can be amortized over a large amount of product if the cost of the raw materials is low. Two important commercial methods of oxygen preparation are the liquefaction and fractional distillation of air and the electrolysis of water.

(1) Distillation of liquid air

There is probably no other process that starts with a raw material as cheap and readily available as the atmosphere which consists of about 21 per cent oxygen, 78 per cent nitrogen, 0.03 per cent carbon dioxide, up to 0.03 per cent water vapor and one per cent other nonreactive or noble gases. The process of liquefaction is sketched in Fig. 2.8. As the liquified air slowly warms, nitrogen (boiling point $-196°C$) boils off first leaving behind liquid oxygen which contains the noble gases and a little residual nitrogen. The liquid oxygen is allowed to boil ($-183°C$) as the gas is compressed into cylinders for sale.

(2) Electrolytic decomposition of water

High purity oxygen is obtained by passing an electrical current through water containing certain dissolved materials. Since the gas is collected over water, it must be dried before it is compressed into cylinders for sale. Electrolytic hydrogen is a by-product of the process.

Physical and chemical properties

Oxygen is a colorless, tasteless, odorless gas at room temperature, with a density 1.1 times that of air. The liquid has a bluish color,

Fig. 2.8

Process for the Liquefaction of Air. Dust, water, and carbon dioxide are removed from the air stream to avoid clogging valves and tubes. After each compression stage, the heat generated is removed, and the air is allowed to expand and cool. Upon sufficient cooling oxygen, nitrogen, and noble gases liquefy. The stages of the apparatus are designed to utilize escaping cool gases in cooling preceding stages.

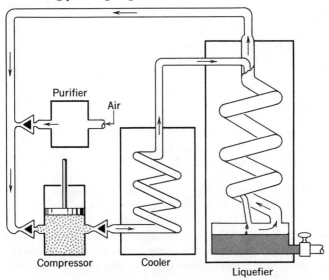

Purifier
Air
Compressor
Cooler
Liquefier

freezes at −219°C, and boils at −183°C. The critical point is −118.4°C and 50.1 atm, making it necessary to transport oxygen as a compressed gas. It is slightly soluble in water; one volume dissolves in thirty-two volumes of water at 0°C. This is sufficient to support aquatic life but is low enough to permit collection of the gas over water.

Oxygen combines directly with many other elements to produce compounds called oxides. The conditions for a reaction, however, vary widely. Some elements ignite spontaneously, while others have to be heated to high temperatures before the reaction begins. Substances containing carbon and hydrogen burn to form water and carbon dioxide, or carbon monoxide when the amount of oxygen available is limited. Details of these reactions are considered in later chapters.

Uses of oxygen

Oxygen is often used to sustain life under unusual circumstances—in high-altitude flying, deep-sea diving, resuscitation, and various types of medical therapy. Commercially, it is widely used in welding and metal-cutting work. Oxygen is used to synthesize many organic materials such as gasoline, methanol (methyl alcohol), ethanol (ethyl alcohol), and other alcohols. It is used in the preparation of nitric acid from ammonia and in the production of certain high-grade steels. Large quantities of liquid oxygen are employed in the propulsion systems of many liquid fuel rockets. The technology developed for the space program makes liquid oxygen readily available at relatively low cost.

Hydrogen
Discovery and occurrence

Hydrogen probably was prepared long before it was recognized as a unique substance. Robert Boyle (1627–1691) made one of the earliest reports (1673) on the properties of hydrogen while discussing the burning of a candle in air. It was one of the "airs" which he prepared by dropping an acid upon iron filings. Henry Cavendish (1731–1810), who published his studies on airs in 1766, is credited with the first characterization of hydrogen. He prepared what he called "inflammable air" by dropping dilute acid upon various metals. He concluded that the same air is obtained with zinc, iron or tin and with what are now known as sulfuric and hydrochloric acids. Since Cavendish believed in phlogiston, he thought his inflammable air was phlogiston that had been released from the metal by the acid.

Cavendish, who made an excellent characterization of hydrogen, is given credit for its discovery. However, it was Lavoisier in 1789, who finally recognized this inflammable air as an element.

Lavoisier named it "hydrogen" or "water producer," since it combines with oxygen to form water.

Very little uncombined hydrogen is found in the earth's atmosphere because of the reactivity of hydrogen at moderately elevated temperatures. Some natural gas wells contain 10 to 30 per cent free hydrogen. The rest of the hydrogen in the earth's crust is chemically combined. About 11 per cent of water by weight is hydrogen. Petroleum, natural gas, and plant and animal matter all contain combined hydrogen. Hydrogen makes up only 0.9 per cent of the earth's crust by weight. This corresponds to a very large gas volume due to its very low density at atmospheric pressure. Oxygen, comprising about 50 per cent of the weight of the earth's crust, would occupy only about three times the volume of hydrogen, if both elements in the earth's crust were converted completely to the free state.

Laboratory preparation

Hydrogen can be prepared in the laboratory by one of the following methods.

(1) **The action of water on certain metals**

Some metals liberate hydrogen from water to form a hydroxide. These "very active" metals include lithium, sodium, potassium, rubidium, cesium, and calcium.

Fig. 2.9
Robert Boyle

Fig. 2.10
Sir Henry Cavendish

very active metal + water →
hydroxide of a very active metal + hydrogen

sodium (Na) + water (H_2O) →
sodium hydroxide (NaOH) + hydrogen (H_2)

(2) The reaction between an acid and certain metals

The very active metals liberate hydrogen from acid solutions with explosive violence. Several other metals do so more sedately. The most commonly used laboratory preparation of hydrogen is the reaction of zinc with hydrochloric acid. Other metals that release hydrogen include magnesium, aluminum, iron, and tin.

zinc (Zn) + hydrochloric acid (HCl) →
zinc chloride ($ZnCl_2$) + hydrogen (H_2)

(3) The action of water on certain metal hydrides

A metal hydride is a chemical combination of a metal and hydrogen. Hydrogen is liberated by the action of water on the hydrides of certain active metals such as sodium, potassium, calcium, and magnesium.

sodium hydride (NaH) + water (H_2O) →
sodium hydroxide (NaOH) + hydrogen (H_2)

Commercial preparation

Hydrogen is prepared commercially by the following methods.

(1) Electrolysis of an aqueous solution

Since the commercial demand for electrolytic oxygen is limited, a solution containing a substantial amount of ordinary salt, sodium chloride, is used for most electrolytic hydrogen production. The products are hydrogen gas, chlorine gas, and a solution of sodium hydroxide.

(2) Bosch process

The classic Bosch process uses hard coal or coke, both of which are almost pure carbon, and superheated steam. At elevated temperatures, the carbon replaces hydrogen from water to form carbon monoxide.

$$C + H_2O \rightarrow CO + H_2$$

The process has been modified in recent years to make use of natural gas (primarily methane—CH_4) instead of coke.

$$CH_4 + H_2O \rightarrow CO + 3H_2$$

Since the separation of the resulting gases is costly, the mixture, called "water gas," usually is used in place of pure hydrogen. The carbon monoxide does not interfere in most applications. If necessary, it can be removed by the addition of more steam which converts it to carbon dioxide (CO_2). CO_2 is then removed by compressing the hydrogen–carbon dioxide mixture over water. Hydrogen is much less soluble than carbon dioxide under these conditions, making the separation possible.

(3) By-product of other reactions

The petroleum and coking industries produce some hydrogen during their operations. Various portions of crude oil and natural gases are reformed to make gasoline and other petroleum products. Some of the hydrogen present in these substances is liberated in this reforming or "cracking" process. Coke is prepared by heating anthracite coal in a limited amount of air. The heat decomposes the chemically combined hydrogen in the coal, and the gas is recovered from the coking ovens along with other decomposition products.

(4) Decomposition of ammonia

Because large volumes of gas are involved, it is very costly to ship substantial quantities of hydrogen or water gas by rail or truck. In order to supply a remote industrial operation economically, hydrogen is combined with atmospheric nitrogen to form ammonia (NH_3). Ammonia is liquefied easily with moderate pressures at room temperatures, while the critical temperature of hydrogen is $-239.9°C$. A tank car of liquid ammonia contains much more hydrogen than one filled with compressed hydrogen gas. The ammonia is decomposed readily to nitrogen and hydrogen at the site of use. In applications using this type of hydrogen, the nitrogen is only a diluent and does not enter into the reaction.

Physical and chemical properties

At room temperature, hydrogen is a colorless, odorless, tasteless gas. The liquid boils at $-253°C$ and freezes at $-259°C$. With the exception of helium, hydrogen possesses the lowest boiling point of any known substance. The critical point is $-239.9°C$ and 12.8 atm. With a density at $0°C$ and 1 atm pressure of 0.0899 g/l, about 0.07 the density of air, hydrogen is the least dense gas known. It is slightly soluble in water; one volume of gas dissolves in 52 volumes of water at $0°C$.

Although relatively unreactive at room temperature, hydrogen becomes increasingly reactive as the temperature rises. At elevated temperatures hydrogen reacts with many metals to form metal hydrides. Nonmetals also form hydrogen compounds under appropriate conditions.

Hydrogen and oxygen can be mixed without any reaction, until a spark or flame initiates the reaction which yields water. When such a reaction takes place, it occurs so rapidly that an explosion results. The explosive composition of a hydrogen-oxygen mixture is from 10 to 90% hydrogen by weight. Thus, when hydrogen is used in the laboratory, it is necessary to burn any excess hydrogen. Since a jet of pure hydrogen can be burned safely, it is necessary to collect and test a small sample of the exit gas to determine the purity of the hydrogen before the exit gas is ignited.

A chlorine-hydrogen mixture illustrates the role of appropriate conditions in a chemical reaction. The gases can be mixed in the dark without any reaction. However, if a red light is directed into the mixture, an explosion will occur. Fluorine, which is chemically similar to chlorine, reacts spontaneously with hydrogen even in the dark.

Uses of hydrogen

Much hydrogen is used to produce ammonia from atmospheric nitrogen. Ammonia is the first step in the production of other nitrogen compounds. There are many metallurgical processes in which a metal is recovered from an oxide by heating the oxide in a stream of hydrogen. The hydrogen combines with the oxygen to form water. The hydrogen atmosphere excludes additional oxygen from the air thereby making it possible to obtain pure metal. Certain limitations are placed upon this process since it cannot be used if the metal forms a stable hydride. There are other cases where hydrogen is the only suitable agent, because coke, or carbon, forms a compound with the metal.

Acids and bases

For organized study of the 103 elements, it is necessary to devise methods of classifying them. One of the earliest and simplest methods of classification is based on their oxide behavior.

Whenever an element reacts with oxygen, an oxide is formed. Most of these oxides dissolve at least to a limited extent in water. If certain colored materials are placed in the water solution, color changes are observed which can be used as the basis of classification. Litmus, a dyestuff extracted from certain lichens, is one of the commonly used materials. If a litmus solution turns blue upon the addition of an elemental oxide, the element is classified as a metal. If the litmus turns red or pink, the element is classified as a nonmetal.

Substances which turn litmus solutions blue are called *bases*, while those which turn litmus red are called *acids*. Since a metal oxide in water turns litmus blue, the oxide and water must react to form a base. Similarly, a nonmetal oxide must react with water to form an acid. This concept of acids, bases, metals, and nonmetals may be summarized in the equations that follow. The concept is enlarged in later chapters.

metal + oxygen → metal oxide
metal oxide + water → base (turns litmus blue)
nonmetal + oxygen → nonmetal oxide
nonmetal oxide + water → acid (turns litmus red)

An example of each case includes the following.

lithium (Li) + oxygen (O_2) → lithium oxide (Li_2O)

lithium oxide (Li_2O) + water (H_2O) →
$\qquad$ lithium hydroxide (LiOH) [a base]

(All metal oxides form bases called hydroxides.)

sulfur (S) + oxygen (O_2) → sulfur dioxide (SO_2)
sulfur dioxide (SO_2) + water (H_2O) →
$\qquad\qquad$ sulfurous acid (H_2SO_3)

If an appropriate amount of acid is allowed to react with a base, water and a substance called a *salt* is produced. This type of reaction is called *neutralization*. If the neutralization is done carefully, the resulting salt solution is neither acidic or basic. The acid and base properties have been neutralized. The neutralization reaction is written as

$\qquad$ base $\qquad$ + $\qquad$ acid $\qquad$ → $\qquad$ salt $\qquad$ + water
sodium hydroxide + sulfuric acid → sodium sulfate + water
$\qquad$ (NaOH) $\qquad\qquad$ (H_2SO_4) $\qquad\qquad$ (Na_2SO_4) $\qquad$ (H_2O)

Activity series

The first part of this chapter describes how certain metals displace hydrogen from an acid, but not from water, while other metals displace hydrogen both from water and from acid. This ability to displace hydrogen is related to the chemical activity of the metal; thus it is possible to rank the metals in order of activity on the basis of this ability. For example, potassium liberates hydrogen from water more vigorously than sodium does, since the evolved hydrogen always ignites with the former and only seldom ignites with the latter. Magnesium does not react with cold water, but

Table 2.2

Activity series

Potassium	*Most active:*
Sodium	*liberate hydrogen*
Calcium	*from cold water*
Magnesium	
Aluminum	
Zinc	*Moderately active:*
Iron	*liberate hydrogen*
Nickel	*from acid solution*
Tin	
Lead	
HYDROGEN	
Copper	*Least active:*
Mercury	*do not liberate*
Silver	*hydrogen from*
Gold	*acid solution* ·

it reacts vigorously with boiling water. Zinc does not liberate hydrogen from water but does so readily when placed in an acid solution. No hydrogen evolution takes place when copper or silver is placed in an acid solution. From many such experiments it is possible to develop the activity series given in Table 2.2.

If copper is used instead of hydrogen as the reference for this system, the same effect is noted. When a metal above copper is inserted into a solution containing copper, the copper comes out of the solution while the metal goes into solution. For example, zinc liberates copper from a copper solution. Since copper is a metal at room temperature it is deposited on the zinc strip and does not escape as a gas. The activity series has a generalized use in the prediction of a chemical reaction. *If a more active metal is placed into a solution of a less active metal, the less active metal is displaced from the solution as the more active metal goes into solution.* Caution: the activity series can be used only for reactions between a metal and a metallic solution. It cannot be used for predicting reactions when two solutions are mixed.

Equivalent weights

In any quantitative approach to the use or study of chemistry, the primary question is, how much of one substance reacts with a given amount of another substance? Some scale of reaction weights is needed. Among the earliest and simplest of these scales is the combining weight or equivalent weight scale. The combining weight is obtained by weighing a substance before and after it has undergone chemical combination with another substance. The only requirements are that a good analytical balance be used for the weighings and that the reaction be carried to completion.

To calibrate a combining weight scale, the combining weights of all elements are expressed in terms of a given weight of a reference element. The combining weight of one element then is that weight which completely reacts with or is equivalent to the combining weight of the reference element. This makes the scale an equivalent weight scale.

Hydrogen, with the lowest density of all elements, was originally chosen as the reference element and assigned a value of 1.0 gram. All other equivalent weights were expressed as the weight of any other element that would combine with 1.0 g of hydrogen. As more elements were discovered, it was found that hydrogen is of limited usefulness as a reference, since many elements do not combine readily with hydrogen. Oxygen was chosen as a more satisfactory reference for the equivalent weight scale, because oxygen reacts with almost all of the elements.

In order to keep the change of values small, the value for the equivalent weight of oxygen was chosen to be exactly 8.00 g. One *equivalent weight* of any element is the weight that reacts with 8.00 g of oxygen. On this basis the equivalent weight of oxygen is 1.008 g, close to its value on the old hydrogen scale. Since hydrogen is liberated by the action of some metals on an acid, the equivalent

hydrogen

weight of an element also may be determined as the weight that reacts with or liberates 1.008 g of hydrogen. This weight of hydrogen gas occupies a volume of 11.2 liters at 0°C and one atm of pressure, leading to the alternate definition of the equivalent weight as that weight of an element that reacts with or liberates 11.2 liters of hydrogen gas measured at 0°C and one atm pressure. The equivalent weight of sodium, for example, is 23 g, while that of calcium is 20 g. Not only do these represent the weight of each metal that combines with 8.0 g of oxygen, they also represent the weight of each metal that liberates 11.2 liters (at 0°C and 1 atm) of hydrogen gas from an acid solution. Further, it is found that 23 g of sodium react with 1.008 g of hydrogen to form sodium hydride. The definition used here is that one equivalent weight of one element reacts with one equivalent weight of another element. The definition of an equivalent weight is broadened in Chapter XII.

Example 2.1 What weight of calcium reacts with 3.00 g of oxygen?
(a) Calculate the number of equivalents of oxygen, which is the same as the number of equivalents of calcium.

$$(3.00 \text{ g oxygen})\left(\frac{1 \text{ equivalent}}{8 \text{ g oxygen}}\right) = 0.375 \text{ equivalent}$$

(b) Convert equivalents of calcium to grams of calcium.

$$(0.375 \text{ eq})\left(\frac{20 \text{ g calcium}}{1 \text{ equivalent}}\right) = 7.50 \text{ g calcium}$$

Example 2.2 What weight of hydrogen reacts with 3.00 g of oxygen?

$$(3.00 \text{ g oxygen})\left(\frac{1 \text{ equivalent}}{8 \text{ g oxygen}}\right) = 0.375 \text{ equivalent}$$

$$(0.375 \text{ eq})\left(\frac{1.008 \text{ g hydrogen}}{1 \text{ equivalent}}\right) = 0.378 \text{ g hydrogen}$$

Example 2.3 What weight of hydrogen reacts with the same weight of calcium that reacts with 3.00 g oxygen (i.e., 7.50 g)?

$$(7.50 \text{ g calcium})\left(\frac{1 \text{ equivalent}}{20 \text{ g calcium}}\right) = 0.375 \text{ equivalent}$$

$$(0.375 \text{ eq})\left(\frac{1.008 \text{ g hydrogen}}{1 \text{ equivalent}}\right) = 0.378 \text{ g hydrogen}$$

Compare this answer with that obtained in Example 2.2.

Example 2.4 Five grams of sodium combine with chlorine to produce 12.71 grams of a sodium–chlorine compound. What is the equivalent weight of chlorine?
(a) Calculate the number of equivalents of sodium which is equal to the number of equivalents of chlorine.

$$(5.00 \text{ g sodium})\left(\frac{1 \text{ equivalent}}{23 \text{ g sodium}}\right) = 0.217 \text{ equivalent}$$

(b) Calculate the weight of chlorine in this reaction which is equal to 0.217 equivalent.

$$12.71 \text{ g} - 5.00 \text{ g} = 7.71 \text{ g chlorine}$$

(c) Calculate the weight of one equivalent of chlorine, i.e., grams chlorine per equivalent.

$$\text{Equivalent weight} = \frac{7.71 \text{ g chlorine}}{0.217 \text{ equivalent}} = 35.5 \text{ g/eq}$$

Example 2.5 What is the equivalent weight of a metal if 450 mg of it liberate 50.4 mg of hydrogen from a hydrochloric acid solution?

(a) Calculate the number of equivalents involved in the reaction.

$$(50.4 \text{ mg hydrogen})\left(\frac{1 \text{ g}}{1000 \text{ mg}}\right)\left(\frac{1 \text{ equivalent}}{1.008 \text{ g hydrogen}}\right) = 0.0500 \text{ eq}$$

(b) Calculate the weight of one equivalent of the metal.

$$\text{Equivalent weight} = \frac{0.450 \text{ g metal}}{0.0500 \text{ eq}} = 9.00 \text{ g/eq}$$

Example 2.6 What weight of cesium would be required to liberate 1000 liters of hydrogen (measured at 0°C and 1 atm) if the equivalent weight of cesium is 133 g?

(a) Calculate the number of equivalents involved in the reaction.

$$(1000 \text{ liters hydrogen})\left(\frac{1 \text{ equivalent}}{11.2 \text{ liters}}\right) = 89.3 \text{ equivalents}$$

(b) Calculate the weight of 89.3 equivalents of cesium.

$$(89.3 \text{ equivalents})\left(\frac{133 \text{ g cesium}}{1 \text{ equivalent}}\right) = 11,877 \text{ g} = 11.9 \text{ kg}$$

SIGNIFICANT TERMS AND CONCEPTS IN CHAPTER II:

Physical properties, chemical properties, phase, melting point, freezing point, normal freezing point, heat of fusion, sublimation, vaporization, heat of vaporization, vapor pressure, boiling point, normal boiling point, variation of melting point and boiling point with pressure, triple point, critical point, critical temperature, critical pressure, distillation, element, compound, chemical symbol, chemical formula, comparison of laboratory and commercial preparations, oxide, hydride, chemical properties of oxygen and hydrogen, acid, base, salt, neutralization, basis and use of the activity series, bases and use of equivalent weights.

Review questions

2.1. List all of the units for the measurement of physical properties which are defined in terms of the properties of water. Define each.

2.2. Can it ever become too cold to ice skate? Explain.
2.3. Distinguish between sublimation and evaporation.
2.4. What properties of water make steam a useful means of transferring heat from a furnace to a room some distance away?
2.5. What phase is present, if the pressure is increased on water at the triple point at a constant temperature?
2.6. Why does the line *oc* in Fig. 2.2 terminate? Why does line *oa* terminate?
2.7. What phase(s) of water exist at: (a) 100°C and 1.0 atm; (b) 200°C and 200 atm; (c) 0.0060 atm and 0.01°C; (d) 110°C and 1.0 atm; (e) −0.1°C and 218 atm; (f) 0.01°C and 0.005 atm?   answers: (a) liquid and vapor (d) vapor
2.8. What elements are present in the substances represented by the following formulas? MgO, NaF, HCl, $LiOH$, CO_2, He, $COCl$.
2.9. Give the products when
    (a) silver oxide (Ag_2O) is heated.
    (b) lead dioxide (PbO_2) is heated.
    (c) sodium chlorate ($NaClO_3$) is heated.
    (d) sodium nitrate ($NaNO_3$) is heated.
    (e) calcium metal is heated in oxygen.
    (f) water is added to barium oxide (BaO).
    (g) phosphorus is burned in oxygen.
    (h) water is added to phosphorus pentoxide (P_2O_5).

2.10. What happens to the color of a solution of barium hydroxide when three drops of litmus solution are added? What happens to a solution of hydrochloric acid?
2.11. When a litmus solution was added to a solution of each of the following oxides, the indicated color was observed. Classify the element other than oxygen as a metal or nonmetal.
    (a) TeO_2 red   (c) Cs_2O blue   (e) Fe_2O_3 blue
    (b) SrO blue   (d) P_2O_5 red   (f) As_2O_3 blue

2.12. Predict the products of the following reactions. (If no reaction takes place, so indicate.)
    (a) Calcium metal in water
    (b) Magnesium metal in sulfuric acid (H_2SO_4)
    (c) Aluminum metal in hydrochloric acid (HCl)
    (d) Tin metal in water
    (e) Calcium hydride (CaH_2) in water
    (f) The conversion of carbon monoxide (CO) to carbon dioxide (CO_2) using steam
    (g) Heating of calcium metal in hydrogen
    (h) Decomposition of ammonia gas
    (i) Copper metal in hydrochloric acid (HCl)
    (j) Silver metal in a solution of copper nitrate ($Cu(NO_3)_2$)

(k) Tin metal in a solution of silver nitrate ($AgNO_3$)
(l) Burning of water gas

Problems

2.13. Calculate the volume occupied by 50.0 g of ice and by 50.0 g of water at 0°C.

2.14. What is the percentage change in volume as water changes to ice?   answer: 9%

2.15. How much heat would be required to melt 1.0 kg of ice at 0°C?   answer: 8×10^4 cal

2.16. How much heat would be required to vaporize 1.00 kg of water at 100°C?

2.17. If the specific heat of ice is 0.500 cal/g-deg, how much heat is required to convert 8.00 grams of ice at -10°C to water at 20°C?

2.18. How much heat is necessary to convert 200 grams of water at 20°C to steam at 100°C?   answer: 1.24×10^5 cal

2.19. How much ice at 0°C is needed to cool 240 grams of water from 40°C to 25°C? Assume that the only useful cooling is the melting of the ice and that the warming of the melted ice has no effect.   answer: 45 g

2.20. How many grams of water can be heated from 20°C to 50°C by the condensation of 1000 grams of steam at 100°C?

2.21. How many grams of ice are needed to condense 400 grams of steam? Assume that only melting of the ice at 0°C is used for cooling.   answer: 2700 g

2.22. What is the final temperature if 20.0 grams of ice at 0°C are added to 400 grams of water at 25°C?

2.23. What is the ratio of oxygen particles to nitrogen particles in the following oxides of nitrogen: (a) N_2O, (b) NO, (c) N_2O_3, (d) N_2O_4, (e) NO_2, (f) N_2O_5?
                                          answers: (a) 1:2, (d) 4:2

2.24. Give the formula, if the following number ratios of particles are found: (a) 1 carbon, 4 hydrogen (b) 2 carbon, 4 hydrogen (c) 1 carbon, 1 hydrogen, 1 chlorine.
                                          answer: (a) CH_4

2.25. If 8.91 g of a metal reacts with 3.10 g of oxygen, what is the equivalent weight of the metal?   answer: 23.0 g

2.26. A sample of metal weighing 10.79 grams was burned in oxygen. The product weighed 11.59 g. What is the equivalent weight of the metal?

2.27. What is the equivalent weight of a metal, if 4.00 g of oxide was formed when 2.40 g of the metal was burned in oxygen?
                                          answer: 12.0 g

2.28. If the equivalent weight of an element is 3.6 g, how much of it reacts with 48 g of oxygen?

2.29. The equivalent weight of gallium is 23.3. How much gallium oxide is formed from 7.00 g of gallium?   answer: 9.4 g

2.30. The equivalent weight of fluorine is 19 g. How much gallium fluoride is formed from 7.00 g of gallium?

2.31. What weights of sodium and fluorine are needed to prepare 8.40 g of sodium fluoride?

answers: 4.6 g sodium, 3.8 g fluorine

2.32. Calculate the equivalent weight of bromine if 40.0 g of calcium bromide are formed from 32 g of bromine.

2.33. What is the volume occupied by 1.00 kg of hydrogen at 0°C and 1 atmosphere pressure?

answer: 1.11×10^4 liters

2.34. What volume measured at 0°C and 1 atmosphere of hydrogen may be dissolved in 100 ml water at 0°C? What weight of hydrogen is this?

2.35. Water consists of about 11% hydrogen by weight. Calculate the volumes of oxygen and hydrogen (at 0°C and 1 atmosphere pressure) that would be generated by the electrolysis of 100 ml of water. (Density of oxygen = 1.43 g/l)

answer: 122 liters hydrogen

2.36. What volume of hydrogen (measured at 0°C and a pressure of 1 atm) is liberated by 1.3 g of potassium reacting with water, if the equivalent weight of potassium is 39 g.

2.37. What is the equivalent weight of a metal, if 0.650 g liberates 224 ml of hydrogen (at 0°C and a pressure of 1 atmosphere) from an acid solution? answer: 32.5 g/eq

2.38. If 3.70 liters of hydrogen (at 0°C and 1 atm) are liberated from an acid by 3.00 g of metal, what is the equivalent weight of the metal?

2.39. What weight of hydrogen is released by the reaction of 1.00 g lithium with water, if the equivalent weight of lithium is 7.00 g? answer: 0.144 g

2.40. When a sample of a metal oxide was treated with 114 ml of H_2 (measured at 0°C and 1 atm pressure) 1.27 g of the pure metal was obtained. What is the equivalent of this metal?

2.41. What weight of calcium (equivalent weight = 20 g) liberates the same amount of hydrogen as 1.15 g of sodium (equivalent weight = 23 g)? answer: 1.00 g calcium

2.42. The density of liquid ammonia is 0.82 g/ml. The hydrogen content is 17.7% by weight. The density of hydrogen is 0.55 g/l at a pressure of 6.8 atm (100 pounds per square inch) and 27°C. If it costs 1 cent per mile for transportation of a tank car holding 1000 gallons of either liquid ammonia or compressed hydrogen, compare the cost of hydrogen in the two forms over a distance of 100 miles (express answers in cents per kilogram of hydrogen).

the gaseous state and atomic theory

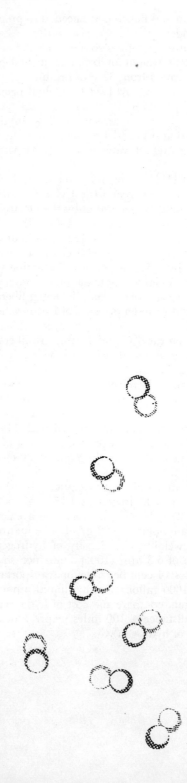

Many theories have been put forth to explain the behavior of matter on the basis of its structure. At one time it was thought that matter was continuous. In this chapter we shall see how the behavior of gases leads to the presently accepted theory that matter is composed of discrete particles.

The gas laws

A gas is that phase of a substance that fills its container completely. To describe fully the physical properties of a gas, it is necessary to specify the three variables: temperature, pressure, and volume.

Boyle's law

Robert Boyle, an English physicist of the seventeenth century, carried out a series of studies which described the pressure–volume relationship of gases. In addition, he proved that the atmosphere exerted a force equivalent to that of a 30-inch high column of mercury. Using this fact, he showed that the product of the pressure, P, and the volume, V, of a given weight of gas at some temperature is a constant, k_B, or

$$PV = k_B$$

This expression may be restated to show that the volume of a constant amount of gas at a constant temperature is inversely proportional to the pressure. This relationship is known as *Boyle's Law*.

$$V = \frac{k_B}{P}$$

Later, more refined measurements on the volume of gases at high pressures show that Boyle's Law does not hold rigorously for most gases at high pressure. However, the behavior predicted by Boyle's Law is within the limits of the errors involved in most experiments on gases at low pressures and at temperatures well above the critical temperature.

Temperature effects

The fact that a gas under a constant pressure expands upon heating and contracts upon cooling is easily observed. Take a balloon filled with air out of a warm building on a cold day. As the gas cools, the size of the balloon decreases.

Jacques Alexandre Charles made the first quantitative studies of the effect of temperature on gases. His work of 1787 was not generally known until Joseph Louis Gay-Lussac published it in 1802. The results of these investigations showed that all gases expand by the same amount for the same rise in temperature. The change in volume of a gas sample at constant pressure was found to be 1/273 of the volume at 0°C for each degree of temperature change. Thus, a gas sample of 273 ml originally at 0°C expands

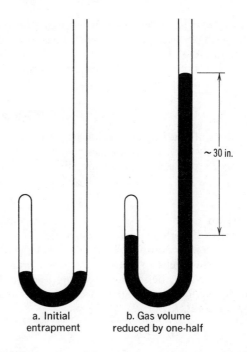

Fig. 3.1

Diagram of Boyle's Experiment. Boyle trapped a quantity of air in the shorter arm of the J-shaped tube. As mercury was added to the longer arm, he measured the volume of the trapped air. Boyle observed that the volume was reduced by one-half when the level of mercury in the longer end was about 30 in. higher than the level in the shorter, closed end.

to 274 ml at $+1°C$ and contracts to 272 ml at $-1°C$ and to 263 ml at $-10°C$.

ABSOLUTE TEMPERATURE SCALE

From the above findings, one would expect a gas to have zero volume at $-273°C$, provided the volume change is constant. Actually, it is not possible to reach this state, because all gases condense to liquids or solids before reaching $-273°C$. Several low-boiling gases have been studied to determine their behavior with respect to temperature and volume. The results indicate that the volume of a gas under constant pressure is a measure of its temperature. That is, all gases show the straight-line behavior sketched in Fig. 3.2 at high temperatures and low pressures. Extrapolation of this straight-line portion leads to a value of $-273.15°C$ as the temperature point at which volume is zero. This temperature is considered to be the minimum temperature, or absolute zero. The scale of temperatures developed from this value is known as the Kelvin scale, after the British physicist, Lord Kelvin, who developed it. The ice point on the Kelvin scale is $273.15°K$. Since a degree on the Kelvin scale is the same as a degree on the Celsius scale, the two are related according to the formula, $°K = °C + 273.15$.

CHARLES' LAW

The volume of a given mass of gas at constant pressure thus is directly proportional to the Kelvin or absolute temperature. One may express this relationship, known as *Charles' Law*, as follows:

$$V = k_C T$$

where V is the volume, T is the absolute temperature, and k_C is a constant.

PRESSURE-TEMPERATURE BEHAVIOR

The gas laws may be combined to state the relationship between the pressure and temperature of a gas. Experiments show that the pressure exerted by a gas confined to a constant volume increases as the temperature increases. For example, the air pressure in tires increases when a car is driven at high speeds over a hot highway. A combination of Boyle's Law and Charles' Law indicates that pressure is directly proportional to the absolute temperature of a gas.

$$P = k_p T$$

Combined gas law

To compare the properties of one sample of gas with another, it is necessary to describe them at the same conditions. The generally

Fig. 3.2

Temperature-Volume Behavior of a Gas. The decrease in the volume of a gas upon cooling at a constant pressure is linear. When the boiling point is approached, deviations appear. Charles' Law is no longer applicable once a gas condenses to a liquid at the boiling point. Extrapolation of the straight-line portion of the curve to a volume of zero leads to a temperature of $-273.15°C$ for all gases.

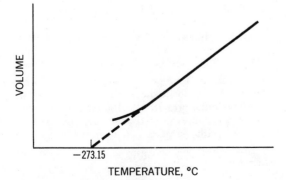

−273.15

TEMPERATURE, °C

accepted *standard conditions* of temperature and pressure (S.T.P.) for the measurement of gas volumes are 0°C and 760 torr. Ordinarily, it is not convenient to measure the volume of a gas at S.T.P., and it is necessary to correct the measured volume to standard conditions using Boyle's and Charles' Laws.

The final volume of a gas V_f is dependent on the initial volume V_i, a factor to correct for the volume change due to the temperature change and a factor to correct for the volume change due to pressure change.

$$V_f = V_i(\text{temperature correction factor}) \times$$
$$(\text{pressure correction factor})$$

The temperature correction factor is the ratio of the absolute temperatures. Recall that for an increase in temperature, there is an increase in volume. Therefore, the ratio of the absolute temperatures is greater than one when the temperature is increased; it is less than one for a decrease in temperature.

The pressure correction term is the ratio of the pressures. Since volume varies inversely with pressure, the pressure correction term is less than one when the pressure is increased, and greater than one when the pressure is decreased. Pressures may be expressed in any unit as long as the same units are used for both.

Although our interest here is primarily in changes of volume, similar expressions can be used for calculating the pressure changes in volume and temperature, and for calculating the temperature after changes in pressure and volume. The appropriate correction factors are developed on the basis of the behavior of gases as they are heated or compressed.

Example 3.1 What is the volume at S.T.P. of a 100 ml sample of hydrogen gas measured at 720 torr and 27°C?

Since the temperature is changed from 27°C to 0°C, the temperature correction factor is less than one or $\dfrac{0 + 273}{27 + 273} = \dfrac{273°\text{K}}{300°\text{K}}$.

The pressure is increased in going to standard conditions with a decrease in volume. The pressure correction factor must be $\dfrac{720 \text{ torr}}{760 \text{ torr}}$ to cause a reduction in volume.

Therefore, the final volume at S.T.P. is

$$V_f = (100 \text{ ml})\left(\frac{273}{300}\right)\left(\frac{720}{760}\right) = 86.2 \text{ ml}$$

Example 3.2 What is the pressure on a sample of air that is compressed from a volume of 2.5 liters to 1.0 liter with a temperature change from 77°C to 17°C? The initial pressure was 700 torr.

A correction for the temperature change must be made. Since the pressure decreases with decreasing temperature, the temperature correction factor is $\dfrac{17 + 273}{77 + 273} = \dfrac{290°\text{K}}{350°\text{K}}$.

The volume compression implies an increase in pressure which leads to a volume correction factor of $\dfrac{2.5 \text{ liters}}{1.0 \text{ liter}}$.

The final pressure is

$$P_f = (700 \text{ torr})\left(\frac{290}{350}\right)\left(\frac{2.5}{1.0}\right) = 1450 \text{ torr}$$

Mixtures of gases

Consider two gases each in a volume V and each at the same pressure P. If the two gases are mixed and no interaction occurs, the pressure remains at P provided the total volume is $2V$. However, if both volumes of gas are mixed together in a container, the total

Fig. 3.3

Pressure-Volume Behavior of Gaseous Mixtures. (a) Two gas samples at constant volume and pressure separated by a diaphragm. (b) Pressure remains constant when diaphragm is removed. (c) Pressure is doubled, if both gases are forced into one chamber.

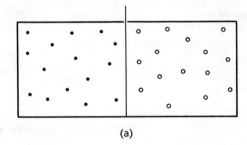

(a)

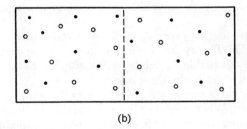

(b)

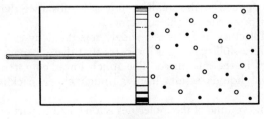

(c)

pressure is the sum of the partial pressures. The partial pressure of a gas is the pressure that is exerted by the gas if it solely occupied the total volume at the temperature of the mixture. The mathematical expression of the Law of Partial Pressures is:

$$P_T = p_1 + p_2 + p_3 + \cdots + p_i + \cdots,$$

where P_T is the total pressure, and p_1, p_2, . . . are the partial pressures of gas 1, gas 2, and so on.

An important application of the Law of Partial Pressures comes when a gas is collected by the displacement of water. The experimentally measured pressure in the container is the sum of the pressure of the dry gas in the container and the vapor pressure of water at the temperature of the experiment. The vapor pressure of water at various temperatures has been carefully measured and is given in Appendix Table III.

Example 3.3 A 100 ml sample of hydrogen was collected over water at 25°C and 720.2 torr. What is the volume of the dry gas at S.T.P.? The vapor pressure of water at 25°C is 23.8 torr.
The partial pressure of the dry hydrogen at 25°C (in 100 ml) is 720.2 − 23.8 = 696.4 torr.
The volume of dry hydrogen at S.T.P. is

$$V_{\text{STP}} = (100 \text{ ml})\left(\frac{273}{298}\right)\left(\frac{696.4}{760.0}\right) = 83.9 \text{ ml}$$

Molecular theory of matter

The relatively simple behavior of gases permits the development of a simple model, or theory, of the gas phase. This model must be consistent with those chosen to explain the behavior of solids and liquids.

On the basis of experimentally observed evidence, the Kinetic-Molecular Theory has been developed as the best explanation presently available for the behavior of gases. Some of the important postulates of the theory are:

(1) A gas is composed of hard, noninteracting particles called molecules. When a solid or liquid is vaporized, the vapor occupies much more volume. This behavior may be explained by postulating some ultimate particle that goes into the gas phase from the surface of the condensed phase. This particle is a *molecule*, which is defined as the smallest unit of a substance that has the chemical properties of the substance.

(2) Molecules in a gas are widely separated by empty space. The compressibility of a gas indicates that there is space between molecules in the gas phase. The much lower compressibility of solids and liquids results from a much closer packing of the molecules.

(3) The volume of the molecules is a negligible part of the total volume of a gas. Near atmospheric pressure, the condensed phase

volume is negligible as compared to the gas volume. For example, the volume of 1 g of liquid water is 1 ml, while 1 g of water vapor occupies a volume of 1367 ml at 1 atm and 27°C.

(4) Molecules are in constant, rapid, random motion. This conclusion is based in part on the fact that gases completely fill their container.

(5) Molecules travel in straight lines between collisions; the average distance moved between collisions is very large compared to the size of the molecules.

(6) Pressure results from the impact of gas molecules on the walls of the container.

(7) Absolute temperature is a measure of the average kinetic energy of the gas molecules. The average kinetic energy is solely a function of the absolute temperature, and is independent of any other property of the gas molecules. Since kinetic energy $= \frac{1}{2} mv^2$ (where m is the mass and v is the velocity), a heavy molecule moves more slowly on the average than a light molecule at the same temperature. At room temperature, the average velocity of hydrogen molecules is much greater than the average velocity of oxygen molecules. Hypothetically, the kinetic energy of gas molecules is zero at absolute zero. Zero kinetic energy implies a velocity of zero which means there is no molecular motion through space. The emphasis here is upon the average kinetic energy, since at temperatures above 0°K, there is a distribution of kinetic

Fig. 3.4

Distribution of Kinetic Energies among Gaseous Molecules at Two Different Temperatures. Curves represent the number of molecules with a given kinetic energy in gaseous samples at absolute temperatures T_1 (solid line) and T_2 (broken line). Since T_2 is twice the value of T_1, the average and most probable kinetic energy values for T_2 are twice those for T_1.

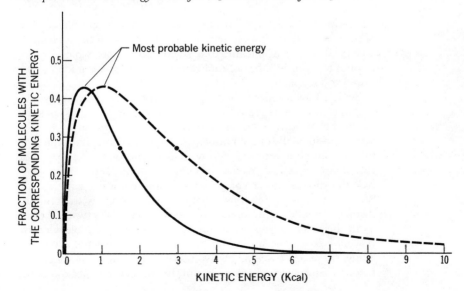

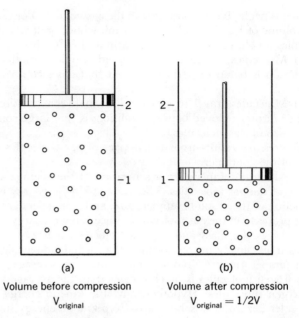

(a)

Volume before compression
$V_{original}$

(b)

Volume after compression
$V_{original} = 1/2V$

Fig. 3.5

Change in the Volume of a Gas Illustrating the Application of the Kinetic-Molecular Theory to Boyle's Law.

energies among the molecules in a gas. This means that at a given temperature, some molecules have little kinetic energy and some molecules have much kinetic energy. The kinetic energy distributions for two different temperatures are shown in Fig. 3.4.

Application to gas laws

The Kinetic-Molecular Theory of gases provides an explanation of the observed gas laws in terms of the behavior of the molecules. The gas laws are applicable to a given mass of gas, which in turn implies a given number of molecules since no gas is added or allowed to escape.

Boyle's Law applies to a sample at constant temperature which means that the average velocity of the molecules remains constant while the pressure and volume change. If the distance between two opposite walls of a container is reduced by one half, the container volume is reduced by one half as shown in Fig. 3.5. The molecules traveling in the vertical direction need travel only half the distance after compression before colliding with a wall. Since the velocity remains constant, the molecules traverse the distance in half the time and collide with the walls twice as often as in the original volume. In an actual container, molecules are traveling in a random fashion so there is no preferred direction. Thus, there are twice as many collisions per unit time (e.g., per second). Since pressure results from the number of collisions of the molecules with the container walls per unit time, the pressure is doubled when the volume is reduced by one half. The extension of this reasoning to other volume changes produces the predicted change in pressure.

When a gas is heated, the average velocity of the molecules increases. If the volume is held constant, the number of collisions per second with the wall increases, resulting in a pressure increase as predicted by Charles' Law.

The validity of the Law of Partial Pressures becomes obvious when one considers that pressure is the result of molecules colliding with the container walls. Thus, if one type of molecule exerts a certain pressure and another type exerts another pressure, the total pressure is the result of the total number of collisions. Increasing the number of molecules in a container results in more molecules colliding with the wall per second and a corresponding increase in pressure unless the volume is increased or the temperature is decreased.

The gas laws are found to be applicable within reasonable accuracy to almost all gases. The agreement between experimentally observed pressure-volume-temperature behavior and that predicted by the gas laws is best at low pressure and at temperatures well above the critical temperature.

The rule of EVEN

The implications of this behavior being relatively independent of the type of gas are many. As indicated previously, the molecules are treated as small hard spheres in the development of the Kinetic-Molecular Theory. Another assumption implicit in this theory is that EQUAL volumes of all gases at the same temperature and pressure contain EQUAL NUMBERS of molecules. While there are alternatives to this assumption, which is referred to as the rule of EVEN in this text, none provides so good an agreement with experimental values in so straightforward a manner. The rule of EVEN is shown to be self-consistent later in this chapter.

Atoms
Law of combining volumes

The fact that molecules are not the simplest form of matter is demonstrated by the *Law of Combining Volumes*. This law was first announced in 1808 by Gay-Lussac who noted a simple regularity in the combining volumes of gases. His law states that gases tend to react in volume ratios that are small whole numbers. While some gaseous reactions are known which do not follow this law, most of the more familiar ones do.

It is found experimentally that at constant pressure and temperature one volume of hydrogen gas reacts with one volume of chlorine gas to produce two volumes of hydrogen chloride gas, or in a more convenient notation:

1 volume hydrogen + 1 volume chlorine →
                              2 volumes hydrogen chloride

If this reaction involved only the combination of one hydrogen molecule with one chlorine molecule to form one hydrogen chloride molecule, there should be only one volume of hydrogen chloride produced if the assumption of the rule of EVEN is made. The alternative is to assume that there are half as many hydrogen chloride molecules per volume as there are hydrogen and chlorine molecules. This is not consistent with the uniform P-V-T behavior of all gases. Accepting the applicability of the rule of EVEN, one may assume that the hydrogen and chlorine molecules are composed of two smaller identical units which are called atoms. The hydrogen chloride molecule is composed of one hydrogen atom and one chlorine atom. Thus, two product molecules result from each molecule of diatomic hydrogen and diatomic chlorine.

Chemical equations

Since large numbers of molecules are involved, the above reaction may be written as follows:

$$nH_2 + nCl_2 \rightarrow 2nHCl$$

In this case, each volume contains n molecules of gas. The two-atom, or diatomic, nature of the molecules is indicated by the subscript 2 on the symbols for the elements.

In this reaction, the number of atoms is conserved, i.e., atoms are not created or destroyed. Furthermore, the experimental volume relationships are retained. The above equality, or equation, expresses the behavior of a large number of molecules. While it is always necessary to deal with large numbers of molecules, a chemical reaction proceeds when one molecule reacts with another. Thus it is correct to write an equation showing the simple ratio of reacting molecules.

$$H_2 + Cl_2 \rightarrow 2HCl$$

This equation is read as, "One molecule of hydrogen [each molecule containing two atoms of hydrogen] reacts with one molecule of chlorine [each molecule containing two atoms of chlorine] to produce two molecules of hydrogen chloride [each molecule containing one hydrogen atom and one chlorine atom]." In reactions involving gases only, the equation also may be interpreted as, "One volume of hydrogen gas reacts with one volume of chlorine gas to produce two volumes of hydrogen chloride gas." Other reactions that illustrate the polyatomic nature of many molecules are shown in Fig. 3.6. With the exception of the monatomic noble gases (He, Ne, Ar, Kr, Xe, Rn), the elements that are gases at room temperatures (H_2, N_2, O_2, F_2, Cl_2) are diatomic.

Additional proof of the fact that these elemental gases are diatomic comes from a consideration of the density of the products and reactants. For example, the density of water vapor is less than the density of oxygen, although hydrogen is added to oxygen.

Fig. 3.6

Reactions That Illustrate the Rule of EVEN *and the Polyatomic Nature of Molecules. The rule of* EVEN *is applicable only if one assumes that the molecules involved are polyatomic.*

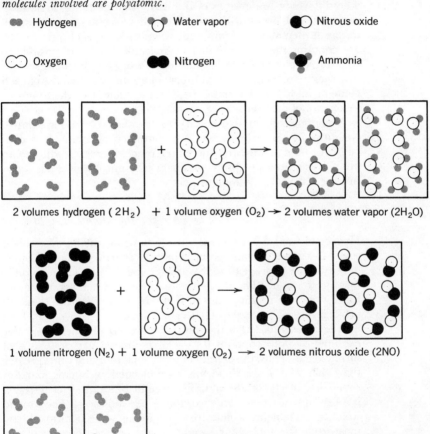

2 volumes hydrogen ($2H_2$) + 1 volume oxygen (O_2) → 2 volumes water vapor ($2H_2O$)

1 volume nitrogen (N_2) + 1 volume oxygen (O_2) → 2 volumes nitrous oxide ($2NO$)

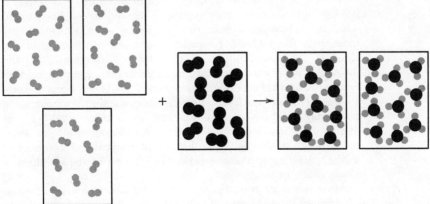

3 volumes hydrogen ($3H_2$) + 1 volume nitrogen (N_2) → 2 volumes ammonia ($2NH_3$)

Ammonia is less dense than nitrogen, although hydrogen is added. Carbon monoxide formed by the reaction of carbon with oxygen is less dense than oxygen. These densities can be explained if one considers that the hydrogen or carbon atoms replace an atom of oxygen or nitrogen in the diatomic molecule.

Atomic and molecular weights

The difference in densities of the various gases at the same temperature and pressure implies that the molecules and atoms of different elements have different weights, since each liter of any gas contains the same number of molecules. It is not possible to weigh a single molecule because of its exceedingly small size. It is necessary to weigh large numbers of atoms or molecules of each element and then determine the relative weight of the atoms or molecules of each substance.

A reference point is necessary to establish a working relative weight scale. Since molecules are composed of atoms, it is convenient to use an atom for such a reference, thereby leading to an atomic weight scale. More precisely it is an atomic mass scale, but the term, atomic weight, persists.

The base for the atomic weight scale

Hydrogen was an early choice as the basis for the atomic weight scale. It has the advantage of being the element with the lowest density. The hydrogen atom was assigned a value of one atomic mass unit (amu). The diatomic molecule had a mass of 2 amu. Since these are relative masses, there are no units other than the arbitrary *atomic mass unit*. Hydrogen provided a convenient base for the determination of the molecular weight of other gases. For example, a bulb contains 0.05 g of hydrogen gas or 0.70 g of nitrogen gas. Thus, the density of nitrogen is fourteen times greater than that of H_2, which means its molecular weight is fourteen times that of H_2, or 28 amu. The weight of an atom of nitrogen is 14 amu since there are two atoms per molecule. The atomic weights of elements which are not gaseous were determined by measuring the molecular weight of gaseous compounds of the element. The contribution of the element in question to the molecular weight is determined from the percentage composition. For example, the compound ethane consists of 80 per cent carbon by weight. Since it is fifteen times more dense than hydrogen, the molecular weight is 30 amu. The carbon contributes 80 per cent of this molecular weight or 24 amu. A value of twelve or some multiple of twelve is found for all of the carbon compounds studied, leading to the assignment of 12 amu as the weight of a single carbon atom.

After many of the atomic and molecular weights had been established using hydrogen as a reference, it was possible to use chemical reactions for a more precise determination of the relative masses. Since oxygen reacts with many more elements than does hydrogen, it is a more convenient reference. A value of exactly 16 amu was assigned to oxygen. On this scale, the hydrogen atom has a value of 1.008 amu. Many precise measurements of atomic weights were made using the oxygen-16 reference.

In recent years, the mass spectrograph has been developed to make very precise determinations of the relative masses of individual atoms. Carbon was selected as the basis of the atomic weight scale partly because of the ease with which carbon is used to calibrate the mass spectrograph. The present basis for the atomic weight scale is a value of exactly 12 amu for the most commonly found type of carbon atom. The atomic masses on the carbon-12 scale differ only slightly from those on the oxygen-16 scale. The atomic weights of the elements based on carbon-12 are given in the table inside the back cover.

Gram-atomic and gram-molecular weights

Chemical reactions occur between atoms and molecules. Therefore, the number of atoms or molecules are more important than the weight in the study of a chemical reaction. While it is not possible to count the number of atoms in a sample, it is possible to

Fig. 3.7

Schematic Diagram of a Magnetic Deflection Mass Spectrograph. Used to determine atomic and molecular masses. Gaseous molecules enter through the slit, acquire a charge, and are accelerated before passing through the magnetic field where they are deflected. With a single unit of charge on the particle, its deflection from a straight line depends on its mass. With some instruments the mass of a particle may be measured to one part per 10 million relative to a reference mass.

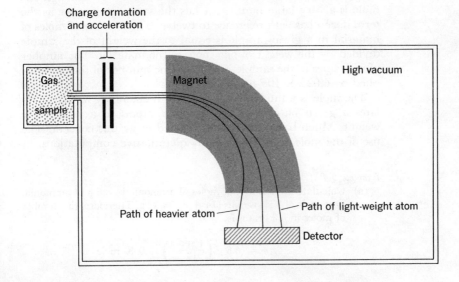

weigh the total number. Thus, the number of atoms must be related to a measurable weight.

Since atomic weights and molecular weights are based on a relative scale, 1.008 g hydrogen, 12.0000 g carbon, and 16.0 g oxygen contain the same number of atoms. There are 100 times as many atoms in 100.8 g hydrogen, 1200 g carbon, and 1600 g oxygen. The weight in grams which is equal to the number representing the atomic weight of an element is called the *gram-atomic weight* of the element. Similarly, one *gram-molecular weight* is the number of grams of a molecular substance that is equal to the number representing the molecular weight of a molecule. It cannot be stressed too strongly that gram-atomic weights and gram-molecular weights have mass units of grams and are measurable on a balance, while atomic weights and molecular weights are measured relative to an assigned value of 12.000 for carbon-12.

The mole

The question persists as to the number of atoms or molecules in a gram-atomic weight or gram-molecular weight. One gram-atomic weight contains the same number of atoms as there are molecules in one gram-molecular weight, since the same reference mass is used for both. Methods have been developed to measure the distance between atoms and their arrangement in a crystalline solid. From these measurements it is possible to calculate the number of atoms in a given volume. Combining this value with the density of the solid, the number of atoms in a given weight is obtained. From studies of this type, it is found that one gram-molecular weight of any substance contains 6.023×10^{23} molecules and one gram-atomic weight contains 6.023×10^{23} atoms.

This number, 6.023×10^{23}, is called the *mole*. Although the mole is a very large number, it has the same significance as the term dozen has with reference to twelve. The number of moles of material in a given sample is equal to the weight of the sample divided by the weight of one mole of the material. The number of molecules in the sample is equal to the number of moles multiplied by 6.023×10^{23} molecules per mole.

The mole is a fundamental concept in chemistry in that it relates a given number of molecules or atoms to a measurable weight. Much basic theory is developed using this concept. The use of the mole greatly aids many quantitative computations.

Example 3.4

(a) Calculate the number of moles of ammonia in 6.8 g of ammonia. One mole of NH_3 weighs $(14 + 3) = 17$ g. Therefore, the number of moles in 6.8 grams is:

$$n = (6.8 \text{ g})\left(\frac{1 \text{ mole}}{17 \text{ g}}\right) = 0.40 \text{ mole}$$

(b) Calculate the number of moles of carbon in 840 g of graphite. One mole of carbon weighs 12 g. Therefore,

$$n = (840 \text{ g})\left(\frac{1 \text{ mole}}{12 \text{ g}}\right) = 70 \text{ moles}$$

Example 3.5
(a) How many molecules are in 8.00 g of Br_2?
Step 1.   Convert weight to moles.

$$\text{Number of moles } Br_2 = (8.00 \text{ g})\left(\frac{1 \text{ mole}}{160 \text{ g}}\right) = 0.0500 \text{ mole}.$$

Step 2.   Convert moles to molecules.

$$\text{Number of molecules} = (5.00 \times 10^{-2} \text{ mole})\left(\frac{6.02 \times 10^{23} \text{ molecules}}{1 \text{ mole}}\right)$$
$$= 3.01 \times 10^{22} \text{ molecules}$$

(b) How many atoms are in 4.00 g of Mg?

$$\text{Number of moles Mg} = (4.00 \text{ g})\left(\frac{1 \text{ mole}}{24 \text{ g}}\right) = 0.167 \text{ mole Mg}$$

$$\text{Number of atoms} = (0.167 \text{ mole})\left(\frac{6.02 \times 10^{23} \text{ atoms}}{1 \text{ mole}}\right)$$
$$= 1.00 \times 10^{23} \text{ atoms}$$

Example 3.6 What is the weight of 1.20×10^{21} atoms of arsenic?

$$\text{Number of moles} = (1.20 \times 10^{21} \text{ atoms})\left(\frac{1 \text{ mole}}{6.02 \times 10^{23} \text{ atoms}}\right)$$
$$= 1.99 \times 10^{-3} \text{ mole}$$
$$\text{weight} = (1.99 \times 10^{-3} \text{ mole})\left(\frac{75 \text{ g As}}{1 \text{ mole}}\right) = 0.149 \text{ g}$$

Example 3.7 How many atoms of oxygen are in 2.40 g of O_2?
Since the number of atoms is required, it is necessary to use the atomic weight of oxygen rather than the molecular weight.

$$\text{Moles of oxygen atoms} = (2.4 \text{ g})\left(\frac{1 \text{ mole}}{16 \text{ g}}\right)$$
$$= 0.15 \text{ mole}$$
$$= (0.15 \text{ mole})\left(\frac{6.02 \times 10^{23} \text{ atoms}}{1 \text{ mole}}\right)$$
$$= 9.0 \times 10^{24} \text{ atoms}$$

The term *mole*, when applied to atoms, refers to a collection of 6.023×10^{23} atoms which weigh the same number of grams as the number representing the atomic weight. When applied to molecules, *mole* refers to a collection of 6.023×10^{23} molecules which weigh the same number of grams as the number representing the molecular weight. *Mole* also refers to the mass of material containing 6.023×10^{23} formula weights of the material. This mass is the same number of grams as the number representing the formula weight. While this convention requires careful reading to determine whether atoms, molecules, or formulas are being discussed, it does reduce the wide variety of terminology.

Example 3.8 How many moles of hydrogen atoms and hydrogen molecules are in 5 g of hydrogen gas?

1 mole of hydrogen atoms weighs 1 g; thus

$$n_H = (5 \text{ g})\left(\frac{1 \text{ mole}}{1 \text{ g}}\right) = 5 \text{ moles}$$

1 mole of hydrogen molecules weighs 2 g; thus

$$n_{H_2} = (5 \text{ g})\left(\frac{1 \text{ mole}}{2 \text{ g}}\right) = 2.5 \text{ moles}$$

Since the mole represents a fixed number of molecules, a chemical equation also represents the number of moles involved. Thus the interpretation for the equation

$$H_2 \quad + \quad Cl_2 \quad \rightarrow \quad 2HCl$$

is

1 molecule H_2 + 1 molecule $Cl_2 \rightarrow$ 2 molecules HCl

or

1 mole H_2 + 1 mole $Cl_2 \rightarrow$ 2 moles HCl

or

1 volume H_2 + 1 volume $Cl_2 \rightarrow$ 2 volumes HCl
(valid for gases only)

The choice of interpretations depends upon the particular application.

Example 3.9 Interpret the following equation in terms of moles, molecules, and liters. $2H_2 + O_2 \rightarrow 2H_2O$

2 moles of hydrogen react with 1 mole of oxygen to form 2 moles of water.

2 molecules of hydrogen react with 1 molecule of oxygen to form 2 molecules of water.

2 liters of hydrogen gas react with 1 liter of oxygen gas to form 2 liters of water vapor.

Example 3.10 Given the equation: $2H_2 + O_2 \rightarrow 2H_2O$

(a) 4 moles O_2 produce _____ moles H_2O
(b) 4 moles O_2 produce _____ molecules H_2O
(c) 4 moles O_2 produce _____ grams H_2O
(d) 6 liters H_2 react with _____ liters O_2 at the same temperature and pressure

(a) 4 moles of O_2 must be expressed in terms of an equivalent number of moles of H_2O using the equation

$$(4 \text{ moles } O_2)\left(\frac{2 \text{ moles } H_2O}{1 \text{ mole } O_2}\right) = 8 \text{ moles } H_2O$$

The term in the second set of parentheses is obtained from the balanced chemical equation.

(b) The number of moles of H_2O is converted to number of molecules.

$$(8 \text{ moles})\left(\frac{6.02 \times 10^{23} \text{ molecules}}{1 \text{ mole}}\right) = 4.8 \times 10^{24} \text{ molecules}$$

(c) The number of moles of H_2O is converted to weight of H_2O.

$$(8 \text{ moles})\left(\frac{18 \text{ g } H_2O}{1 \text{ mole}}\right) = 144 \text{ g } H_2O$$

(d) The equation provides the ratio required to convert volume of one gas to an equivalent volume of another gas.

$$(6 \text{ liters } H_2)\left(\frac{1 \text{ liter } O_2}{2 \text{ liters } H_2}\right) = 3 \text{ liters } O_2$$

Gram-molecular volume

It is found that one mole of a gas at 0°C and 1 atm pressure occupies a volume of 22.4 liters, which is called the *gram-molecular volume*. Assuming ideality, the molecular weight of a gas is approximated by weighing a known volume of gas, correcting the volume to S.T.P., and then multiplying the weight by the factor $(22.4/V)$, where V is the corrected volume in liters. This results in the weight of 22.4 liters which is the same number of grams as the molecular weight.

Example 3.11 The density of CO_2 is 1.96 g/l at S.T.P. What is the molecular weight?

$$\left(\frac{1.96 \text{ g}}{1 \text{ liter}}\right)\left(\frac{22.4 \text{ l}}{1 \text{ mole}}\right) = 44 \text{ g/mole}$$

The molecular weight is 44 amu.

Example 3.12 The weight of 3.2 liters of a gas at S.T.P. is 9.15 g. What is the molecular weight of the gas?

$$(9.15 \text{ g})\left(\frac{22.4 \text{ l/mole}}{3.2 \text{ l}}\right) = 64 \text{ g/mole}$$

The molecular weight is 64 amu.

The ideal gas law

A gas is said to be ideal if its pressure-volume-temperature behavior is described by Boyle's and Charles' Laws. It is possible to combine these laws into one ideal gas law which may be derived also from Kinetic-Molecular Theory.

$$PV = RT$$

The constant, R, may be evaluated using the values of the gram-molecular volume: $(1 \text{ atm})(22.4 \text{ liters}) = R(273°K)$,

$$R = 0.08205 \frac{\text{l-atm}}{\text{mole-deg}}$$

This value is for one mole of gas. The ideal gas law is generalized for n moles of gas.

$$PV = nRT,$$

where n is the number of moles of gas and T is the absolute temperature. The value of the gas constant R depends upon the units of pressure and volume. If P is expressed in atmospheres and V in liters, R has a value of 0.08205 liter-atm/mole-deg.

Example 3.13 What is the volume occupied by 12.8 grams of oxygen at 57°C and 646 torr? Assume ideality.

$$n = (12.8 \text{ g})\left(\frac{1 \text{ mole}}{32 \text{ g}}\right) = 0.400 \text{ mole}$$

$$P = (646 \text{ torr})\left(\frac{1 \text{ atm}}{760 \text{ torr}}\right) = 0.850 \text{ atm}$$

$$T = 57 + 273 = 330°\text{K}$$

$$(0.850 \text{ atm})V = (0.400 \text{ mole})(0.08205 \text{ liter-atm/mole-deg})(330°\text{K})$$

$$V = \frac{(0.400 \text{ mole})(0.08205 \text{ liter-atm/mole-deg})(330°\text{K})}{0.850 \text{ atm}} = 12.7 \text{ liters}$$

No real gas is truly ideal, but all gases approach ideality well above the critical temperature and at low pressures. The finite size of the gas molecules and their interactions cause deviations from ideality at high pressures and low temperatures.

It is a relatively simple task to verify the earlier assumption of the rule of EVEN using the ideal gas law. The expression of the ideal gas law for gases 1 and 2 is

$$P_1V_1 = n_1RT_1$$
$$P_2V_2 = n_2RT_2$$

The rule of EVEN implies the conditions

$$P_1 = P_2, \ V_1 = V_2, \text{ and } T_1 = T_2$$

Therefore,

$$P_1V_1 = P_2V_2$$
$$n_1RT_1 = n_2RT_2$$
$$n_1 = n_2$$

SIGNIFICANT TERMS AND CONCEPTS IN CHAPTER III:

Boyle's law, Charles' Law, Absolute or Kelvin temperature scale, standard conditions (S.T.P.), P-V-T behavior of gases, ideal gas law, partial pressure, Kinetic-Molecular Theory, molecule, distribution of kinetic energies among gas molecules and its relationship to the absolute temperature, EVEN, atoms, chemical equation and its interpretation, carbon-12 base for atomic weight scale, atomic and molecular weights, gram-atomic and gram-molecular weights, mole, use of moles in a chemical equation, gram-molecular volume.

Review questions

3.1. Why is mercury commonly used as the liquid in direct reading barometers?
3.2. There is a deviation from a straight line at low temperatures in Fig. 3.2. Explain.
3.3. How is the mathematical statement of Charles' law rewritten for use with the Celsius temperature scale?
3.4. Which of the parts of the Kinetic-Molecular Theory are not rigorously applicable to a real gas?
3.5. How does the mole relate number of molecules and weight?
3.6. How does the mole relate number of molecules and the volume of a gas?
3.7. Show that the ideal gas law reduces to Boyle's Law and to Charles' Law under appropriate conditions.
3.8. Three one-liter flasks at 25°C contain the following gases at the indicated pressures. Flask A: H_2 at 500 torr. Flask B: H_2 at 1000 torr. Flask C: O_2 at 1000 torr.
   (a) Which flask contains the largest number of molecules?
   (b) Which flask contains the most rapidly moving (on the average) molecules?
   (c) Which flask contains the molecules with the greatest average kinetic energy?

Problems

3.9. What is the volume of 5.00 liters of gas when the pressure is changed from 640 torr to 1.0 atm?   answer: 4.21 liters
3.10. What is the final volume of a gas sample at 100 torr if it occupies a volume of 250 ml at a pressure of 800 torr?
3.11. What must be the pressure (in atmospheres) on a sample of gas to contain it in a 1.00 liter volume if it occupies a volume of 2.50 liters at 720 torr?
3.12. What is the final volume of a gas sample at 0°C if it occupies 640 ml at 100°C?
3.13. What is the final volume of a gas sample at 240°C if it occupies 5.00 liters at −10°C?   answer: 9.75 l
3.14. What is the final temperature of a gas if the volume is changed from 2.20 liters at 40°C to 1.00 liter?
3.15. A sample of gas occupies a volume of 300 ml at 27°C and 720 torr. What will be the volume at 500°C and 800° torr?
     answer: 696 ml
3.16. A volume of 1500 ml of hydrogen is at 17°C and 720 torr. What would be the volume occupied by the hydrogen at S.T.P.?
3.17. A sample of gas occupies a volume of 1.50 liters at 740 torr and 30°C. What is the pressure of the gas if the volume is 3.50 liters at −33°C?
3.18. A sample of gas occupies a volume of 4.60 liters at 700 torr

and 22°C. What is the temperature of the gas if the volume is 8.20 liters and the pressure is 1000 torr?

3.19. A gas occupies a volume of 70.0 ml when collected over water. The barometric pressure is 717 torr and the water temperature is 15°C. What volume does the dry gas occupy at 25°C and 800 torr?

3.20. What volume will be occupied by 2.6 grams of SiF_4 gas at 247°C and 684 torr?

3.21. What volume will be occupied by 0.76 grams of F_2 gas at 800°C and 570 torr?   answer: 2.3 liters

3.22. A sample of an unknown liquid was vaporized at 100°C. The container was found to have a volume of 41.0 ml. The sample weighed 0.114 g. The barometric pressure was 722 torr. What is the molecular weight of the compound?

3.23. Calculate the molecular weight, given the data: Sample weight 0.244 g, pressure 773 torr, volume 52.0 ml, temperature 80°C.

3.24. One volume of gas A reacts with two volumes of gas B to produce one volume of product gas. What is the formula of the product if (a) A and B are monatomic molecules, (b) A and B are diatomic molecules, (c) A is monatomic and B is diatomic, (d) A is diatomic and B is monatomic?

3.25. If the density of hydrogen at room temperature is 0.0800 g/l, what is the weight of 5.00 liters of argon under the same conditions?

3.26. What is the weight (in grams) of: (a) 10 moles of oxygen gas, (b) 6.02×10^{24} molecules of oxygen, (c) 6.02×10^{24} atoms of oxygen, (d) a single oxygen molecule, (e) a single oxygen atom?   answer: (a) 320 g

3.27. How many atoms are in (a) 10 g aluminum, (b) 10 g sulfur, (c) 10 g carbon, (d) 10 g mercury? answer: (a) 2.2×10^{23}

3.28. (a) 0.800 mole CH_4 = _____ g = _____ molecules
   (b) 40.0 g SO_3 = _____ moles = _____ molecules
   (c) 9.00×10^{23} molecules CO_2 = _____ moles = _____ g
   (d) 3.2 moles O_2 = _____ g = _____ molecules = _____ atoms
   (e) 0.600 g N_2O_5 = _____ moles = _____ molecules = _____ atoms
   (f) 6.02×10^6 molecules N_2 = _____ moles = _____ g = _____ atoms

answer: (a) 12.8 g, 4.82×10^{23} molecules

3.29. Given the equation: $2SO_2 + O_2 \rightarrow 2SO_3$
   (a) 5 molecules of O_2 react with _____ molecules of SO_2
   (b) 8 moles of O_2 react with _____ moles of SO_2
   (c) 5 molecules of SO_2 would form _____ molecules of SO_3
   (d) 4 moles of SO_2 would form _____ liters of SO_3 (at 25°C, 1 atm)

answer: (a) 10

four

the language of chemistry

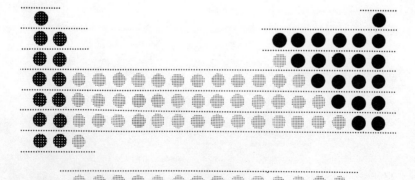

It is not possible to remember all of the chemical and physical properties of the 103 elements and their compounds. Many classifications which attempt to group the elements systematically into families with similar properties have been developed. In addition, rules for writing and naming the multitude of compounds are necessary. It is possible to express a chemical reaction in terms of a chemical equation which provides a quantitative as well as a qualitative understanding of a chemical reaction.

The periodic law

If one studies the chemical and physical properties of the elements in order of increasing atomic weight, one notes that similarities in properties occur at regular intervals. When elements of similar properties are grouped, the sequence generally follows the order of atomic weights, although there are a few obviously misplaced elements. For example, the almost inert gas, argon, and the very active metal, potassium, must be interchanged in the sequence of atomic weights to place them in a chemically similar group. Other changes such as this are also found.

On the basis of empirical evidence, it is desirable to number each element beginning with hydrogen. This number, called the atomic number, parallels the atomic weight listing except at those points where the properties require a change in sequence. Thus, potassium, with an atomic weight of 39.10, has an atomic number of 19, while argon is number 18 with a higher weight of 39.95. As the understanding of the behavior of atoms increased, the definition (but not the value) of the atomic number was changed so that now the atomic number is much more important than the atomic weight in the correlation of properties. The recurrent, or periodic, nature of the properties of the elements is illustrated in Fig. 4.1.

One of the early attempts to make a periodic classification of the elements was made by John A. Newlands in 1863. He observed that the properties seemed to recur with every eighth element. The so-called law of octaves holds for the lightweight elements, if the noble gas elements (helium, neon, argon) which were not discovered until the early part of the twentieth century are not included.

About the same time that Newlands published his law of octaves in England, Lothar Meyer in Germany published a more extensive table showing the periodic character of 56 elements. The credit for the most useful periodic table must go to the Russian, Dmitri I. Mendeleev, who published his work from 1869 to 1871. Mendeleev put his primary emphasis upon chemical similarities. While arranging the elements in order of their atomic weight, Mendeleev left blanks or assumed the atomic weights to be in error wherever discrepancies would otherwise appear. Since argon was unknown at the time, the reversal of potassium and argon was not a problem to him. Only two other reversals were

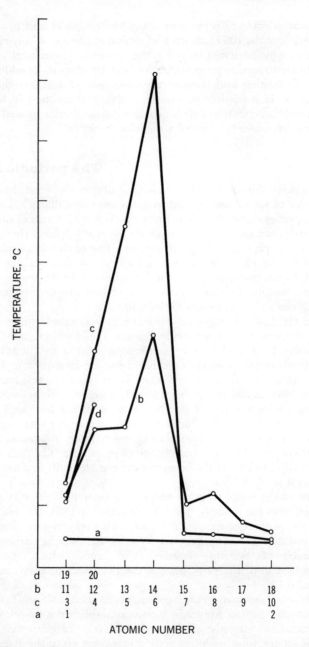

Fig. 4.1

Melting Points of the Elements As a Function of Atomic Number. Includes first 20 elements. Curve is broken into sections to show minimum values for elements 2, 10, and 18 above each other at the right. The maxima occurring at elements 6 and 14 are above each other. Shape of each section is the same qualitatively. Similar curves are obtained when other properties are plotted.

necessary: cobalt (58.93) and nickel (58.71), and tellurium (127.6) and iodine (126.9). The genius of Mendeleev's system was in his prediction of chemical and physical properties of elements not yet discovered. At least three elements were discovered within fifteen years using Mendeleev's predictions. With these triumphs to its credit, the Mendeleev table was accepted readily.

Fig. 4.2

Dmitri Mendeleev

The early tables were strictly empirical. As the understanding of its theoretical basis developed, modifications of the periodic table were made. Several forms are now available. A commonly used long form of the table, which arranges the elements in the order of atomic number, is shown inside the front cover of this book. The elements in a vertical column or *group* form a family with similar chemical and physical properties. The horizontal rows are known as *periods*, throughout which the properties vary in a regular fashion.

Design of the long form periodic table

The *Group Number* is shown as a Roman numeral at the top of each column. The *A* and *B* designation developed when the transition metals were thought to be subgroups of the other families and is still used as a convenience. It is also convenient to place hydrogen in Group IA, although it is unlike the other members of the group in many ways. The period is designated by an Arabic numeral to the left.

Each square represents an element. At the top is the atomic number which designates its position in the sequence of elements. At the bottom of each square is the atomic weight of the element. The symbol for the element is given in the center of each square.

The metals are found on the left-hand side of the table while the nonmetals are on the right-hand side, although the Group VIIIA elements are neither metals nor nonmetals. A diagonal line through boron (B), silicon (Si), arsenic (As), and tellurium (Te) roughly divides the metals and nonmetals. Since metallic and nonmetallic properties vary uniformly in a period, there is no sharp boundary between the two. Thus the elements on and just to the left of the dividing line are *amphoteric*, that is, they behave as both metals and nonmetals. The amphoteric elements, or *metalloids*, are intermediate between metals and nonmetals. The amphoteric nature of the metalloids is illustrated by the fact that the water insoluble oxides of these elements dissolve in either an acid or base.

The *B* Groups or transition metals are, as the name implies, a group of metals with properties intermediate between the very metallic IA and IIA Groups and the metalloids. The chemistry of the transition metals is extremely varied, but it is uniform enough for them to be considered as one large family.

The lanthanide and actinide series represent two large subdivisions of Group IIIB. The elements in each series are quite similar in physical and chemical properties and require very sophisticated techniques for their separation. Similarly, the chemistry of both series is very close; many of the properties of the actinide ele-

Fig. 4.3
Melting Points and Boiling Points of the Elements

IA	IIA	IIIB	IVB	VB	VIB	VIIB	VIIIB			IB	IIB	IIIA	IVA	VA	VIA	VIIA	VIIIA
H 0.09*																	**He** 0.18*
Li 0.53	**Be** 1.85				TRANSITION METALS							**B** 2.46	**C** 2.25	**N** 1.25*	**O** 1.43*	**F** 1.70*	**Ne** 0.90*
Na 0.97	**Mg** 1.74											**Al** 2.70	**Si** 2.33	**P†** 2.20	**S** 2.06	**Cl** 3.21*	**Ar** 1.74*
K 0.86	**Ca** 1.55	**Sc** 2.99	**Ti** 4.50	**V** 5.68	**Cr** 7.20	**Mn** 7.48	**Fe** 7.87	**Co** 8.79	**Ni** 8.91	**Cu** 8.93	**Zn** 7.13	**Ga** 5.91	**Ge** 5.32	**As** 5.78	**Se** 4.81	**Br** 3.12	**Kr** 3.74*
Rb 1.53	**Sr** 2.58	**Y** 5.51	**Zr** 6.51	**Nb** 8.57	**Mo** 10.22	**Tc** —	**Ru** 12.44	**Rh** 12.42	**Pd** 12.04	**Ag** 10.50	**Cd** 8.64	**In** 7.29	**Sn** 7.29	**Sb** 6.70	**Te** 6.23	**I** 4.94	**Xe** 5.90*
Cs 1.87	**Ba** 3.60	**La** 6.19	**Hf** 13.25	**Ta** 16.63	**W** 19.26	**Re** 21.03	**Os** 22.58	**Ir** 22.66	**Pt** 21.47	**Au** 19.30	**Hg** 13.53	**Tl** 11.85	**Pb** 11.34	**Bi** 9.81	**Po** 9.32	**At** —	**Rn** 9.9*
Fr —	**Ra** —	**Ac** —															

— Symbol
— Density (g/cc)

*Densities for gases are expressed in g/l.
**Graphite form
†Red phosphorus

LANTHANIDES	**Ce** 6.9	**Pr** 6.8	**Nd** 7.02	**Pm** —	**Sm** 7.52	**Eu** 5.17	**Gd** 7.87	**Tb** 8.25	**Dy** 8.44	**Ho** 8.80	**Er** 4.8	**Tm** 9.32	**Yb** 7.03	**Lu** 9.85
ACTINIDES	**Th** 11.5	**Pa** 15.37	**U** 18.97	**Np** —	**Pu** 17.91	**Am** 13.67	**Cm** —	**Bk** —	**Cf** —	**Es** —	**Fm** —	**Md** —	**No** —	**Lw** —

Fig. 4.4

Densities of the Elements

ments can be predicted by analogy with the corresponding lanthanide.

All of the actinides with atomic numbers 93 and above do not occur in nature but are prepared synthetically. Francium (atomic number 87), astatine (atomic number 85), promethium (atomic number 61), and technetium (atomic number 43) are non-actinides that are not found in nature.

Certain groups in the Periodic Table have been given special names of historical significance. These include: Group IA (except hydrogen), alkali metals; Group IIA, alkaline earths; Group VIA, chalcogens; Group VIIA, halogens; and Group VIIIA, noble gases.

Periodic properties

Values of the melting point, boiling point, and density for many of the elements are shown in Figs. 4.3 and 4.4. Atomic radii are shown in the Periodic Table of Fig. 4.5. It is apparent that there are certain general trends in the physical properties of the elements. In general, the values for the elements in any one group increase with increasing atomic weight. One outstanding exception to the general rule occurs with the melting and boiling points of the alkali metals (Group IA), where the opposite trend is observed.

Several trends also are observed within a period. The melting points, boiling points, and densities reach a maximum value in

Group IVA, followed by a sharp drop in Group VA, an increase in Groups VIA and VIIA, and another drop in Group VIIIA. There are small changes in all of the physical properties of the transition metals, lanthanide series, and actinide series elements.

A periodicity is observed in chemical properties also. The metallic character of a group increases with atomic weight. Thus, cesium is the most reactive metallic element that is naturally occurring. Conversely, the lightest element in any group has the most nonmetallic character. Since the nonmetallic character increases when going from Group IA to Group VIIA, fluorine is the most reactive nonmetallic element.

Charged atoms

The metallic character of an element is demonstrated frequently in a chemical reaction by the acquisition of a positive charge by an atom. Nonmetallic atoms become negatively charged in such a reaction. These charged particles are *ions*. The term refers to any charged species, positive or negative, monatomic (one atom) or polyatomic (many atoms). The positively charged ions frequently are called *cations* (cat'-ion), and the negatively charged ions are called *anions* (an'-ion).

Ions may have more than one unit of electrical charge. The number of charges is indicated by a superscript following the symbol along with a + or − to show the type of charge. The digit is omitted when there is only one charge; it is permissible to use as many + or − signs as there are charges. Some examples in-

Fig. 4.5

Atomic Radii of the Elements. The atomic radius represents the effective size of the atom in combination with another atom to form a molecule. The isolated atom probably is somewhat larger, but its size cannot be measured experimentally.

IA																	VIII A
H 0.30	II A											III A	IV A	V A	VI A	VII A	He 0.93
Li 1.225	Be 0.889											B 0.80	C 0.771	N 0.74	O 0.74	F 0.72	Ne 1.12
Na 1.572	Mg 1.364	III B	IV B	V B	VI B	VII B		VIII B			I B	II B	Al 1.248	Si 1.173	P 1.10	S 1.04	Cl 0.994	Ar 1.54
K 2.025	Ca 1.736	Sc 1.439	Ti 1.324	V 1.224	Cr 1.172	Mn 1.168	Fe 1.165	Co 1.157	Ni 1.149	Cu 1.173	Zn 1.249	Ga 1.245	Ge 1.223	As 1.21	Se 1.17	Br 1.14	Kr 1.69
Rb 2.16	Sr 1.914	Y 1.616	Zr 1.454	Nb 1.342	Mo 1.291	Tc —	Ru 1.241	Rh 1.247	Pd 1.278	Ag 1.339	Cd 1.413	In 1.497	Sn 1.412	Sb 1.41	Te 1.37	I 1.334	Xe 1.90
Cs 2.35	Ba 1.981	La 1.690	Hf 1.442	Ta 1.343	W 1.299	Re 1.278	Os 1.255	Ir 1.260	Pt 1.290	Au 1.336	Hg 1.440	Tl 1.549	Pb 1.538	Bi 1.52	Po 1.53	At —	Rn —

— Symbol
— Atomic radius (Å)

LANTHANIDE SERIES	Ce 1.646	Pr 1.648	Nd 1.642	Pm —	Sm 1.66	Eu 1.850	Gd 1.614	Tb 1.592	Dy 1.589	Ho 1.580	Er 1.567	Tm 1.562	Yb 1.699	Lu 1.557

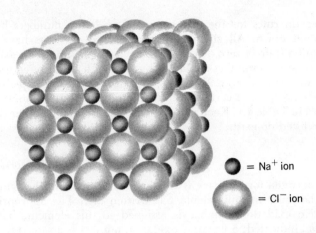

= Na⁺ ion

= Cl⁻ ion

Fig. 4.6
Arrangement of Ions in Sodium Chloride

clude, Na^+, Mg^{2+} or Mg^{+2} or Mg^{++}, Al^{3+} or Al^{+3} or Al^{+++}, S^{-2} or $S^=$ or S^{2-}, F^-, and Cl^-.

In a compound composed of ions, the total number of positive charges is equal to the total number of negative charges. In such a compound, each positive ion is surrounded by negative ions; thus it is associated equally with all of the negative ions. The negative ions are surrounded in turn by positive ions. An ionic solid, such as sodium chloride (NaCl) shown in Fig. 4.6, is made up of an array of positive and negative ions held together by the electrostatic forces of attraction between particles with unlike charges. When such a solid is placed in water, the arrangement of ions breaks up, if the forces of attraction between the water molecules and the ions are greater than the forces of attraction between ions. Such a solid is said to be soluble in water. If the forces of interionic attraction are greater, very few ions are broken out of the array. The solid then is said to be insoluble in water.

Chemical formulas

Much chemical information is contained in a chemical formula. Chemical symbols are used to designate the elements that make up a molecule. The number of atoms is indicated by a subscript after the symbol. In the case of an ionic solid, the formula indicates the ratio of the ions in the solid. Every compound, ionic or molecular, is characterized by a unique formula.

Oxidation numbers

Chemical formulas may be predicted by the use of oxidation numbers. Since all chemical compounds are electrically neutral, the total number of positive oxidation numbers must equal the total of the negative oxidation numbers.

Certain rules for the assignment of oxidation numbers have been set down. All chemically uncombined elements have an oxidation state of zero. Na and H_2, for example, are in an oxidation state of zero. The oxidation number of a monatomic ion is the same as its charge. Elements in each *A* group in the periodic table tend to have certain commonly found oxidation numbers, shown in Table 4.1. Keep in mind that oxidation states other than those listed do exist.

Formula writing

In a formula for a binary (two element) compound, the symbol for the more metallic element is written first. The appropriate positive oxidation number is assigned to this element, but is seldom indicated; a negative oxidation number is assigned to the more nonmetallic element. Since the total of positive numbers must equal the total of negative numbers to attain a neutral species, each symbol is followed by an integer subscript indicating the number of atoms of the element required for neutrality. If the subscript is one, it is omitted.

Example 4.1 Predict the formulas of the binary compounds formed by the following pairs of elements.
  (a) Sodium and chlorine
  (b) Potassium and oxygen
  (c) Aluminum and oxygen
  (d) Calcium and nitrogen
  (e) Phosphorus and oxygen
answers:
  (a) oxidation number of Na $= +1$; of Cl $= -1$. Formula: NaCl
  (b) oxidation number of K $= +1$; of O $= -2$. Formula: K_2O

Table 4.1

Oxidation Numbers
Commonly Found
in the Groups
of the Periodic Table

Group	Oxidation Number*
IA	$+1$
IIA	$+2$
IIIA	$+3$
IVA	$-4, +2, +4$
VA	$-3, +3, +5$
VIA	$-2, +4, +6$
VIIA	$-1, +1, +3, +5, +7$

*The number first listed
is the charge most often acquired
in an ionic compound.

Table 4.2

Some Common Radical Ions

71

*Chemical
nomenclature*

Formula	Name	Formula	Name
NH_4^+	ammonium	$CrO_4^=$	chromate
$CO_3^=$	carbonate	$Cr_2O_7^=$	dichromate
$SO_4^=$	sulfate	SiO_4^{4-}	silicate
$SO_3^=$	sulfite	ClO_3^-	chlorate
$S_2O_3^=$	thiosulfate	ClO_4^-	perchlorate
MnO_4^-	permanganate	$C_2H_3O_2^-$	acetate
PO_4^{3-}	phosphate	CN^-	cyanide
NO_3^-	nitrate	OH^-	hydroxide
NO_2^-	nitrite		

(c) Al_2O_3
(d) Ca_3N_2
(e) Table 4.1 indicates that phosphorus may have a $+3$ and a $+5$ oxidation state. In the absence of other data, two formulas are possible, P_2O_3 and P_2O_5.

When dealing with compounds containing more than two elements, it is necessary to recognize that there are groups of atoms which behave as a single unit. Usually these groups exist as ions and their charge can be used as a kind of "pseudo-oxidation number" for the purposes of writing formulas. The group is enclosed in parentheses if more than one group occurs in the formula of the compound. An appropriate subscript follows. Several of the more common of these groups, whose members frequently are called radical ions, are listed in Table 4.2. It should be noted that most of the radical ions listed are those that contain oxygen and that the ammonium ion (NH_4^+) is the only common positively charged radical ion.

Example 4.2 On the basis of the discussion in this chapter, predict the formulas of compounds containing the following groups of elements.
(a) Sodium, carbon, oxygen
(b) Nitrogen, hydrogen, chlorine
(c) Aluminum, sulfur, oxygen
(d) Nitrogen, phosphorus, hydrogen, oxygen
  answers: (a) Na_2CO_3 (b) NH_4Cl (c) $Al_2(SO_4)_3$ (d) $(NH_4)_3PO_4$

Chemical nomenclature

A chemical formula provides the simplest and clearest method of designating chemical compounds. However there are many circumstances where a name is highly desirable. Certain rules are necessary for transforming a formula into a unique name for the compound. International agreement on uniform rules of nomenclature makes for rapid communication and easy understanding. The rules for naming inorganic compounds suggested by the International Union of Pure and Applied Chemistry (IUPAC) are used as the basis of the discussion that follows. Because of their widespread use, systematic names are discussed first.

Binary compounds

The more metallic element is named first. The last syllable of the nonmetallic element is dropped and replaced with the suffix, *-ide*. For example, chlorine becomes chloride. Occasionally it is necessary to modify the spelling slightly in order to pronounce the word easily, such as in hydride and oxide. The name of a binary compound always ends in *-ide*; this is true also for hydrox*ide* (OH⁻) and cyan*ide* (CN⁻).

The more metallic element is named as follows:
(a) A compound of a metal and a nonmetal
If the metal exists only in one oxidation state, the name of the element is used.

$$Al_2O_3 \text{ aluminum ox}ide \qquad NaCl \text{ sodium chlor}ide$$

If the metal can exist in two oxidation states, the higher oxidation state is denoted by an *-ic* ending, while the lower state is denoted by an *-ous* ending. The transition metals commonly exhibit multiple oxidation states (Table 4.3). Some examples are ferrous sulfate ($FeSO_4$) and ferric sulfate [$Fe_2(SO_4)_3$], and stannous chloride ($SnCl_2$) and stannic chloride ($SnCl_4$).

Table 4.3
Common Metals with Two Oxidation States

Cuprous	Cu^+	Mercurous	Hg_2^{++}
Cupric	Cu^{++}	Mercuric	Hg^{++}
Ferrous	Fe^{++}	Chromous	Cr^{++}
Ferric	Fe^{3+}	Chromic	Cr^{3+}
Manganous	Mn^{++}	Stannous	Sn^{++}
		Stannic	Sn^{4+}

(b) A compound of two nonmetals
Each element is prefixed to designate the number of atoms of each in the compound. The commonly used prefixes are given in Table 4.4. The name of the more nonmetallic element still ends in *-ide*. Some examples are *di*nitrogen *tri*oxide (N_2O_3), *di*chlorine *hept*oxide (Cl_2O_7), *mono*phosphorus *penta*chloride (PCl_5), and *mono*sulfur *hexa*fluoride. Note that the prefix *mono-* need not be used.
(c) Binary acids
Aqueous solutions of binary compounds containing hydrogen ions and negative ions are called acids. The nonaqueous com-

pounds are named as binary hydrogen compounds. The aqueous solutions are named as acids; the nonmetal is prefixed by *hydro-* and the suffix *-ic* replaces the last syllable. For example, HCl is used to designate hydrogen chloride, the dry gas, and hydrochloric acid, the solution that results when the gas is passed into water. H_2S is hydrosulfuric acid, while the dry gas is hydrogen sulfide. The cyanide radical ion (CN^-) was thought to be an element at one time. For this reason, the names hydrocyanic acid and hydrogen cyanide (HCN) exist, although the compounds are not binary.

Table 4.4

*Commonly used
prefixes*

mono	1	hexa	6
di	2	hepta	7
tri	3	octa	8
tetra	4	nona	9
penta	5	deca	10

Ternary compounds

Ternary (three element) salts considered in this text involve the radical ions given in Table 4.2. Except for the ammonium group, which is treated as a metal ion with a $+1$ charge, these radical ions are treated in the same way as the nonmetals in binary compounds. The appropriate metal name is followed by the name of the radical. Note that the groups ending in *-ate* have one more oxygen atom than those ending in *-ite*. For those cases where there is a third possibility, the prefix *per-* denotes one more atom of oxygen than in the *-ate* group. $KClO_4$ is potassium perchlorate, while $KClO_3$ is potassium chlorate.

The prefix *hypo-* denotes one less atom of oxygen than in the *-ite* group. KClO is potassium hypochlorite; $KClO_2$ is potassium chlorite.

The names of ternary acids are based on the names of their corresponding salts. If the salt name ends in *-ite*, the acid name ends in *-ous*. The salt name ending in *-ate* corresponds to the acid name ending in *-ic*.

$NaClO$ = sodium hypochlorite	$HClO$ = hypochlorous acid
$NaClO_2$ = sodium chlorite	$HClO_2$ = chlorous acid
$NaClO_3$ = sodium chlorate	$HClO_3$ = chloric acid
$NaClO_4$ = sodium perchlorate	$HClO_4$ = perchloric acid
$NaNO_2$ = sodium nitrite	HNO_2 = nitrous acid
$NaNO_3$ = sodium nitrate	HNO_3 = nitric acid

An acid salt is formed by the stepwise loss of hydrogen from a polyprotic (many hydrogen) acid. The preferred nomenclature for acid salts is to include the word hydrogen in the name with appropriate prefixes when needed to prevent ambiguities. Thus, $NaHSO_4$ is sodium hydrogen sulfate and NaH_2PO_4 is sodium dihydrogen phosphate. Other systems have developed. When half of the hydrogens are removed from a two-hydrogen acid, the prefix *bi-* or the notation *acid* is used, as in HSO_4^-, the bisulfate or acid sulfate ion.

There is a wide variety of names for the three-hydrogen acids such as H_3PO_4. These include:

NaH_2PO_4—primary sodium phosphate
monosodium phosphate
monobasic sodium phosphate
Na_2HPO_4—secondary sodium phosphate
disodium phosphate
dibasic sodium phosphate
Na_3PO_4—tertiary sodium phosphate
trisodium phosphate (probably the best)
tribasic sodium phosphate
normal sodium phosphate
sodium phosphate (most common)

The Stock notation

The Stock notation is particularly useful for naming compounds involving metals that exhibit more than one oxidation state. The IUPAC recommendations are (1) that the Stock notation be used in place of the older *-ic* and *-ous* suffixes to designate oxidation states, and (2) that it not be used for compounds of nonmetals. In this system the ratio of the constituent atoms in the compound is indicated indirectly by placing Roman numerals corresponding to the oxidation number in parentheses immediately following the name of the metal. An Arabic 0 is used for a case where the formal oxidation number is zero. Some examples include:

$CuCl_2$ copper(II) chloride, read "copper two chloride"
UCl_6 uranium(VI) chloride
MnO_2 manganese(IV) oxide

The Stock notation is useful for naming more complex compounds, such as $(NH_4)_3Fe(C_2O_4)_3$, ammonium trioxalatoferrate(III), but these are outside the scope of this text and the rules are not considered.

Trivial names

Many common compounds have names that were established long before any system was devised. Many of these trivial names are recognized only in commerce, but a few are acceptable in a chemistry laboratory. Water (H_2O), ammonia (NH_3), and phosphine (PH_3) are included in the latter group. Soda (Na_2CO_3) and quicklime (CaO) are examples of persistent industrial names.

Determination of oxidation numbers

It is a relatively simple matter to determine the oxidation number for an element using the principle of neutrality, when the formula of the compound is known. With few exceptions, hydrogen in a compound is assigned an oxidation number of $+1$ and oxygen a value of -2. Using these values and those predicted by Table 4.1 the oxidation state of the unknown element usually can be determined. If the element exists in a radical ion, the difference in positive and negative oxidation numbers must equal the charge on the ion.

Example 4.3 Determine the oxidation state of the underlined element in each of the following.

    (a) $\underline{P}_2O_5$ (d) $\underline{Cr}_2O_7^=$

    (b) $Ca_3(\underline{As}O_4)_2$ (e) $\underline{Cu}Cl_4^=$

    (c) $H_2\underline{S}_2O_7$

          answers: (a) $+5$ (b) $+5$ (c) $+6$ (d) $+6$ (e) $+2$

Writing a chemical equation

The use of formulas in a chemical equation permits the condensation of a great deal of information into a short space. In order to be able to write a chemical equation, it is necessary to know the products of the reaction. With no prior experience, it is impossible to predict the products. One of the goals of this text is to record the results of previous experiments so that intelligent predictions may be made about the products of a reaction that has not been studied. One such listing is the activity series discussed in Chapter II.

Once the products and reactants for a reaction are known, the symbols for the reactants are written on the left-hand side of an arrow; the symbols for the products are on the right-hand side. In order for this to be an equation, an equality must exist between the reactant atoms and product atoms, since it is not possible to create or destroy mass in an ordinary chemical reaction. Neither is it possible to transform an atom of one element to another element. Thus, there must be the same number of atoms of each element on the product side as on the reactant side of the equation. The equality is achieved by balancing the equation. This involves changing the coefficients of formulas, but never the subscripts, until the goal is achieved. At present, it is necessary to limit equation balancing to simple reactions which can be balanced by inspection. In this method the coefficients are systematically adjusted until the equation is balanced. If a radical ion is involved in the reaction, it is usually more convenient to balance the radical ion as a group rather than each atom.

Example 4.4 Balance the equation for the burning of ethane in oxygen to produce water and carbon dioxide.

Step (1) The reaction products are given as water and carbon dioxide.

Step (2) The formulas for the products and reactants are:
ethane — C_2H_6,   water — H_2O,
oxygen — O_2,   carbon dioxide — CO_2.

Step (3) The unbalanced equation is $C_2H_6 + O_2 \rightarrow CO_2 + H_2O$.

Step (4) Balance the equation.

Two atoms of carbon on the reactant side require two atoms of carbon on the product side. This can be achieved only by having two molecules of CO_2. The six hydrogen atoms are balanced by having three molecules of water. Now it is necessary to balance the oxygen atoms; the two CO_2 molecules require four atoms of oxygen, and three H_2O molecules require three atoms of oxygen for a total of seven atoms of oxygen on the product side. Since oxygen comes in diatomic molecular units, one could write $7/2$ O_2; however, this expression implies splitting of a molecule. It is usually more desirable at this state of development to multiply all of the coefficients by two in order to have an integer number of oxygen molecules. The balanced equation is

$$2C_2H_6 + 7O_2 \rightarrow 4CO_2 + 6H_2O$$

Other information often is included in the equation. A downward arrow ($\downarrow$) is placed beside a product to indicate the formation of a precipitate. An upward arrow ($\uparrow$) beside a product denotes that the product comes off as a gas. Often the physical state of the substance is indicated in parentheses after the formula; for example, $H_2O(l)$ indicates that water is a liquid in the reaction, while $H_2O(g)$ indicates that water is a gas. Solids are designated as (s). Special conditions such as heat or pressure are indicated by an appropriate notation above the arrow. The fact that a reaction must be heated is indicated by a delta Δ over or under the arrow. The notation $\xrightarrow{100°C}$ indicates that the reaction is carried out at 100°C. The need for a pressure of 1000 atm for a reaction to occur is indicated by $\xrightarrow{1000\,atm}$.

It is often possible to correlate more information about some chemical reactions, if only the ions involved are included in the equation. For example, whenever a solution of any barium salt is mixed with a solution containing sulfate ions, a precipitate of barium sulfate appears. Rather than write (and remember) all of the combinations of barium salts, such as $BaCl_2$, BaI_2, $Ba(NO_3)_2$, with sulfate salts, such as Na_2SO_4, K_2SO_4, $(NH_4)_2SO_4$, it is easier to write

$$Ba^{++} + SO_4^= \rightarrow BaSO_4\downarrow$$

This equation indicates that barium ions from any source react with sulfate ions from any source to form a precipitate of $BaSO_4$. The other ions in the solution do not affect this reaction and are not included. If there is a reaction between the other ions, these ions should also be included. For example, if a $Ba(OH)_2$ solution is mixed with a H_2SO_4 solution, there is a reaction between the H^+ and OH^- ions as well as between the Ba^{++} and $SO_4^=$ ions. The ionic equation for this reaction is written

$$Ba^{++} + 2OH^- + 2H^+ + SO_4^= \rightarrow BaSO_4\downarrow + 2H_2O$$

Ionic equations are written only for reactions that take place in solution.

When balancing ionic equations, there must be an equality of charge on both sides of the equation in addition to the atomic balance. For example, aluminum reacts with hydrogen ions of an acid to form hydrogen and the aluminum ion. In unbalanced ionic form:

$$Al + H^+ \rightarrow H_2\uparrow + Al^{3+}$$

A coefficient of 2 for H^+ would provide atomic balance but not charge balance:

$$Al + 2H^+ \rightarrow H_2\uparrow + Al^{3+}$$

To obtain the same number of positive charges on both sides of the equation, the hydrogen ions are multiplied by 3, and the aluminum ions are multiplied by 2, to give a $+6$ on both sides as well as a balance of atoms.

$$2Al + 6H^+ \rightarrow 3H_2\uparrow + 2Al^{3+}$$

Calculations with chemical equations

Another important application of the balanced chemical equation is in making quantitative calculations involving products and reactants. The coefficients in the chemical equation indicate the ratio in which moles of reactants react and moles of products are formed. Since the weight of a mole of any substance or the volume occupied by a mole of a gas are easily determined, all of the calculations make use of the mole concept. First, the given mass or volume of matter is converted to number of moles. In the second step, the number of moles of the other substance in question equivalent to this number of moles is determined using the ratio of the coefficients in the balanced equation. In the final step, the calculated number of moles of the second substance is converted to the required units. The procedure is illustrated best by reference to Examples 4.5 and 4.6.

Example 4.5 (a) Calculate the weight of water produced when 5.00 grams of ethane are burned in oxygen. (b) What volume of CO_2 (measured at 25°C and 740 torr) is produced in this reaction?

(a)

Step (1) Write the balanced equation for the reaction.
This was done in Example 4.4.

$$2C_2H_6 + 7O_2 \rightarrow 4CO_2 + 6H_2O$$

Step (2) Convert the weight of ethane into moles of C_2H_6.

$$\text{Moles } C_2H_6 = (5.00 \text{ g})\left(\frac{1 \text{ mole}}{30 \text{ g } C_2H_6}\right) = 0.167 \text{ mole}$$

Step (3) Calculate the number of moles of H_2O produced by this number of moles of C_2H_6. From the balanced equation, it is seen that 6 moles H_2O are produced from 2 moles C_2H_6.

$$\text{Moles } H_2O = (0.167 \text{ mole } C_2H_6)\left(\frac{6 \text{ moles } H_2O}{2 \text{ moles } C_2H_6}\right)$$
$$= 0.500 \text{ mole}$$

Step (4) Convert moles of H_2O to weight of H_2O.

$$\text{Wt. } H_2O = (0.500 \text{ mole})\left(\frac{18 \text{ g}}{1 \text{ mole}}\right) = 9.00 \text{ g } H_2O$$

answer: 9.00 g H_2O

(b)
Steps (1) and (2) are the same as above.

Step (3) Calculate number of moles of CO_2 produced by 0.167 moles C_2H_6.

$$\text{Moles } CO_2 = (0.167 \text{ moles } C_2H_6)\left(\frac{4 \text{ moles } CO_2}{2 \text{ moles } C_2H_6}\right)$$
$$= 0.333 \text{ mole}$$

Step (4) Convert 0.333 mole CO_2 to the volume of gas using the ideal gas law.

$$PV = nRT$$

$$\left(\frac{740 \text{ torr}}{760 \text{ torr/atm}}\right)V = (0.333 \text{ mole})\left(0.0821 \frac{\text{l-atm}}{\text{mole-deg}}\right)(298°K)$$

$$V = \frac{(0.333)(0.0821)(298)(760)}{740} = 8.37 \text{ liters}$$

Example 4.6 What weight of oxygen would be required to burn 30.0 grams of magnesium metal? What volume (at 42°C and 800 torr) of oxygen would be required?

$$2Mg + O_2 \rightarrow 2MgO$$

$$\text{Moles } O_2 = (30 \text{ g Mg})\left(\frac{1 \text{ mole Mg}}{24 \text{ g Mg}}\right)\left(\frac{1 \text{ mole } O_2}{2 \text{ moles Mg}}\right) = 0.625 \text{ mole}$$

$$\text{Weight of } O_2 = (0.625 \text{ mole})\left(\frac{32 \text{ g } O_2}{1 \text{ mole}}\right) = 20.0 \text{ grams}$$

Volume of O_2 gas:

$$V = \frac{nRT}{P} = \frac{(0.625 \text{ mole})\left(0.0821 \frac{\text{l-atm}}{\text{mole-deg}}\right)(315°K)\left(760 \frac{\text{torr}}{\text{atm}}\right)}{800 \text{ torr}}$$

$$V = 15.4 \text{ liters}$$

SIGNIFICANT TERMS AND CONCEPTS IN CHAPTER IV:

Periodicity of physical and chemical properties, group, period; location of metals, nonmetals, and metalloids in the periodic table, transition metals, lanthanides, actinides; ion, anion, cation, formulas, oxidation numbers, rules of nomenclature; balancing chemical equations, ionic equations, calculations involving an equation.

Review questions

4.1. What trend is observed in the density of the elements in: (a) Group VIIA, (b) Group IIA, (c) Period 2, (d) the transition metals of Period 4, (e) the Lanthanide Series?

4.2. Mendeleev predicted the existence of the element, germanium, before its discovery. Compare the melting point and density of germanium with the adjacent elements in: (a) the same period, (b) the same group.

4.3. Which element in each of the following groups is the most metallic? (a) P, O, F; (b) C, B, Be; (c) Ca, Rb, Mg; (d) P, S, Sc; (e) Sn, Pb, I.

4.4. Give the oxidation number of the underscored element in each of the following:

$\underline{P}$ $\underline{P}Br_3$ $\underline{Ba}O$ $\underline{Cl}_2O_7$ $K_2\underline{Mn}O_4$ $\underline{N}Cl_3$

$\underline{Xe}F_4$ $\underline{V}_2O_5$ $\underline{Hg}_2Cl_2$ $\underline{Br}_2$ $P\underline{Br}_3$ $\underline{O}_2$

$Na_2\underline{S}O_4$ $\underline{Cu}(CN)_4^=$ $H\underline{Cl}O_3$ $\underline{Fe}SO_4$ $\underline{Os}O_4$ $H_2\underline{Se}O_3$

4.5. Write the formula of each compound formed by the combination of the ions in row *a* with each of the ions in row *b*. Name each.

a. Na^+, Mg^{2+}, NH_4^+, Fe^{3+}, Fe^{2+}, Cu^{2+}, Cu^+, Sn^{2+}, Sn^{4+}, Zn^{2+}, Al^{3+}, K^+

b. Cl^-, $SO_4^=$, OH^-, NO_3^-, $CO_3^=$, $SO_3^=$, $O^=$, $S^=$, SiO_4^{4-}

4.6. Write the formula of the acid associated with the ions in row *b* of the preceding question. Name each acid.

4.7. Give the formula for each of the following:

(a) perchloric acid
(b) nitrous acid
(c) hydrobromic acid
(d) acetic acid
(e) phosphorous acid
(f) cuprous iodide
(g) vanadium(III) sulfate
(h) tungsten(VI) nitride
(i) ammonium dichromate
(j) sodium thiosulfate
(k) disulfur decafluoride

4.8. If $KMnO_4$ is potassium permanganate, then permanganic acid is ____. If metavanadic acid is HVO_3, $NaVO_3$ is ____.

4.9. Give the name and formula for:

(a) An oxide that reacts with water to form sodium hydroxide.
(b) The acid required to form calcium nitrate by neutralization.

    (c) An oxide which will form sulfuric acid upon addition of water.

    (d) The salt formed by neutralizing sulfuric acid with ammonium hydroxide.

    (e) A potassium compound that is a base.

4.10. Give the name for each of the following:

    (a) PBr_3, (b) N_2O_5, (c) N_2O_4, (d) SiF_4, (e) IF_7, (f) XeF_6, (g) P_3N_5, (h) P_4S_7.

4.11. Balance the following:

    (a) $Na + Cl_2 \rightarrow NaCl$

    (b) $Ca + N_2 \rightarrow Ca_3N_2$

    (c) $K + O_2 \rightarrow K_2O$

    (d) Aluminum + oxygen to produce aluminum oxide

    (e) Iron + chlorine to produce ferric chloride

    (f) Burning acetylene (C_2H_2) in oxygen to obtain carbon dioxide and water

    (g) The precipitation of silver chloride when silver ions and chloride ions are mixed

    (h) $Cu^{++} + CN^- \rightarrow Cu(CN)_4^=$

    (i) The replacement of silver ions in solution by zinc

Problems

4.12. From the data in Figs. 4.3 and 4.4 estimate the density, melting point, boiling point, and physical state at room temperature for technetium (number 43), astatine (85), and promethium (61).

4.13. Nitrogen and hydrogen react to form ammonia (NH_3) gas.

    (a) What weight of ammonia is obtained from 100 grams of nitrogen?   answer: 121 g

    (b) What weight of hydrogen is needed to prepare 100 grams of ammonia?

    (c) What volume of NH_3 may be prepared from 10 liters of nitrogen and 10 liters of hydrogen?   answer: 6.7 liters

    (d) How many liters of which gas remains unreacted in part (c)?

    (e) How many grams of nitrogen are needed to prepare 5.6 liters of NH_3 at S.T.P.?

    (f) How many milliliters of NH_3 (at 27°C and 740 torr) are prepared from 0.060 g of hydrogen?   answer: 506 ml

    (g) How many moles of NH_3 are prepared from 2.0 moles of nitrogen?   answer: 4.0 moles

    (h) How many grams of NH_3 are prepared from 0.80 mole of hydrogen?

    (i) How many liters of hydrogen (at 17°C and 700 torr) are required to react with 0.60 mole of nitrogen?   answer: 46.5 liters

(j) What volume of NH_3 (at 700°K and 3.0 atm) is prepared from 10.00 liters of hydrogen measured at 27°C and 1.0 atm?   answer: 5.18 liters

4.14. When sulfur reacts with oxygen, sulfur trioxide (a gas) may be formed under appropriate conditions.

(a) How many moles of sulfur react with 18 g of oxygen?

(b) How many grams of sulfur trioxide are formed from 3.0 g of oxygen and excess sulfur?

(c) How many grams of sulfur trioxide are formed when 10 g of sulfur and 12 g of oxygen are mixed?

(d) How much of the excess reactant remains after the reaction in part (c) is completed?

(e) What weight of sulfur is required to produce 1.68 liters of sulfur trioxide at S.T.P.?

(f) What weight of sulfur reacts with 10.0 liters of oxygen at 27°C and 780 torr?

(g) What weight of sulfur trioxide is prepared from 1.0 g of sulfur?

(h) How many moles of oxygen are required to produce 12 moles of sulfur trioxide?

(i) How many liters of sulfur trioxide at 500°K and 10 atm are formed from 5.0 liters of oxygen measured at 17°C and 1 atm?

4.15. Magnesium nitride reacts with water to form magnesium hydroxide and ammonia (NH_3).

(a) What weight of magnesium hydroxide is formed from 10.0 g of magnesium nitride?

(b) What weight of water is required to form 1.0 g NH_3?

(c) What volume of NH_3 at 27°C and 1.10 atm is formed when 2.90 g of magnesium hydroxide are prepared?

(d) How many moles of NH_3 are formed from 4.0 g of magnesium nitride?

(e) What weight of water is required to form one billion (1×10^9) molecules of NH_3?

When two or more substances are mixed together, a chemical reaction may or may not take place. If no reaction occurs, the result is called a mixture. If a reaction does take place, the product may be a mixture of new compounds. It is necessary to distinguish between a mixture and a compound. A particular type of mixture, a solution, is considered in some detail later in this chapter.

Compounds and mixtures

Compounds are chemical combinations of the elements. Their composition throughout is uniform. Chemical reactions are required to recover the components of the compound.

Mixtures consist of two or more compounds or elements. The distinguishing characteristic of a mixture is that it may be resolved into its components by the use of physical means. Evaporation, freezing, and magnetic separation are among the common physical techniques for obtaining the components of a mixture.

Iron and sulfur offer a classic example of elements, compounds, and mixtures. The elements may be separated from a mixture of powdered iron and sulfur by use of a magnet to recover the iron or by dissolving the sulfur in carbon disulfide. If the mixture is heated, a reaction takes place with the formation of ferrous sulfide, a compound. If the elements have been mixed in the ratio required to form the compound, it is not possible to recover iron with a magnet nor sulfur with carbon disulfide.

Mixtures may be classified further on the basis of their composition. Mixtures are *heterogenous* if the composition is different from sample to sample within the mixture. A *homogenous* mixture is one in which the composition is uniform throughout.

Solutions

A solution is a homogenous mixture in which one or more substances (solutes) are dispersed in another (solvent) on an atomic or molecular scale. In many cases, it is somewhat arbitrary as to which component of the solution is called the solvent and which components are called the solutes. Usually, the component present in the greatest amount is called the solvent. For example, if a drop of alcohol is placed in a glass of water, the alcohol is usually considered to be the solute and water to be the solvent.

There are many criteria for classifying solutions. It is possible to use several of these for the same solution. Two of the more important criteria to be considered are the phases of the solute and solvent, and the amount of solute in the solution.

Gaseous, liquid, or solid solutes may dissolve in gaseous, liquid, or solid solvents to give nine types of solutions when classification is made on the basis of phases. A careful study of the following examples shows that a sharp distinction between a true solution and a mixture is not always possible. Examples of solutions classified according to phase include:

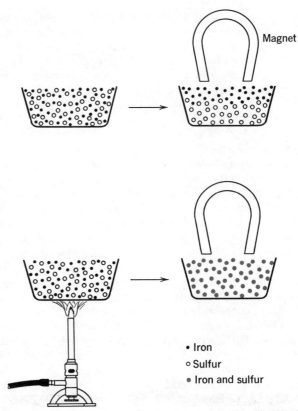

Magnet

• Iron
○ Sulfur
• Iron and sulfur

Fig. 5.1

Behavior of Iron and Sulfur. Iron and sulfur form a mixture that can be separated readily by a magnet. Once the mixture is heated, the magnet no longer has an effect; a chemical reaction has taken place, and the properties of iron and sulfur have been modified.

A gas in a gas—the atmosphere
A liquid in a gas—fog
A solid in a gas—smoke

A gas in a liquid—carbonated water
A liquid in a liquid—alcohol in water
A solid in a liquid—sugar in water

A gas in a solid—meringue
A liquid in a solid—a water drop on a sugar cube
A solid in a solid—an alloy

Most of the solutions considered in this chapter are those having a liquid solvent. Although most of the examples involve water as the solvent, the general applicability of the principles should be recognized.

Solutions may be unsaturated, saturated, or supersaturated depending on the amount of solute present relative to the maximum amount that can be retained stably in solution. A solution that contains the maximum amount of solute is said to be *saturated*. If the amount of solute is less than this maximum, the solution is *unsaturated*. Under certain conditions, it is possible to have more solute in a solution than there is in a saturated solution. Such a solution is said to be *supersaturated*. To make a supersaturated solution, a saturated solution is prepared at a temperature at which the amount of solute contained in solution is greater than at the final temperature. If the container has no scratches or irregularities and if there are no particles in the solution, the excess solute does not precipitate upon cooling and a super-saturated solution is formed.

If the container wall is scratched, or if a dust particle or a seed crystal is added, the excess solute precipitates almost at once. Apparently the particles of some solutes need a nucleus about which to start forming a crystal. In the absence of some such particle or rough surface, the solute particles cannot become oriented properly for crystal growth. Once started, the crystal growth does not stop until all excess solute precipitates, and a saturated solution remains.

Solubility

Not all substances go into solution to an equal extent. The amount of solute that dissolves in a given amount of solvent is called the

Fig. 5.2

Effect of a Crystal on a Solution. (a) A crystal of material dropped into an unsaturated solution dissolves; (b) a saturated solution undergoes no visible change; (c) a supersaturated solution causes excess solute to precipitate.

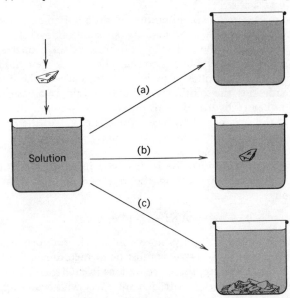

solubility. Usually the solubility of solids and liquids in a liquid solvent is expressed in number of grams of solute per 100 grams of solvent, while gas solubility in liquids is expressed in terms of gas volume measured at S.T.P.

Solubility is dependent on the nature of the solute and solvent, on temperature, and on pressure. The interaction between solute particles and solvent molecules plays an important role in solubility. For example, AgCl is not soluble in water but is readily dissolved in liquid ammonia; NaCl is soluble in water and insoluble in ammonia.

An increase in the temperature always reduces the solubility of a gas in a liquid. The reduction in solubility of dissolved air accounts for the formation of small gas bubbles on the walls of the container when water is heated. The solubility of a solid or liquid in a liquid solvent usually increases with increasing temperature. The number of exceptions to this generalization is great enough to make it of limited usefulness, however.

An increase in the pressure of a gas over a liquid always increases the solubility of the gas. For example, bottled carbonated beverages froth upon opening since the CO_2 pressure above the liquid is lowered and carbon dioxide escapes from the solution. Pressure has little effect on the solubility of liquids or solids in liquids.

Acids, bases, and salts

It is noted in Chapter II that an aqueous solution of a nonmetal oxide is considered to be an acid and an aqueous solution of a metal oxide is a base. This definition at one time led to the erroneous conclusion that only compounds containing oxygen could behave as acids.

The next step in expanding the definition of an acid is to recognize that hydrogen ions in an aqueous solution are related to the acid properties, while hydroxide ions provide the properties of the base. Every aqueous solution contains both hydrogen and hydroxide ions. If the number of hydrogen ions exceeds the number of hydroxide ions, the solution is said to be acidic. In a basic solution, the number of hydroxide ions exceeds the number of hydrogen ions. If the number of hydrogen ions is equal to the number of hydroxide ions, the solution is *neutral*, that is, it shows neither acidic nor basic properties.

When sodium hydroxide is dissolved in water, OH^- ions are released, thereby increasing the number of OH^- ions in the solution.

$$NaOH \rightarrow Na^+ + OH^-$$

The situation is slightly more complex in the formation of an acidic solution, since H^+ ions must be formed during the solution process. For example, there are no ions in HCl gas. When the gas passes into water, the hydrogen interacts with water molecules

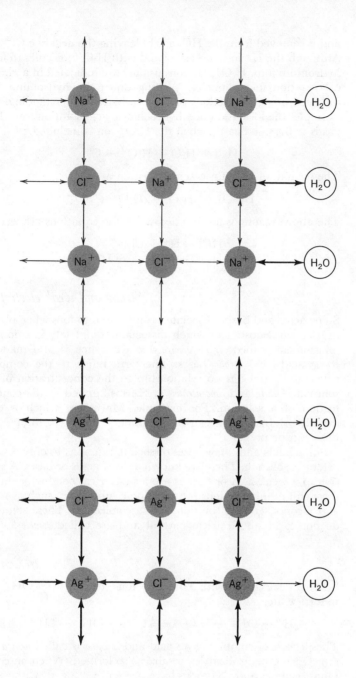

Fig. 5.3

Solid Solubility. The strength of interionic forces between ions of a solid compared to the force of attraction between solid ions and water molecules determine solubility. NaCl is soluble, because the force of attraction between ions and water molecules is greater. AgCl is insoluble in water, because the interionic forces are stronger.

and is removed from the HCl as H^+ leaving the negative Cl^- ion. Although the H^+ ions are associated with H_2O molecules to form hydronium ions, H_3O^+, H^+ ions usually are indicated in a chemical reaction for simplicity. Writing down the hydronium ions involved in some reactions provides a better understanding. For example, the formation of a hydrochloric acid solution from HCl gas is understood easily when the H_3O^+ ion is included.

$$HCl + H_2O \rightarrow H_3O^+ + Cl^-$$

The formation of sulfuric acid is written as follows.

$$H_2SO_4 + 2H_2O \rightarrow 2H_3O^+ + SO_4^=$$

The above reactions are implied when the equations are written

$$HCl \rightarrow H^+ + Cl^-$$
$$H_2SO_4 \rightarrow 2H^+ + SO_4^=$$

Strong and weak electrolytes

Some acids and bases dissociate completely into ions when placed in solution. Substances which dissociate completely into ions in solution are called *strong electrolytes*. Reference is also made to *strong* acids and *strong* bases. The term refers to the complete dissociation and has no relationship to the concentration of the solution. *Dilute* and *concentrated* are terms applied to the concentration of a solution. For example, $Mg(OH)_2$, which is only slightly soluble, is a strong base; although only very dilute solutions can be prepared.

Some acids and a few bases dissociate into ions to only a small extent in solution. These are known as *weak* acids or bases. A solution of a weak acid or base is a poor electrical conductor due to the small number of ions present. Some substances, such as sugar and alcohol, go into solution only as molecules. These solutions do not carry an electrical current and are called *nonelectrolytes*.

Neutralization

When an acid reacts with a base, H^+ ions combine with OH^- ions to form water.

$$H^+ + OH^- \rightarrow H_2O \quad \text{or} \quad H_3O^+ + OH^- \rightarrow 2H_2O$$

The process of combining an acid and a base is called *neutralization*. During neutralization, a salt is also formed. When an equal number of H^+ and OH^- ions have been mixed together, the solution is said to be at the *equivalence point*. The solution at the equivalence point has the same properties as a solution prepared by adding the salt to pure water. Due to interactions of the salt ions with the water, the solution at the equivalence point may not be neutral, i.e., the numbers of free H^+ ions and free OH^- ions are not equal. Salt solutions resulting from the neutralization of a strong

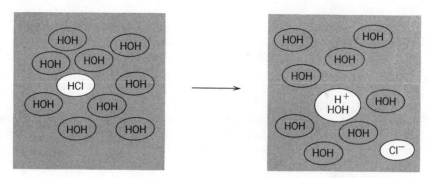

Fig. 5.4

Behavior of HCl in Water. A water molecule has a greater attractive force for the H+ ion than does the Cl− ion. Thus, HCl gas dissociates into H₃O+ ions and Cl− ions when it passes into water. The solution is hydrochloric acid.

acid and a strong base are neutral at the equivalence point. Salt solutions from the neutralization of a weak acid or base are not neutral at the equivalence point. The relationship between neutrality and equivalence point is discussed in Chapter XI.

Solutions of almost all salts are strong electrolytes. This means that to whatever extent a salt dissolves, it breaks up completely into ions. Many salts can be recovered as solids from the neutralization reaction. If the salt is soluble, it is necessary to evaporate the water to reduce the volume of solvent. Often the salts are insoluble and precipitate upon formation. Table 5.1 lists some solubility rules that aid in the prediction of chemical reactions.

Fig. 5.5

Composition of Electrolyte Solutions. Molecules of a strong electrolyte such as HCl dissociate into ions when in solution. Only a few molecules are dissociated in a solution of a weak electrolyte such as HCN. No dissociation occurs when a nonelectrolyte such as ethyl alcohol (C₂H₅OH) is placed in solution.

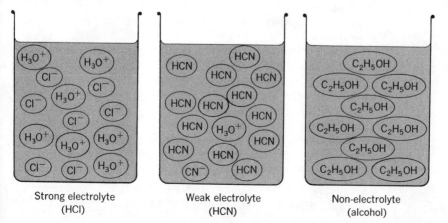

Strong electrolyte
(HCl)

Weak electrolyte
(HCN)

Non-electrolyte
(alcohol)

Table 5.1
Solubility Rules

Water Soluble Salts

All sodium, potassium, and ammonium salts.

All nitrates, chlorates, and acetates, except silver acetate.

All metal chlorides, bromides, and iodides, except those of lead, silver, and mercury(I).

All sulfates, except those of lead, mercury(I), barium, calcium, antimony, and silver.

Hydroxides and oxides of sodium and potassium, and ammonium hydroxide are very soluble.

Hydroxides and oxides of calcium and barium are moderately soluble.

Water Insoluble Salts

Metal sulfides, except those of barium, calcium, magnesium, sodium, potassium, and ammonium.

Metal carbonates, phosphates, sulfites, and chromates, except those of sodium, potassium, and ammonium.

Metal oxides and hydroxides not listed as soluble.

Dilute Acid Soluble Salts

All water soluble salts.

Water insoluble carbonates, phosphates, sulfites, chromates, oxides, and hydroxides.

Net ionic equations

Only the reacting species are indicated in most chemical reactions. Thus, formulas for strong electrolytes in solution are written in ionic form. Formulas for nonelectrolytes are written in the molecular form. Weak electrolytes also are written in the form of molecules since this is the species that predominates in solution. The formulas for gases and solids also are written in a molecular form. Equations showing only the reacting species are called *net ionic equations*.

Some helpful rules to aid in the writing of net ionic reactions are given below.

(a) Almost all salts are strong electrolytes. The few exceptions are noted when encountered.

(b) All of the soluble metal hydroxides (primarily those of Group IA) are strong electrolytes. Most of the insoluble metal hydroxides dissociate to ions to the extent of their solubility.

(c) Ammonium hydroxide (NH_4OH) is the only commonly encountered weak base within the limits of the present definition.

(d) Several acids are classified as weak or strong in Table 5.2. Some examples of net ionic equations are:

(a)   strong acid + strong base → salt + water
$$(H^+ + Cl^-) + (Na^+ + OH^-) \rightarrow (Na^+ + Cl^-) + H_2O$$

Net: H^+ + OH^- $\rightarrow$ H_2O

(The Na^+ and Cl^- ions are unaffected by this reaction.)

(b) weak acid + strong base $\rightarrow$ salt   + water

$(HC_2H_3O_2) + (Na^+ + OH^-) \rightarrow (Na^+ + C_2H_3O_2^-) + H_2O$

Net: $HC_2H_3O_2$ + OH^- $\rightarrow$ $C_2H_3O_2^-$ + H_2O

(c) formation of a precipitate

$(Ag^+ + NO_3^-) + (H^+ + Cl^-) \rightarrow (H^+ + NO_3^-) + AgCl(s)$

Net: Ag^+ + Cl^- $\rightarrow$ $AgCl(s)$

$(Cu^{++} + 2NO_3^-) + H_2S \rightarrow 2(H^+ + NO_3^-) + CuS(s)$

Net: Cu^{++} + $H_2S \rightarrow$ $2H^+ + CuS(s)$

(d) formation of a gas

$Mg + 2(H^+ + Cl^-) \rightarrow (Mg^{++} + 2Cl^-) + H_2(g)$

Net: $Mg + 2H^+$ $\rightarrow$ Mg^{++} + $H_2(g)$

$(2Na^+ + CO_3^=) + 2(H^+ + Cl^-) \rightarrow 2(Na^+ + Cl^-) +$
$CO_2(g) + H_2O$

Net: $CO_3^=$ + $2H^+$ $\rightarrow$ $CO_2(g)$ + H_2O

Concentration scales

For quantitative chemical studies it is necessary to know the amount of solute in a given amount of solvent or solution, or the concentration of the solution. Since water is the solvent most commonly used in the laboratory, this discussion centers on aqueous solutions. It should be remembered that the discussion is applicable to other solvents.

A *standard solution* is one for which the concentration of the solute has been determined carefully. Few chemicals are available at a purity sufficiently high to permit direct weighing of the solute. Usually it is necessary to standardize a solution after it has been prepared to an approximate concentration. For example, the highest commercial grade sodium hydroxide contains about 98%

Table 5.2

Strong and Weak Acids

Strong Acids		Weak Acids	
Hydrobromic	HBr	Acetic	$HC_2H_3O_2$
Hydrochloric	HCl	Carbonic	H_2CO_3
Hydriodic	HI	Hydrofluoric	HF
Nitric	HNO_3	Hydrosulfuric	H_2S
Phosphoric	H_3PO_4	Hypobromous	HOBr
Sulfuric	H_2SO_4	Hypochlorus	HOCl
		Oxalic	$H_2C_2O_4$
		Sulfurous	H_2SO_3

NaOH. The concentration of OH^- ions in a solution prepared from this material is determined by measuring the amount of this solution required to neutralize a known amount of H^+ ions.

Several concentration scales have been developed. Some scales are very specialized and are used in certain types of laboratories. Other laboratories have modified the common concentration scales to meet their needs. The five types that are considered here (per cent by weight, per cent by volume, molar, normal, and molal) are the most frequently encountered scales.

Per cent by weight

This is the simplest and most obvious concentration scale. One need only know the weight of the solute and the weight of the solution to obtain the per cent by weight from the relation:

$$\frac{\text{weight of solute}}{\text{weight of solution}} \times 100 = \% \text{ by weight}$$

This scale, unlike the molarity, normality, and molality scales, may be used with any solute, since there is no need to know the molecular or equivalent weight. It has the further advantage of being unaffected by a change in temperature.

Example 5.1 What is the per cent by weight of a solution if 2.50 g of solute remain after 175 g of solution are evaporated to dryness?

$$\frac{2.5 \text{ g solute}}{175 \text{ g solution}} \times 100 = 1.43\% \text{ solute by weight}$$

Per cent by volume

The per cent by volume concentration scale is useful primarily with liquid–liquid solutions. The values change with temperature due to variations in density of the liquids. Since the volumes of many liquids are not additive, one must decide the volume contribution of the solute to the final solution. Usually the per cent by volume is based on the volume of solute that is diluted to make a volume of solution. Thus, a 50% by volume solution of alcohol in water is prepared by diluting 500 ml of alcohol to 1.00 liter of solution. This would require somewhat more than 500 ml of water, since the volume obtained by mixing 500 ml alcohol and 500 ml water is less than 1000 ml.

Molar solutions

The *molarity* of a solution, indicated by the symbol M, is the number of moles of solute per liter of solution. This scale is also temperature dependent. A solution of a given molarity is prepared by weighing the appropriate amount of solute and adding sufficient solvent to make the required volume of solution.

Example 5.2 How would one prepare 250 ml of 0.30 M NaOH?

The formula weight of NaOH = 40

Weight of NaOH required = (0.30 moles/l)(0.250 liter)(40 g/mole)

$$= 3.0 \text{ g}$$

Thus, one would weigh out 3.0 g NaOH and add enough water to make 250 ml of solution.

Example 5.3 If 100.0 g of K_2SO_4 are dissolved in 2.10 l of solution, what is the molarity?

Formula weight of K_2SO_4 = 174

$$\text{Moles } K_2SO_4 = (100.0 \text{ g})\left(\frac{1 \text{ mole}}{174 \text{ g}}\right) = 0.575 \text{ mole}$$

$$\text{Molarity} = \frac{0.575 \text{ moles}}{2.10 \text{ liters}} = 0.274 \text{ } M$$

Normal solutions

The *normality* of a solution, designated by the symbol N, is defined as the number of equivalents of solute per liter of solution. Normal solutions are also dependent on temperature. For an acid or base one *equivalent* is the weight of the substance that contains one mole of replaceable H^+ or OH^- ions. A replaceable H^+ or OH^- ion is one that forms water in a neutralization reaction.

The normality scale is useful primarily because one equivalent of a substance reacts with one equivalent of any other substance. Since the scale gives the number of equivalents per liter, it is easy to make the necessary calculations. The normality of a solution is some integer multiple of the molarity, since there are one, two, or three replaceable ions in every acid or base molecule.

Example 5.4 What is the normality of a solution containing 17.5 g H_3PO_4 per 750 ml of solution? What is the molarity?

Molecular weight of H_3PO_4 = 98

Number of replaceable hydrogen ions = 3

Equivalent weight of H_3PO_4 = 98/3 = 32.7 g

$$\text{Number of equivalents} = (17.5 \text{ g})\left(\frac{1 \text{ eq}}{32.7 \text{ g}}\right) = 0.535 \text{ eq}$$

$$\text{Normality} = \frac{0.535 \text{ eq}}{0.750 \text{ l}} = 0.713 \text{ } N$$

Molarity = 1/3 × N = 1/3(0.713) = 0.238 M

The normality scale is particularly useful in the standardization of acids and bases. Standardization usually is accomplished by *titration*, the careful addition of one solution to a measured quantity of another until a reaction is completed as shown by an indicator. The neutralization reaction is of interest during an acid–base titration. When equal numbers of H^+ and OH^- ions have been mixed, the equivalence point is reached. The point is shown

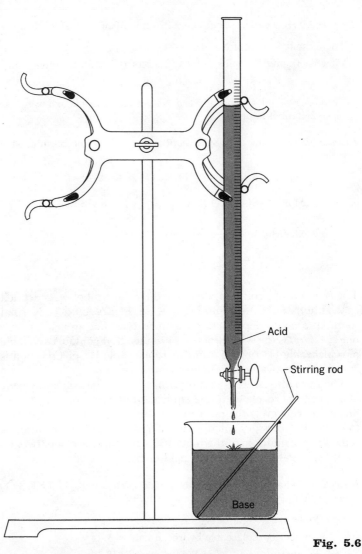

Fig. 5.6

Acid–Base Titration. A buret is used to measure the quantity of acid that is equivalent to the measured volume of base. The equivalence point is determined by the use of an indicator added to the solution.

by an indicator, a substance which changes color as the concentration of H^+ or OH^- ions changes. Common acid–base indicators include litmus, phenolphthalein, and methyl orange, all of which are complex molecular compounds.

The concentration of H^+ or OH^- ions in a solution is determined by comparison with a solution of a primary standard or to a solution that has been compared to such a standard solution. A primary standard is a substance that is obtainable in very high purity so that the number of H^+ or OH^- ions can be determined directly from the weight of the substance. Two commonly used standards are potassium hydrogen phthalate and oxalic acid, both of which are H^+ ion sources.

The normality scale is used in acid-base titrations, since the number of equivalents of acid is equal to the number of equivalents of base at the equivalence point. A useful relationship can be developed.

$$\text{Number of equivalents} = (\text{equivalents/liter})(\text{liters})$$
$$= (\text{Normality})(\text{Volume}).$$
$$\text{Number of equivalents of acid} = N_A V_A$$
$$= \text{number of equivalents of base}$$
$$= N_B V_B$$
$$N_A V_A = N_B V_B$$

Example 5.5 What volume of 6.0 N H_2SO_4 is required to neutralize 180 g of pure NaOH?

Equivalent weight of NaOH = 40 g

$$\text{Number of equivalents of NaOH} = (180 \text{ g})\left(\frac{1 \text{ eq}}{40 \text{ g}}\right) = 4.5 \text{ eq}$$

Number of equivalents of H_2SO_4 required = 4.5 eq

$$\text{Volume } H_2SO_4 = \frac{4.5 \text{ eq}}{6.0 \text{ eq/l}} = 0.75 \text{ l} = 750 \text{ ml}$$

alternatively: $N_{acid} \, V_{acid}$ = equivalents base

$$(6 \text{ eq/l})(x) = \frac{180 \text{ g}}{40 \text{ g/l}}$$

$$x = 0.75 \text{ liter} = V_{acid}$$

Molal solutions

The molality of a solution, represented by the symbol m, is equal to the number of moles of solute in 1000 g or 1.0 kg of solvent. The molality of a solution does not vary with the temperature.

Example 5.6 What is the molality of a solution prepared by mixing 13 g of benzene, C_6H_6, and 225 g of toluene, C_7H_8?

Molecular weight of benzene = 78

$$\text{Moles of benzene} = (13 \text{ g})\left(\frac{1 \text{ mole}}{78 \text{ g}}\right) = 0.167 \text{ mole}$$

$$\text{Molality (of benzene)} = \frac{0.167 \text{ mole}}{0.225 \text{ kg}} = 0.74 \text{ m}$$

Since benzene is also a liquid, the molality of toluene in benzene may be calculated also:

$$\text{Molality (of toluene)} = \frac{(225 \text{ g})/(92 \text{ g/mole})}{(0.013 \text{ kg})} = 19 \text{ m}$$

Colligative properties

The molal concentration scale is used in the study of the properties of solutions, since the number of solvent particles remains at a constant number. It is particularly useful for *colligative properties* (independent of substance). These include the closely related properties of freezing point depression, boiling point elevation, and osmotic pressure. All of these properties depend upon the ratio of the number of solute particles to the number of solvent particles. The relationship for each of these properties can be derived from basic principles. The final result is given here for each case without proof. These results are valid only if (a) the solute is nonvolatile (does not exert a measurable vapor pressure); (b) the solution is dilute (because of the approximations used in the derivation); and (c) the solute does not dissociate upon dissolving (since the colligative properties are based on number of particles). Any dissociation changes the results.

Elevation of the boiling point

Since a nonvolatile solute lowers the vapor pressure of a solution, the solution must be heated to a higher temperature before its vapor pressure is equal to the atmospheric pressure. The change in the boiling point, ΔT_b, can be measured quite accurately experimentally. The increase in the boiling point is proportional to the molality of the solution.

$$\Delta T_b = K_b m$$

The molal boiling point constant K_b is characteristic of the solvent and does not depend upon the solute. Values of K_b and the boiling points of several solvents are given in Table 5.3. The molecular weight of a solute can be determined from the observed rise in boiling point, since the rise is proportional to the molality. In a molecular weight determination the boiling point of a weighed amount of pure solvent is observed. The boiling point is measured after a weighed amount of solute is added. The molality of the solution is calculated from the temperature rise. Molecular

Table 5.3

Molal Boiling Point Constants and Boiling Points

Liquid	Boiling Point (°C)	K_b
Water	100.0	0.512
Benzene	80.10	2.53
Carbon-tetrachloride	76.54	5.03
Chloroform	61.73	3.63
Acetone	56.2	1.71

weight is determined from the weights of solute and solvent and the molality.

Example 5.7 What is the boiling point of a benzene solution containing 4.00 g of naphthalene ($C_{10}H_8$) in 600 g of benzene?

$$\text{Molality} = \frac{(4.00 \text{ g})/(128 \text{ g/mole})}{0.6 \text{ kg}} = 0.0521 \ m$$

$$\Delta T_b = (2.53)(0.0521) = 0.132°C$$

$$\text{Boiling point} = 80.10°C + 0.13°C = 80.23°C$$

Example 5.8 When 1.000 g of a solute is added to 150.0 g of CCl_4 the boiling point is 77.06°C. What is the molecular weight of the solute?

$$\text{Molality} = \frac{\Delta T_b}{K_b} = \frac{77.06 - 76.54}{5.03} = \frac{0.52}{5.03} = 0.103 \ m$$

$$\text{Molality} = \frac{(\text{wt solute})}{(\text{molecular wt})}/\text{kg solvent} = \left(\frac{1.000 \text{ g}}{MW}\right)/0.150 \text{ kg}$$

Equating the two expressions for the molality,

$$\left(\frac{1.000 \text{ g}}{MW}\right)/0.150 \text{ kg} = 0.103 \ m$$

$$MW = \frac{1.000}{(0.150)(0.103)} = 64$$

Table 5.4

Molal Freezing Point Constants and Freezing Points

Liquid	Freezing Point (°C)	K_f
Water	0.00	1.86
Benzene	5.53	4.90
Phenol	40.90	7.40
Acetic acid	16.63	3.90

Depression of the freezing point

The nonvolatile solute depresses the freezing point of a solution, since the vapor pressure of the solution is equal to the vapor pressure of the solid at the freezing point. The freezing point depression ΔT_f for dilute solutions is proportional to the molality.

$$\Delta T_f = K_f m$$

K_f is the molal freezing point constant which is characteristic of the solvent. Values of K_f for some liquids are given in Table 5.4. Freezing point methods are very useful for molecular weight determinations, since the freezing point does not vary within the experimental error with atmospheric pressure changes. The methods of molecular weight determination using the freezing point depression are similar to those for boiling point elevation.

Example 5.9 What is the freezing point of an aqueous solution containing 10.0 g of ethylene glycol, $C_2H_6O_2$, in 1000 g of solution?

$$\text{Moles of ethylene glycol} = (10.0 \text{ g})\left(\frac{1 \text{ mole}}{62 \text{ g}}\right) = 0.161 \text{ mole}$$

$$\text{Weight of water} = 1000 \text{ g} - 10.0 \text{ g} = 990 \text{ g}$$

$$\text{Molality} = \frac{0.161 \text{ moles}}{0.9 \text{ kg}} = 0.163 \text{ m}$$

$$\Delta T_f = (1.86)(0.163) = 0.303°C$$

$$\text{Freezing Point} = 0°C - 0.30° = -0.30°C$$

Example 5.10 The freezing point of a phenol solution is 39.8°C when 5.08 g of solute is added to 264 g phenol. What is the molecular weight of the solute?

$$\text{Molality} = \frac{\Delta T_f}{K_f} = \frac{40.9 - 39.8}{7.40} = \frac{1.1}{7.40} = 0.15 \text{ m}$$

Also,

$$\text{Molality} = \left(\frac{\text{weight of solute}}{\text{molecular weight}}\right)/\text{kg solvent}$$

$$= \left(\frac{5.08 \text{ g}}{MW}\right)/0.264 \text{ kg} = 0.15$$

$$MW = \frac{5.08}{(0.264)(0.15)} = 128$$

The freezing point depression concept has a very important application in automotive antifreeze. Permanent antifreeze is ethylene glycol with rust preventatives and other additives. Charts are supplied showing the ratio of antifreeze (ethylene glycol) to water that is required to obtain the desired freezing point. The values on this chart are calculated from the relationship $\Delta T_f = K_f m$.

Osmotic pressure

If a solution and a solvent are separated by a semipermeable membrane (one through which solvent molecules may pass but solute particles may not), solvent flows through the membrane in an attempt to equalize the concentration. *Osmotic pressure* is defined as the pressure that would have to be applied to the solution to prevent passage of pure solvent into the solution through the membrane. If a solution is put into one arm of a U-tube of appropriate dimensions and some pure solvent is placed in the other arm separated by a semipermeable membrane, the liquid level on the solution side rises as solvent enters. At some height, the gravitational force on the solution is equal to the force that drives

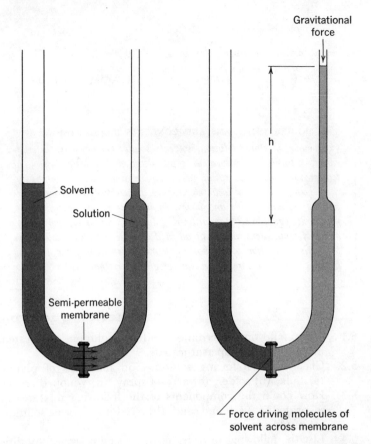

**Gravitational
force**

h

Solvent

Solution

Semi-permeable
membrane

Force driving molecules of
solvent across membrane

Fig. 5.7

*Osmotic Pressure. Molecules of solvent pass through a semipermeable
membrane to equalize the concentrations on both sides. As the volume of
solution increases, it rises in the small-diameter tube. At some height h the
gravitational force on the column of solution is exactly equal to the force
driving the solvent molecules through the membrane. Under these conditions
there is no net transfer of solvent molecules across the membrane.*

the solvent molecules through the membrane. The osmotic pressure π is calculated from the height; since $\pi = hdg$, where h is
height of the liquid column, d is the liquid density, and g is the
gravitational constant.

The relation between the osmotic pressure and the molality for
dilute aqueous solutions is

$$\pi = mRT,$$

where R is the gas constant and T is the absolute temperature.

Example 5.11 A glycerin solution with a density of 1.0700 g/ml contains
310.3 g of glycerin, ($C_3H_8O_3$), per liter. Estimate the osmotic pressure
at 20°C.

$$\text{moles of glycerin} = (310.3 \text{ g})\left(\frac{1 \text{ mole}}{92 \text{ g}}\right) = 3.37 \text{ moles}$$

$$\text{weight of water in 1 liter solution} = 1070.0 \text{ g} - 310.3 \text{ g} = 759.7 \text{ g}$$

$$\pi = \left(\frac{3.37 \text{ moles}}{0.760 \text{ kg}}\right)\left(0.0820 \frac{\text{l-atm}}{\text{mole-deg}}\right)(293°\text{K}) = 106 \text{ atm}$$

SIGNIFICANT TERMS AND CONCEPTS IN CHAPTER V:

Compound, mixture, solution, solvent, solute, homogenous, heterogenous, saturated, unsaturated, supersaturated, solubility, effect of temperature and pressure on gas solubility and on solid solubility, acid, base, strong and weak electrolytes, nonelectrolytes, strong acids and bases, weak acids and bases, equivalence point, neutral point, net ionic equations, standardized solutions, molarity, normality, molality, equivalent weight of an acid or base, titration, colligative properties, elevation of the boiling point, depression of the freezing point, osmotic pressure, molecular weight determinations.

Review questions

5.1. How could one determine whether a solution is saturated, unsaturated, or supersaturated?

5.2. Classify the following solutions on the basis of phases: (a) milk, (b) solder, (c) aerosol spray, (d) whipped cream.

5.3. How could the components of the following mixtures be separated? (a) salt and sand, (b) a sodium chloride solution, (c) muddy water.

5.4. List the following in order of increasing oxygen solubility.
(a) H_2O at 0°C and 1 atm pressure
(b) H_2O at 50°C and 1 atm pressure
(c) H_2O at 50°C and 5 atm pressure
(d) H_2O at 0°C and 0.5 atm pressure

5.5. Why are the solubility rules for gases in liquids applicable only if there is no chemical reaction?

5.6. Write net ionic reactions for the following, clearly showing precipitates and gases:
(a) silver nitrate solution and sodium chloride solution
(b) nitric acid and potassium hydroxide
(c) lead nitrate solution and sulfuric acid
(d) ammonium hydroxide and hydrobromic acid
(e) acetic acid and barium oxide (solid)
(f) copper(II) chloride solution and hydrosulfuric acid
(g) potassium chromate solution and barium hydroxide
(h) potassium chloride and sodium nitrate
(i) calcium carbonate (solid) and hydrochloric acid

Problems

5.7. A solution containing 62.6 g KBr per liter has a density of

1.043 g/ml. What is the percentage composition by weight? What is the molarity?

5.8. How many grams of $MgCl_2$ are required to prepare 300 ml of 0.500 M $MgCl_2$?   answer: 14.2 g

5.9. How many grams of $ZnBr_2$ are required to prepare 400 ml of 0.600 M $ZnBr_2$?

5.10. Both hydrogens are replaceable in oxalic acid, HOOCCOOH. How many grams of oxalic acid are in 5.60 liters of a 0.250 N solution?

5.11. What is the molarity of an oxalic acid ($H_2C_2O_4$) solution prepared from 3.60 g oxalic acid in 600 ml of solution?

5.12. What volume of 0.20 M $CuSO_4$ can be prepared from 1.0 kg $CuSO_4$?

5.13. What volume of 0.100 N $Ba(OH)_2$ can be prepared from 342 g $Ba(OH)_2$?   answer: 40.0 l

5.14. What weight of H_2SO_4 is in 450 ml of 6.00 N sulfuric acid?

5.15. What is the normality of a phosphoric acid that contains 1.00 g H_3PO_4 in 200 ml of solution?

5.16. What is the normality of a NaOH solution if 24.00 ml of it is neutralized by 20.40 ml of 0.320 N sulfuric acid?

answer: 0.272 N

5.17. Exactly 10.00 ml of 0.250 N NaOH is required to reach the equivalence point when titrating 12.20 ml acetic acid. What is the normality of the acetic acid?

5.18. What volume of 0.825 N H_2SO_4 can be neutralized by 100 ml of 0.602 N KOH?

5.19. If 18.18 ml of NaOH are required to reach the equivalence point when titrating a solution containing 4.50 g oxalic acid (see Problem 5.10), what is the normality of the NaOH solution?   answer: 5.50 N

5.20. If 10.15 ml of $Ba(OH)_2$ are required to reach the equivalence point when titrating a solution containing 1.00 g oxalic acid, what is the normality and molarity of the $Ba(OH)_2$ solution?

5.21. What is the molecular weight of a solute if a solution containing 61.8 g in 600 g of water freezes at $-0.56°C$?

answer: 342

5.22. If 0.46 g toluene (C_7H_8) is added to 400 g benzene (C_6H_6), what is the freezing point of the solution?

5.23. What is the boiling point of a solution containing 17.1 g sucrose ($C_{12}H_{22}O_{11}$) in 200 g water?   answer: 100.13°C

5.24. Estimate the osmotic pressure of the solution in Problem 5.23.

structure of the atom   six

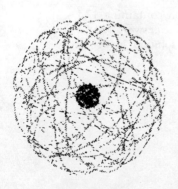

From a study of gases, we may conclude that matter is composed of atoms. Yet no one has ever seen an atom. Their existence is postulated from the development of theories or models which fit the experimentally observed results. The technique of fitting theory to observations is used to arrive at the present understanding of the structure of the atom. There has been a continual change in theories as new data become available. Present theories fit today's observations. There is always the possibility that tomorrow's discoveries may require a complete revision of theory.

The hard-sphere model

Early theories on the structure of matter

As with so many things, theories on the structure of matter begin with the Greeks. Democritus, who lived in the fifth century B.C., is one of the first atomists. Democritus and the other early atomists reasoned that matter can be divided only to a certain point. These small, indivisible particles were called *atoms*. The form of the particles determined the physical properties. For example, liquid particles were smooth and solids were rough. Bitter material had hooks on the particles that stuck to the tongue.

During the next century Aristotle's philosophy replaced the atomic theory. Aristotle thought that four elements—fire, earth, water, and air—existed. All natural phenomena could be explained by the transfer of these elements from one piece of matter to another. Since both Aristotle and the atomists depended solely on reason and not experiment, the apparently better reasoning prevailed.

For the next two thousand years alchemists were guided by Aristotle's arguments. Because matter was interconvertible, it did not seem foolish to try to find the philosopher's stone that would transmute base matter into gold, the perfect metal. The alchemists boiled and cooked almost everything. They discovered many chemical reactions and developed many pieces of apparatus but failed to draw any conclusions from their work. Eventually, a few of the alchemists began to see that their discoveries could not be explained adequately by Aristotelian logic.

Near the end of the seventeenth century, the phlogiston–calx theory was postulated by Stahl. This was a revival of the atomists' theory, since phlogiston and calx were elements held together by forces which today would be called gravitational. Stahl's theory (a model) attempted to explain experimental facts. Once the hold of Aristotle's theory had been broken, modification and change of theories took place readily. Early in the eighteenth century, Hales developed the pneumatic trough which permitted the study of pure gases. These studies showed that air was not an element and definitely brought an end to Aristotle's theory. The phlogiston–calx theory was disproved by Antoine Lavoisier in the latter part of the eighteenth century.

By the end of the eighteenth century, very few people questioned the existence of atoms. About 160 years ago, John Dalton, the English physicist, was able to summarize the knowledge of his day in his atomic theory which, severely modified, serves as the basis for the development of much of the present-day theory of the structure of matter. Dalton's theory of the structure of matter can be set down as follows:

(1) Chemical elements are composed of indivisible atoms.
(2) Atoms can be neither created nor annihilated.
(3) Atoms of the same element are identical and have the same mass.
(4) Atoms of different elements have different masses.
(5) Combination may occur between atoms of two or more elements in whole number ratios to form compounds.

Today it is recognized that atoms are composed of smaller units. It is also possible to split an atom and to create or annihilate matter—but not in the course of an ordinary chemical reaction. Furthermore, it is well established that atoms of the same element

Fig. 6.1

The Four Elements of Aristotle. Greek philosophers thought that all matter was composed of four elements, each with its characteristic properties. Earth (represented by a cube) was dry and heavy; water (icosahedron) was wet and relatively heavy; air (octahedron) was cold and relatively light; fire (tetrahedron) was hot and light. A substance called ether filled all voids. Changes in matter were transformations of the shapes, and properties were transferred from one piece of matter to another.

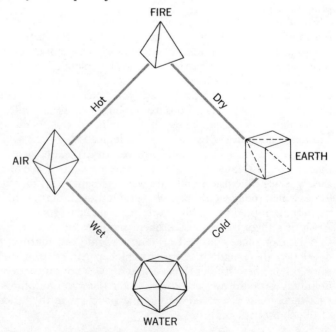

Fig. 6.2

Aristotle

Fig. 6.3

John Dalton

may have different masses. However, when one measures the average weight of a large number of atoms of a single element, the atomic weight is constant for most natural samples. Since most chemical reactions involve large numbers of atoms, parts 3 and 4 of Dalton's theory are valid for average values. Although it is possible to find many exceptions to part 5 of the theory with present-day techniques, there is still a host of compounds that demonstrate the combination of atoms in small, whole number ratios.

While Dalton's model of the atom as being a small, hard, impenetrable, movable sphere is no longer acceptable, it should be noted that many of the advances in chemistry during the nineteenth century were made using this simple picture to correlate experimental results. Even today, it is possible to use the hard-sphere model for an easy explanation of the gross behavior of many systems as, for example, that of an ideal gas. In other words, the more complex models of today's theoreticians approximate the early simple model under appropriate conditions.

One underlying feature of Dalton's theory is still very much a part of present-day thought. In the course of an ordinary chemical reaction the mass of each of the reacting atoms does not change, nor is one element changed into another. It is these principles that permitted the development of chemistry.

Spectroscopy

The hard-sphere model of the atom could not be used to explain the spectra emitted by atoms. Spectroscopy, the study of light emitted or absorbed by atoms or molecules, developed during the latter half of the nineteenth century. Atomic spectra consist of a series of lines. The simplest spectrum is that of hydrogen atoms. A portion of the spectrum, which occurs in the visible and near-ultraviolet region, is shown in Fig. 6.5. Other groups of lines in the atomic hydrogen spectrum are observed in other wavelength ranges. Any model of the atom should provide an explanation of the observed spectral lines.

Discovery of the electron

In 1897, J. J. Thomson, while studying cathode rays, demonstrated that the atom is composed of smaller units. He showed that cathode rays consist of negatively charged particles with a mass about 1/1850 that of the hydrogen atom. He obtained the same particle using any cathode material and any gas. Thomson concluded that these negative particles, which he called *electrons*, are present in all matter. The hard-sphere model of the atom was modified so that electrons were embedded in a positively charged sphere at fairly definite locations. This model had one very serious shortcoming—there was no way to correlate the electron arrangement with the observed spectra of atoms.

The nuclear model

Radioactivity attracted the attention of many experimenters after its discovery in 1896. Ernest Rutherford bombarded thin metal foils with alpha rays, known to be positively charged particles emitted by a radioactive source. Rutherford found that one out of about every 8000 alpha particles did not go through the foil but was "reflected" back at unexpected angles.

Once observed, the back-scattering of alpha particles needed an explanation. Therefore, in 1911, Rutherford postulated a nuclear

Fig. 6.4

Sketch of a Spectrograph. Light emitted by the source or excited sample passes through the slit onto a grating, or through a prism, where wavelengths (colors) of light are bent at slightly different angles and separated. An image of the slit appears at the detector at points corresponding to the wavelengths in the light beam. Light emitted by atoms results in a series of well defined lines.

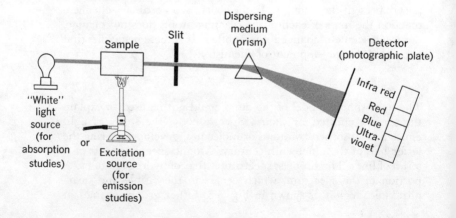

model of the atom to replace the hard-sphere model. In this model the positive charge and almost all of the mass is contained in a very small volume, the nucleus. Electrons are in the space about this nucleus. Since the atom is neutral, the number of electrons is equal to the number of positive charges on the nucleus. Rutherford's experiments lead to an estimate of 10^{-12} to 10^{-13} cm for the radius of the nucleus. Experimental data from other studies indicate an atomic radius of about 10^{-8} cm. Thus, the nucleus occupies only an insignificant portion of the total volume of an atom. Since the radius of an electron is estimated to be about 10^{-13} cm, most of the volume occupied by an atom is empty space.

This nuclear model is almost universally accepted, but it presents the very difficult problem of determining how the electrons

Å
3647

3798
3835
3889
3970
4102
4340
4861

Fig. 6.5

Balmer Series of the Atomic Hydrogen Spectrum. These spectral lines of hydrogen atoms which occur in the visible and ultraviolet regions were observed by Johann Balmer in 1885. The wavelength λ of the lines is represented by

$$\lambda = \frac{n^2}{n^2 - 4} (3645.6 \times 10^{-8}) \, cm,$$

where n is an integer greater than 2.   6563

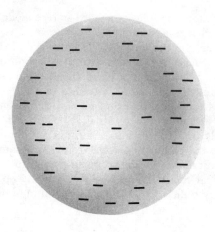

Fig. 6.6

Thomson Model of the Atom. The negatively charged electrons are embedded in a sphere of positive charge. The total atom is neutral.

are arranged about the nucleus. There appears to be no definitive method of precisely locating the position of an electron within an atom. Thus, it is necessary to postulate an arrangement of electrons that predicts the experimentally observed results.

On the basis of classical or Newtonian physics, the nuclear atom should not exist for two reasons:

1. There is no way for oppositely charged particles to be at rest within an atom. The unlike charges attract; the only stable situation is for the positive and negative charges to touch. This is not what the postulated nuclear model predicts.

2. The electrons would remain at some distance from the nucleus, if they were moving in a circle about the nucleus at a velocity such that the centrifugal or outward force is equal to the force of attraction between the charged particles. But when an electron is moving in the field of a charged nucleus, the electron should radiate energy and spiral toward the nucleus. Calculations show that the electron should collide with the nucleus in about 10^{-8} seconds. Furthermore, the radiated energy would not be in the form of discrete wavelengths as is observed.

Since atoms exist and apparently have electrons arranged at some distance from the nucleus, it is necessary to develop a further theory that results in the prediction of chemical properties.

The Bohr model

One of the first of the more successful attempts to explain the observed spectrum of hydrogen atoms was made by the Danish physicist, Niels Bohr, in 1913. In order to explain the observed facts, Bohr introduced three assumptions for the hydrogen atom which consists of a positively charged nucleus and a single electron. These assumptions are:

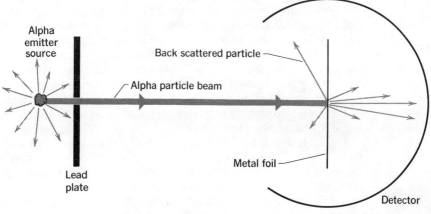

Fig. 6.7

The Rutherford Experiment. Rutherford bombarded pieces of thin gold foil with a beam of alpha particles. Most particles passed through the foil; only a few were bounced back or scattered. From this experiment Rutherford concluded that the atom is mostly empty space.

Fig. 6.8

Scattering of Alpha Particles by Nuclei. By studying the angles at which alpha particles are scattered, it is possible to estimate how closely the particles approach a nucleus. From the values obtained, the radius of the nucleus has been estimated to be 10^{-12} to 10^{-13} centimeters.

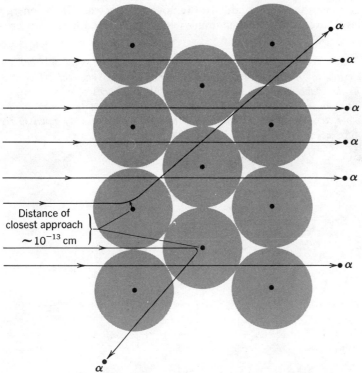

1. According to classical theory the electron can be at any distance from the nucleus; its energy is dependent upon the distance of separation. Bohr assumed that the electron is only at certain distances from the nucleus and that only certain discrete energies exist for the atom. In other words, the energy is quantized. In a simple picture for the hydrogen atom, the electron moves in one of several possible spherical paths about the nucleus.

2. The electron, although it is moving, does not emit radiation while in one of these orbits or energy levels.

3. The emission and absorption of radiation are associated with transitions or "jumps" between two of these levels. The energy gained during absorption or the energy lost during emission is emitted as a packet or *quantum* of radiant energy. The energy of this quantum is equal to the difference in energy of the higher state, E_a, and the lower state, E_b, or: $\Delta E = E_a - E_b$.

This energy difference, ΔE, is observed as emitted or absorbed light of a particular wavelength. The relationship is given by: $\Delta E = hc/\lambda$, where h is the proportionality constant known as Planck's constant, c is the speed of light, and λ (lambda) is the wavelength. Combining measured values of ΔE with an arbitrary reference energy, it is possible to assign values to each of the energy levels. A value of zero is customarily assigned as the energy of the level corresponding to that point at which the electron is completely removed from the influence of the nucleus. All other levels are of lower energy, since the electron is attracted to the nucleus and energy must be added to remove the electron. If the energy levels are numbered beginning with one for the lowest and pro-

Fig. 6.9

Bohr's Model of the Hydrogen Atom. Niels Bohr suggested that the electron in the hydrogen atom lies in one of several spherical orbits at a fixed distance from the nucleus. Each orbit corresponds to a given energy. At room temperature the electron occupies the ground state of $n = 1$. To move to other orbits the electron must absorb energy exactly equal to the difference in energies of the various orbits.

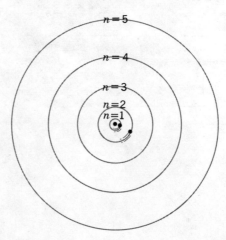

| **Fig. 6.10** | **Fig. 6.11** |
| *Lord Rutherford* | *Niels Bohr* |

ceeding by integer values, the energy of the nth level, E_n, is

$$E_n = \frac{\text{constant}}{n_2}$$

Since n can only be an integer, the energy can take on only certain values as determined by n^2.

Agreement with the spectroscopic expression for the wave lengths of the hydrogen spectrum is obtained readily by taking the difference between two energy levels, E_{n_2} and E_{n_1}.

By extending the theory further and making more assumptions, the radii r of the orbits of the electron in the hydrogen atom are calculated to be:

$$r = 0.529 \times 10^{-8} n^2 \text{ centimeters} = 0.529 n^2 \text{ Angstroms}$$

This indicates that the electron is farther from the nucleus in the higher energy level and is infinitely far away when the energy of the system becomes zero. Since the electron cannot be located precisely, there is no direct experimental check on these values. However, the values for the lower energy levels appear to be reasonable when compared with other data on atomic dimensions.

The Bohr model proved to be very successful in predicting the wavelengths emitted and absorbed by the hydrogen atom. New series of wavelengths were predicted and found which aided in the rapid acceptance of the theory. Attempts were made to extend this model to elements other than hydrogen. A qualitative model similar to a miniature solar system developed, with electrons occupying spherical orbitals at relatively fixed distances. This simple picture permitted the correlation of much chemical knowledge. However, in order to achieve partial quantitative agreement between the theoretical model and observed properties, it is necessary to introduce various corrections into the theoretical model. Numerous factors for each element do not follow any pattern and cannot be predicted on the basis of any theory.

The new quantum mechanical model

The need for a better model for the structure of atoms other than hydrogen led to the development of the new quantum mechanics by Erwin Schroedinger, Werner Heisenberg, and P. A. M. Dirac in the period between 1925 and 1932. The model used by each of these men is essentially a mathematical expression. Each man used a different method of approach, but obtained practically the same results. The discussion to follow proceeds along the lines used by Schroedinger.

Quantum numbers

The electrons about the nucleus of an atom can be arranged in an infinite number of ways with a different energy for each arrangement. However, as in the case of the Bohr model, only certain arrangements of electrons and the corresponding energies are possible for the system. The problem is to describe this arrangement or state of the system. Bohr and others chose to use a physical picture to express this arrangement. In the new quantum mechanics theory, the state of the system is given by a mathematical expression known as the wave function and designated by the symbol ψ (psi). The wave function cannot be derived from experimental data, nor does it permit any physical pictures to be drawn.

In the solution of the mathematical equations, the energy associated with each allowed arrangement of electrons, or state of the system, is calculated. Thus, each wave function has a corresponding energy. Each of the wave functions for a particular atom is characterized by a set of three quantum numbers. It is convenient to use these quantum numbers to index the energy associated with each wave function. Such an indexing system permits comparison of the energy levels of one atom with another.

The three quantum numbers are the principal quantum number, symbolized as n, the azimuthal quantum number, l, and the magnetic quantum number, m. The possible values are limited by the mathematics used to solve for the relationship between the energy and wave function. For a given value of n, l varies by integer values from 0 to $(n - 1)$. For a given value of l, the value of m varies by integer values from $-l$ to $+l$.

RESULTS FOR THE HYDROGEN ATOM

When the methods of quantum mechanics are applied to the simplest atomic system, the hydrogen atom, the results are very

Fig. 6.12

Energy Level Diagram for the Hydrogen Atom. When an electron moves from a higher energy state to a lower, the difference in energy (ΔE) is emitted as a single packet. The wavelength λ of light resulting from the transition is

$$\Delta E = hc/\lambda.$$

Calculated wavelengths agree with experimentally determined spectral lines. Each final energy level provides a series of lines in different parts of the spectrum.

simple. The energy of each allowed arrangement of the electron about the nucleus is found to be dependent only upon the value of the principal quantum number n.

$$E_n = \frac{-\text{constant}}{n^2}$$

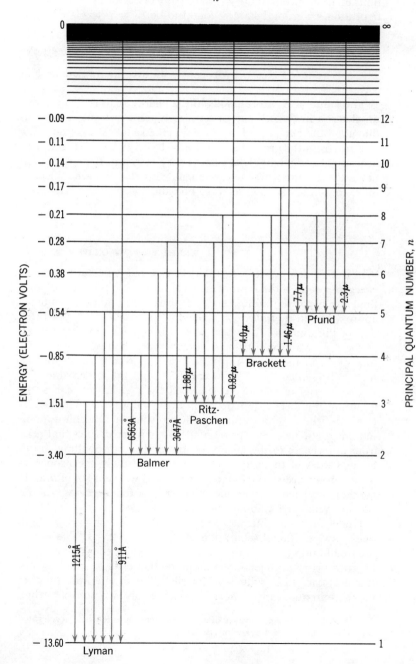

Thus, n becomes the index for the energy level. There are several wave functions representing different allowed values of l and m, but the energies of these states do not change, except as the value of n changes. The highest energy state is $E = 0$ which corresponds to a value of $n = \infty$. When the constant is evaluated in the usual units of the electron-volt (eV*) the energy of the lowest energy configuration, or ground state, is found to be $E_1 = -13.60$ eV. This corresponds to a value of $n = 1$. The energy of the state or arrangement corresponding to $n = 2$ is $E_2 = \dfrac{-13.60}{4} = -3.40$ eV. The energy levels of the hydrogen atom are diagramed in Fig. 6.12.

The value of E_n corresponds to the energy required to remove an electron in the nth energy level to a point just outside the influence of the nucleus. Thus, it would take 13.60 eV to remove the electron from the ground state, or $n = 1$ energy level. It would be necessary to add 3.40 eV to remove an electron in the $n = 2$ level. Since these values are in agreement with the observed spectral lines, the theory is considered to be valid.

RESULTS FOR OTHER ATOMS

While it is not possible to make a rigorous calculation of the energy for each of the arrangements of the electrons in atoms other than the hydrogen atom, certain features are apparent from the approximation methods used. Energy no longer is solely a function of the quantum number, n; it also depends upon the value of the l quantum number. In other words, the presence of electron–electron repulsions introduces an energy difference for the states represented by different values of l but the same value of n.

The energy of the levels described by a given set of n and l quantum numbers is independent of the values of m. Under certain conditions, such as placing the emitting or absorbing atoms in a magnetic field, it is possible to obtain spectral lines that arise from differences in the energy of the levels corresponding to different values of the m quantum number. Usually the properties of the atoms are studied under conditions where a set of n and l values is sufficient to describe the energy of the electrons, and no reference need be made to the value of m.

Under favorable but more extreme conditions, it is possible to detect an additional separation of the energy levels. The effects are small and are indicative of small changes in energy. Since the Schroedinger approach offers no prediction of these small effects, it is necessary to introduce arbitrarily a fourth quantum number m_s, the spin quantum number. There are only two possible values

---

* 1 electron-volt is the energy gained by an electron when it is accelerated through a potential difference of 1 volt.

$$1 \text{ eV} = 1.60 \times 10^{-12} \text{ erg} = 3.83 \times 10^{-20} \text{ calorie}$$

for m_s, namely, $+1/2$ and $-1/2$. Although the term *spin* is derived from an older, but presently unacceptable concept of an electron spinning on its axis, the spin quantum number is developed in the Dirac approach and as such has no physical significance. It is not necessary to become involved in the definition of the spin quantum number if one only considers that there is a spin quantum number symbolized as m_s that has two values, $+1/2$ and $-1/2$. In many notations the two spin values are distinguished by an arrow up and an arrow down.

THE PAULI EXCLUSION PRINCIPLE

When the calculations of quantum mechanics are extended to atoms with several electrons, it is necessary to introduce the Pauli Exclusion Principle. While the mathematical arguments of the Pauli Principle are beyond the scope of this text, a useful simplification may be stated as follows:

In any system of fundamental, identical particles (such as electrons in an atom), no two particles may have an identical set of quantum numbers.

The first consequence of this Exclusion Principle is to show that there is a limit on the number of electrons in any one energy level. Secondly, when the Pauli Exclusion Principle is combined with the restrictions placed on the values of the quantum numbers as obtained by quantum mechanics, it is possible to correlate the periodic table with the electronic structure of the atoms.

ENERGY LEVEL NOTATION

As discussed above, the energy of an electronic level depends upon the values of the quantum numbers, n and l. In order to keep the

Table 6.1

*Symbols for the Values
of the Quantum Number, l*

l value	letter
0	s
1	p
2	d
3	f
4	g
5	h
6	i
7*	k

* For l values greater than 7,
the sequence is alphabetical
beginning with l.

designation of these levels relatively simple, it is necessary to adopt a shorthand notation to index them.

The electronic energy levels are designated first by an Arabic numeral which represents the value of the principal quantum number, n, followed by a small letter representing the value of the azimuthal quantum number, l. The letters used to represent the

Fig. 6.13

Probability of Finding an Electron in a Thin Spherical Shell of Radius r, as a Function of the Radius for the Ground State of the Hydrogen Atom. The quantum model shows that the electron of the hydrogen atom is found most often 0.529 Å from the nucleus; however, it is possible to find the electron at other distances.

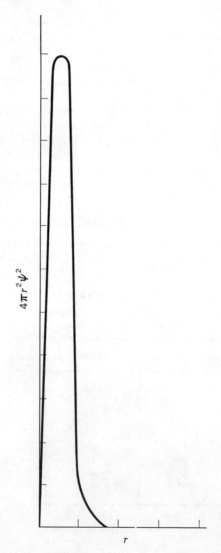

values of *l*, given in Table 6.1, result from early spectroscopic notations for spectral lines.

A 1*s* electron is an electron which has a principal quantum number of one and an azimuthal quantum number of zero. A 3*p* electron represents the state corresponding to $n = 3$, $l = 1$.

Locating the electron

According to another theoretical concept, there is a finite limit to the accuracy with which one may locate a particle experimentally. The error in the location of the heavy nucleus is very small. However, the error in locating a lightweight electron is about one atomic diameter. This means that it is possible to associate an electron with one atom but it is impossible to determine where the electron is within the atom.

The wave function does not give a physical picture of the arrangement of electrons in an atom. When the appropriate calculations are made, correct values of the energies as well as useful predictions of chemical properties are obtained. It has been suggested that the value of the square of the wave function, ψ^2, can be related to the probability of finding the electron at the point for which ψ^2 is evaluated.

In this mathematical model of the atom it is no longer possible to fix the location of the electron exactly. Rather, it is necessary to speak in terms of a probability of finding the electron at some point. When in its ground state, the electron in a hydrogen atom may be found anywhere from the center of the nucleus out to an infinite distance; although the probability of finding it at either extreme is almost zero. The most probable, but not the only, distance from the nucleus is 0.529 Å. If one were to imagine a three-dimensional plot of the probability of finding the electron when it is in the ground state of hydrogen, where the density increases as the probability (Fig. 6.14), the result would be a gradual darkening from the center outward until a maximum density is reached at 0.529 Å from the nucleus. Then the darkening decreases as the distance increases until at some ill-defined point no darkening would be detected. This cloudy ball frequently is called an electron cloud. This electron cloud is not to be considered as the electron smeared out over the entire region. Rather,

Fig. 6.14

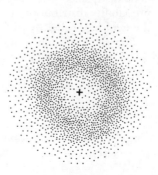

Electron Cloud. Represents the results of a hypothetical experiment during which the electron is precisely located many times. The very dark area shows the region where the electron most often is found. For hydrogen this is 0.529 Å from the nucleus. The hypothesis cannot be verified experimentally.

it should be viewed as the observable result of a very rapidly moving small particle.

If similar calculations of the probability distribution are made for levels other than the 1*s*, it is found that the distribution is spherical for all *s* levels. In other words, the most probable location for an electron in an *s* level (an *s* electron) is in a thin spherical shell. The value of the principal quantum number, *n*, determines the radius of this sphere.

If one draws the most probable distribution surfaces for *p* electrons, one finds the result to be two spherical shells tangent at the nucleus. However, since $l = 1$, there are three *p* states, corresponding to $m = 1$, $m = 0$, and $m = -1$, which have the same energy. It is possible to relate these distributions to the usual *x*, *y*, *z* coordinate system and to speak of p_x, p_y, and p_z orbitals.

Usually it is more convenient to draw only the cross section of the probability distributions and refer to these as *s* electrons, *p* electrons, and so on. When this terminology is encountered, one must remember that it refers to the planar cross section of the most probable location of the electron in that state, or the cross section of the contour of the greatest value of the product of $4\pi r^2$ and the square of the wave function describing the particular energy state.

Quantum number summary

From the solution of the wave equation it is found that a particular electronic state is described by four quantum numbers. For most purposes the energy of an electronic state depends solely upon the values of the principal and the azimuthal quantum numbers.

The principal quantum number *n* takes on integer values from one to infinity. The value of *n* is related to the most probable distance between the electron and the nucleus.

The azimuthal quantum number *l* takes on integer values from zero to $(n - 1)$ for a given value of *n*. The value of *l* is related to the shape of the electron probability distribution.

The magnetic quantum number *m* takes on integer values from $-l$ to $+l$ for any given value of *l*. The effect of the magnetic quantum number cannot be observed in the absence of a magnetic field, since the value of *m* is related to the orientation of the probability distribution in the magnetic field. Each orientation in the field has a slightly different energy.

The electron spin quantum number m_s has only two values, $+1/2$ and $-1/2$, which correspond to some residual energy. The energy difference of the two orientations in a strong magnetic field is very small.

The periodic classification

The electron configuration (a listing of the energy levels occupied by electrons) of the elements may be determined on the basis of

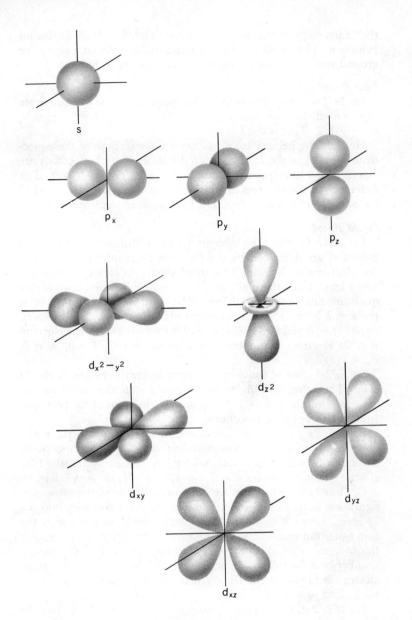

Fig. 6.15

*Most Probable Location of an Electron in $l = 0$ (s orbital), $l = 1$
(p orbital), and $l = 2$ (d orbital) Energy Levels. Drawings represent
three-dimensional surfaces calculated to be the most probable locations of an
electron in the energy level. The shape of the probability distribution is
characteristic of the l quantum number value; size is a function of the n
quantum number value. Each orientation shown above can be related to
the m quantum number value and is energetically equivalent for a given l
value.*

the limits imposed by quantum theory and the Pauli Exclusion Principle. The periodic table is based on the lowest energy, or ground state, electron configurations which are as follows.

First Period

H: $1s$ The single electron in hydrogen is in the ground state represented by the quantum numbers $n = 1$, $l = 0$, $m = 0$, $m_s = -1/2$. This is the $1s$ state.

He: $1s^2$ The helium atom has two electrons. Both of these electrons may be in the $1s$ state since the states of both electrons are described by the quantum numbers $n = 1$, $l = 0$, $m = 0$. The difference in the two sets of quantum numbers is that $m_s = -1/2$ for one electron and $m_s = +1/2$ for the other electron.

Second Period

Li: $1s^2 2s$ Two of the three electrons in lithium go into the $1s$ state and are described by the same set of quantum numbers as the electrons in helium. The third electron cannot go into the $n = 1$ level, since there are only two possible combinations of the quantum numbers for that level. The third electron must exist at the $n = 2$ level. There are two possible values of l in this level, namely $l = 0$ and $l = 1$. Since $l = 0$ is the lower level, the electron is a $2s$ electron with quantum numbers $n = 2$, $l = 0$, $m = 0$, $m_s = -1/2$.

Be: $1s^2 2s^2$ Two of the four electrons in beryllium are in the $1s$ state. The other two electrons go into a state described by the quantum numbers, $n = 2$, $l = 0$, $m = 0$; the spins of the two electrons are in opposite directions.

B: $1s^2 2s^2 2p$ Four of the five boron electrons go into the states described by the sets of quantum numbers for beryllium. Since there can be only two s electrons for any given n value, the fifth electron must go into the $n = 2$, $l = 1$, $m = -1$, $m_s = -1/2$ level.

C: $1s^2 2s^2 2p^2$ The first five electrons of carbon have the same configuration as those in boron. The sixth electron also goes into the $2p$ level. There is good spectroscopic evidence to show that the spin quantum numbers of the two $2p$ electrons are the same. For this to be possible, it is necessary that the value of the m quantum number be different for the two p orbitals. This means that a single electron is in two of the three p orbitals. These are referred to as the p_x and p_y orbitals.

N: $1s^2 2s^2 2p^3$ There is spectroscopic evidence to show that the three $2p$ electrons have aligned spins which means that there is one electron in each of the three p orbitals. For convenience, these are sometimes designated as $2p_x\, 2p_y\, 2p_z$. It should be noted that the energies of the three p states are identical in the absence of a magnetic field. The energy difference between this and other possible configurations is due to the spin alignment. In other words, it would require the expenditure of some energy to have one of the electrons spin in an opposite direction.

O: $1s^2 2s^2 2p^4$ Seven of the oxygen electrons have the same configuration as the nitrogen electrons. The eighth electron of oxygen must go into a p orbital and fill it. Thus the two electrons in the one p orbital have opposed spins and different m_s values. The filled oxygen orbital is usually designated as the $2p_z$. Thus, the configuration for the p electrons in oxygen is $2p_x2p_y2p_z^2$.

F: $1s^22s^22p^5$ The ninth electron in fluorine fills another p orbital which is customarily designated as $2p_y$. Thus, the p electron configuration is $2p_x2p_y^22p_z^2$.

Ne: $1s^22s^22p^6$ The tenth electron fills the last p orbital which shows that there are six p electrons for any given n value. In the case of neon, the $n = 2$ level also is filled, since all possible combinations of quantum numbers have been used.

Third Period

An eleventh electron now must enter the $n = 3$ level. The filling of the $n = 3$ state takes place for sodium through argon in the same manner as the $n = 2$ state. Thus, the electron configuration for argon is

$$1s^2\ 2s^2\ 2p^6\ 3s^2\ 3p^6.$$

The 18 electrons in argon do not exhaust all of the possible combinations of quantum numbers for the $n = 3$ state, since l may also have a value of 2 leading to $3d$ electronic states.

Fourth Period

The nineteenth electron in potassium does not enter the $3d$ state but rather the $4s$ state, since this leads to a slightly lower energy. The $4s$ state is filled with the 20th electron as in calcium. The $3d$ level is then filled, starting with scandium and ending with zinc. There are five possible orientations of the d electron probability distributions corresponding to the $m = -2, -1, 0, 1, 2$ values. Thus, ten electrons are possible in the d states. As with the p electrons, the alignment of electron spins is preferred as the first five d orbitals are being filled. The fact that the $4s$ and $3d$ states are energetically close together is illustrated by there being only one $4s$ electron in chromium and copper, while the $3d$ orbitals are half or completely filled (Table 6.2). After thirty electrons have been used in zinc, the next six electrons fill the $4p$ level from gallium through krypton.

Fifth, Sixth, and Seventh Periods

After the $4p$ level is filled, the $5s$, $4d$, $5p$, and $6s$ levels fill in order, making a total of 56 electrons for barium. In lanthanum the next electron goes into the $5d$ level. Beginning with cerium, fourteen electrons go into the $4f$ level, creating the so-called lanthanide or rare earth series. After the $4f$ level is filled, the $5d$ level is filled followed by the $6p$ level. The $7s$ level is filled next followed by the actinide series which is analogous to the lanthanide series. The actinide series ends with element 103. The electron configuration of the man-made elements above 99 is not observed experimentally due to the fact that so few atoms of these elements have been prepared. However, it is possible to predict the configuration from theory.

Table 6.2

Electron Configuration of Elemental Gaseous Atoms in the Ground State

Atomic Number	Element	1s	2s	2p	3s	3p	3d	4s	4p	4d	4f	5s	5p	5d	5f
1	H	1													
2	He	2													
3	Li	2	1												
4	Be	2	2												
5	B	2	2	1											
6	C	2	2	2											
7	N	2	2	3											
8	O	2	2	4											
9	F	2	2	5											
10	Ne	2	2	6											
11	Na	2	2	6	1										
12	Mg	2	2	6	2										
13	Al	2	2	6	2	1									
14	Si	2	2	6	2	2									
15	P	2	2	6	2	3									
16	S	2	2	6	2	4									
17	Cl	2	2	6	2	5									
18	Ar	2	2	6	2	6									
19	K	2	2	6	2	6		1							
20	Ca	2	2	6	2	6		2							
21	Sc	2	2	6	2	6	1	2							
22	Ti	2	2	6	2	6	2	2							
23	V	2	2	6	2	6	3	2							
24	Cr	2	2	6	2	6	5	1							
25	Mn	2	2	6	2	6	5	2							
26	Fe	2	2	6	2	6	6	2							
27	Co	2	2	6	2	6	7	2							
28	Ni	2	2	6	2	6	8	2							
29	Cu	2	2	6	2	6	10	1							
30	Zn	2	2	6	2	6	10	2							
31	Ga	2	2	6	2	6	10	2	1						
32	Ge	2	2	6	2	6	10	2	2						
33	As	2	2	6	2	6	10	2	3						
34	Se	2	2	6	2	6	10	2	4						
35	Br	2	2	6	2	6	10	2	5						
36	Kr	2	2	6	2	6	10	2	6						
37	Rb	2	2	6	2	6	10	2	6			1			
38	Sr	2	2	6	2	6	10	2	6			2			
39	Y	2	2	6	2	6	10	2	6	1		2			
40	Zr	2	2	6	2	6	10	2	6	2		2			
41	Nb	2	2	6	2	6	10	2	6	4		1			
42	Mo	2	2	6	2	6	10	2	6	5		1			
43	Tc	2	2	6	2	6	10	2	6	5		2			
44	Ru	2	2	6	2	6	10	2	6	7		1			
45	Rh	2	2	6	2	6	10	2	6	8		1			
46	Pd	2	2	6	2	6	10	2	6	10					
47	Ag	2	2	6	2	6	10	2	6	10		1			
48	Cd	2	2	6	2	6	10	2	6	10		2			
49	In	2	2	6	2	6	10	2	6	10		2	1		
50	Sn	2	2	6	2	6	10	2	6	10		2	2		
51	Sb	2	2	6	2	6	10	2	6	10		2	3		
52	Te	2	2	6	2	6	10	2	6	10		2	4		
53	I	2	2	6	2	6	10	2	6	10		2	5		
54	Xe	2	2	6	2	6	10	2	6	10		2	6		

Transition Metals I (elements 21–30)

Transition Metals II (elements 39–48)

Atomic Number	Element	1s	2s2p	3s3p3d	4s	4p	4d	4f	5s	5p	5d	5f	6s	6p	6d	7s
55	Cs	2	8	18	2	6	10		2	6			1			
56	Ba	2	8	18	2	6	10		2	6			2			
57	La	2	8	18	2	6	10		2	6	1		2			
58	Ce	2	8	18	2	6	10	2	2	6			2			
59	Pr	2	8	18	2	6	10	3	2	6			2			
60	Nd	2	8	18	2	6	10	4	2	6			2			
61	Pm	2	8	18	2	6	10	5	2	6			2			
62	Sm	2	8	18	2	6	10	6	2	6			2			
63	Eu	2	8	18	2	6	10	7	2	6			2			
64	Gd	2	8	18	2	6	10	7	2	6			2			
65	Tb	2	8	18	2	6	10	9	2	6			2			
66	Dy	2	8	18	2	6	10	10	2	6			2			
67	Ho	2	8	18	2	6	10	11	2	6			2			
68	Er	2	8	18	2	6	10	12	2	6			2			
69	Tm	2	8	18	2	6	10	13	2	6			2			
70	Yb	2	8	18	2	6	10	14	2	6			2			
71	Lu	2	8	18	2	6	10	14	2	6	1		2			
72	Hf	2	8	18	2	6	10	14	2	6	2		2			
73	Ta	2	8	18	2	6	10	14	2	6	3		2			
74	W	2	8	18	2	6	10	14	2	6	4		2			
75	Re	2	8	18	2	6	10	14	2	6	5		2			
76	Os	2	8	18	2	6	10	14	2	6	6		2			
77	Ir	2	8	18	2	6	10	14	2	6	7		2			
78	Pt	2	8	18	2	6	10	14	2	6	9		1			
79	Au	2	8	18	2	6	10	14	2	6	10		1			
80	Hg	2	8	18	2	6	10	14	2	6	10		2			
81	Tl	2	8	18	2	6	10	14	2	6	10		2	1		
82	Pb	2	8	18	2	6	10	14	2	6	10		2	2		
83	Bi	2	8	18	2	6	10	14	2	6	10		2	3		
84	Po	2	8	18	2	6	10	14	2	6	10		2	4		
85	At	2	8	18	2	6	10	14	2	6	10		2	5		
86	Rn	2	8	18	2	6	10	14	2	6	10		2	6		
87	Fr	2	8	18			32		2	6	10		2	6		1
88	Ra	2	8	18			32		2	6	10		2	6		2
89	Ac	2	8	18			32		2	6	10		2	6	1	2
90	Th	2	8	18			32		2	6	10		2	6	2	2
91	Pa	2	8	18			32		2	6	10	2	2	6	1	2
92	U	2	8	18			32		2	6	10	3	2	6	1	2
93*	Np	2	8	18			32		2	6	10	4	2	6	1	2
94*	Pu	2	8	18			32		2	6	10	6	2	6		2
95*	Am	2	8	18			32		2	6	10	7	2	6		2
96*	Cm	2	8	18			32		2	6	10	7	2	6	1	2
97*	Bk	2	8	18			32		2	6	10	8	2	6	1	2
98*	Cf	2	8	18			32		2	6	10	9	2	6	1	2
99*	Es	2	8	18			32		2	6	10	10	2	6	1	2
100*	Fm	2	8	18			32		2	6	10	11	2	6	1	2
101*	Md	2	8	18			32		2	6	10	12	2	6	1	2
102*	No	2	8	18			32		2	6	10	13	2	6	1	2
103*	Lw	2	8	18			32		2	6	10	14	2	6	1	2

Side brackets: Lanthanides (57–71); Transition Metals III; Actinides (89–103).

* Predicted

A careful study of Table 6.2, which lists the ground state electron configuration of the elements, shows that there are some irregularities in the configuration of the elements with many electrons. This is due to the small separations of the energy levels. Thus, electron–electron interactions may cause certain configurations to be more stable than others. Also there is some question as to the exact ground state configuration in some cases, since the spectra are very complex.

The following generalizations can be made about the electronic configuration and the periodic table.
(1) All elements in Group IA have a single *s* electron in the highest level of the ground state.
(2) All elements in Group IIA have two *s* electrons in the highest energy level of the ground state.
(3) The elements in Group IIIA, IVA, VA, VIA, VIIA and the noble gases have one to six *p* electrons respectively in the highest energy level of the ground state.
(4) The transition elements result from the filling of *d* orbitals.
(5) The lanthanide and actinide series result from the filling of *f* orbitals.

Electronic arrangement and physical properties

In Chapter IV it is noted that several physical properties of the elements are periodic. It is possible to explain this behavior, at least qualitatively, on the basis of electronic arrangements in the atoms.

We have found that the atomic radii of the elements become larger with increasing atomic weight within a given group of the periodic table. This observation reflects the fact that the most probable location of an electron at a higher energy level is farther from the nucleus. Thus, the 6*s* electron of cesium is more likely to be found farther from the nucleus than is the 3*s* electron of sodium. However, because of increased nuclear charge, the most probable location of an electron in the 6*s* state of cesium is closer to the nucleus than is that of an electron in the 6*s* state of sodium.

The increase in density with increasing atomic number within a group arises from the nuclear attraction for electrons. The nuclear mass, which is almost equal to the atomic mass, increases more rapidly than does the volume occupied by the atom. Thus, elements of higher atomic weight have higher density.

The atomic radius is found to decrease within a given period except in Group VIIIA, where the noble gas configuration is reached. The decrease is due to an increasing nuclear charge which attracts electrons that are entering approximately the same energy level. It is not yet clear why the rather stable noble gas configuration leads to a larger atomic radius.

Electron arrangement and chemical properties

Chemical properties are related closely to electronic configuration. Electrons in the filled shells or energy levels do not appreciably affect the chemical properties of the atom. It is the arrangement of electrons in the unfilled highest energy states or outer shells that has the greatest influence on chemical properties. Electrons in unfilled inner shells have only a limited effect on the chemical properties. For example, the $4f$ electrons in the elements of the lanthanide series play only a small role in the chemistry of these elements. Thus, these elements are very similar chemically.

The electron configurations of the noble gases appear to be very stable. There is a great tendency for atoms with one or two electrons more than the noble gas configuration to lose those electrons to form positive ions. Similarly, atoms with one to three electrons less than the noble gas configuration readily take on electrons, and attain the configuration by the formation of a negative ion. Thus, the $3s$ electron in a sodium atom is lost readily in a chemical reaction to form a Na^+ ion with the electron configuration of neon. The $3p$ level of chlorine is filled readily with an electron in a chemical reaction to form a Cl^- ion.

The energy required to remove an electron to just outside the influence (field) of the nucleus is called the *ionization potential*. Certain trends in ionization potentials are observed. The ionization potential for the removal of the first electron generally increases with increasing atomic number within a given period of the periodic table. The higher nuclear charge and the smaller atomic size account for the increased stability of the atoms. The ionization potential within a single group or family of elements decreases with increasing atomic number. This reflects the increasing size of the atom and the lessening of the nuclear attraction.

The change in ionization potentials for the first, second, and subsequent electrons is strong evidence for the existence of stable

Table 6.3

Successive Ionization Potentials for the Elements of the Third Period

	1st electron	2nd electron	3rd electron	4th electron	5th electron
Na	5.12 eV	47.1 eV	70.7 eV		
Mg	7.61	15.0	79.7	108.9 eV	
Al	5.96	18.7	28.3	119.4	153.4 eV
Si	8.12	16.3	33.4	44.9	165.6
P	10.9	19.6	30.0	51.1	64.7
S	10.30	23.3	34.9	47.1	63.0
Cl	12.95	23.7	39.7	53.2	67.4
Ar	15.68	27.8	40.8	61.	78.0
K	4.32	31.7	46.5		
Ca	6.09	11.8	51.0	69.7	

electronic configurations. The stable electronic configurations for ions of the lightweight elements are the same as those of the noble gas atoms. The values in Table 6.3 for the elements of the third period show substantial increases in the ionization potential when the neon electronic structure is entered after one electron is removed from sodium, two electrons from magnesium, three electrons from aluminum, and so on. This very large increase reflects the stability of the $2s^22p^6$ arrangement of electrons. Likewise the values for potassium and calcium show the stability of the $3s^23p^6$ configuration.

When an atom takes on an electron to form a negative ion, energy is liberated. If the neutral atom and the ion are gases with the ground state electron configurations, this energy is called the *electron affinity*. The electron affinity for metals is essentially zero. In general, the electron affinity of the nonmetals increases as the noble gas structure is approached and decreases with increasing atomic number. The most notable exception to this rule is fluorine which has an electron affinity less than that of chlorine.

Atomic number

Although electronic arrangement and the periodic nature of the properties of the elements are closely related, the atomic number is not defined in terms of electrons. Rather, the atomic number is the number of positive charges on the nucleus. Thus, in the course of a chemical reaction the number of electrons about a particular nucleus may change, but the element may be identified throughout. The number of electrons in the neutral atom is equal to the number of positive charges on the nucleus. Therefore, in the neutral atom the atomic number is equal to the number of electrons about the positive nucleus.

SIGNIFICANT TERMS AND CONCEPTS IN CHAPTER VI:

Dalton's atomic theory, the spectroscopic experiment, electron, Rutherford's nuclear model, the Bohr model, quantized energy levels, quantum numbers—significance and range of values of each, spectral lines and energy levels of the hydrogen atom, Pauli Exclusion Principle, letters corresponding to values of l, electron configurations, electron probability distributions, relationship of electron configuration to the periodic table and periodic properties, ionization potential, electron affinity, atomic number.

Review questions

6.1. Compare the picture of the atom obtained from Bohr's theory with that from quantum theory.

6.2. Why are the energies of the allowed levels for an electron in an atom always negative?

6.3. What energy level is being filled with the 12th electron in an atom, the 23rd electron, the 34th electron, the 46th electron, the 65th electron, the 80th electron? (Assume a ground state configuration and no magnetic field.)

6.4. Indicate the electronic states involved when the outer or highest energy electron in each of the following atoms is excited from the ground state to the next available energy level. (a) Na (b) Ar (c) Ca (d) I.   answer: (a) $3s \rightarrow 3p$

6.5. Write the ground state electron configuration for each of the following: (a) C (b) Sc (c) Kr (d) Cs (e) Nd (f) Na$^+$ (g) F$^-$ (h) S$^=$.   answer: (a) C: $1s^2 2s^2 2p^2$

6.6. What is the maximum number of electrons in any s orbital, p orbital, d orbital, f orbital?

6.7. What are the values of the n and l quantum numbers for each of the following energy levels? (a) $2s$ (b) $4f$ (c) $6p$ (d) $8g$ (e) $3p$ (f) $5s$.   answer: (a) $n = 2$, $l = 0$

6.8. What are the possible values of the m quantum number for each of the levels in Problem 6.7?   answer: (a) $m = 0$

6.9. What are the possible values of the spin quantum number for each of the levels in Problem 6.7?

answer: (a) $m_s = +\frac{1}{2}$, $-\frac{1}{2}$

6.10. Give the notation for the energy levels with the following quantum numbers: (a) $n = 5, l = 2$ (b) $n = 1, l = 0$ (c) $n = 6, l = 5$ (d) $n = 6, l = 4$ (e) $n = 12, l = 8$.

answer: (a) $5d$

6.11. Using the Bohr model of the atom, calculate the value of n for the energy level involved in the transition to give the 4102 Å line of the Balmer Series.

the chemical bond

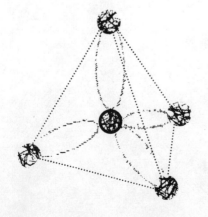

Chemical bonding is the result of interactions between electrons of one atom and those of another atom. A chemical reaction is the rearrangement of these electron interactions to form different compounds. Thus, the more that is known about the principles of chemical bond formation, the greater is the understanding of chemistry. For our purposes, it is convenient to consider only three types of bonding: ionic, covalent, and metallic.

Ionic bonds

A positive and a negative ion are formed when one or more electrons are lost by an atom of one element and are gained by atoms of another element. Metals characteristically lose electrons to form positively charged ions, and the number of positive charges on the nucleus then exceeds the number of electrons about the nucleus. The gain of electrons by nonmetals results in more electrons than positive charges, producing negative ions. Negatively charged polyatomic ions consisting of two or more nonmetals contain an excess of electrons equal to the negative charge.

Substances composed of ions are held together by electrostatic forces of attraction between oppositely charged particles. These attractive forces lead to what is called the *ionic bond*. In general, ionic bonding is found in solids which are characterized by high melting points and high boiling points. These high values indicate that the ionic bond is quite strong and that substantial amounts of energy (such as heat) must be supplied to overcome the forces of attraction. Ionic solids are hard and brittle as a result of these strong ionic bonds.

It is not possible to associate one ion with only one other ion in a solid. Rather, the ions of a solid are arranged in a three-dimensional array such that one ion is surrounded by several ions of the opposite charge, although the total number of positive and negative ions in the crystal are such that the crystal is electrically neutral. In the sense that the bonds extend from one ion to the next, the entire crystal is a single giant molecule. The chemical formula of an ionic substance represents the ratio of ions in the crystal.

In the formation of an ionic compound electrons are removed from a metal atom and attached to a nonmetal atom. Certain qualitative considerations may be given to the energies involved in this process. Electrons are removed easily from atoms with low ionization potentials. The Group IA metals have the lowest ionization potentials of any group and are found to form +1 ions very readily. Conversely, the negative ions formed from atoms with a large electron affinity are very stable. Furthermore, the energy released as the negative ion is formed is used in other energy consuming processes such as ionization of metal atoms. The halogens (Group VIIA) as a group have the largest electron affinities.

On the basis of this discussion one would predict the formation of an ionic compound when a metal with a low ionization poten-

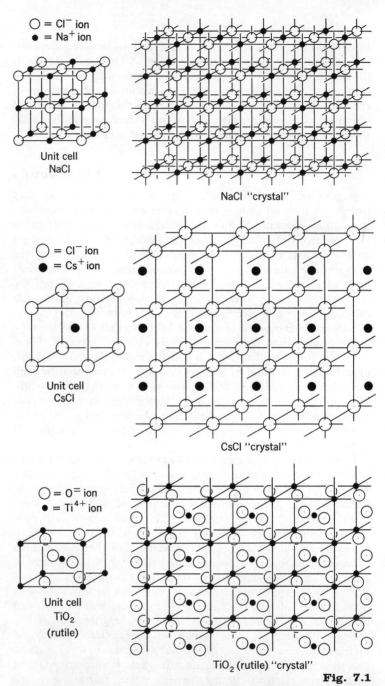

Fig. 7.1

*Structures of Some Typical Ionic Compounds. The ratio of ions in the
basic repeating unit, the simple unit cell, does not correspond to a compound
formula unless allowance is made for the fact that ions along each unit
cell edge are shared with adjacent units. In this diagram the crystals have
been limited to a thickness of one unit cell for clarity; lines between spheres
are aids to visualization and are not related to any bonds.*

Fig. 7.2

Comparison of Ionic Radii and Atomic Radii

	IA	IIA	IIIA	IVA	VA	VIA	VIIA	VIIIA
He 0.93	Li 1.22 Li^+ 0.60	Be 0.89 Be^{++} 0.31	B 0.80	C 0.77	N 0.74 N^{3-} 1.71	O 0.74 $O^=$ 1.40	F 0.72 F^- 1.36	Ne 1.12
Ne 1.12	Na 1.57 Na^+ 0.95	Mg 1.36 Mg^{++} 0.65	Al 1.25 Al^{3+} 0.50	Si 1.17	P 1.10 P^{3-} 2.12	S 1.04 $S^=$ 1.84	Cl 0.99 Cl^- 1.81	Ar 1.54
Ar 1.54	K 2.02 K^+ 1.33	Ca 1.74 Ca^{++} 0.99	Ga 1.24 Ga^{3+} 0.62	Ge 1.22 Ge^{4+} 0.53	As 1.21 As^{5+} 0.47	Se 1.17 $Se^=$ 1.98	Br 1.14 Br^- 1.95	Kr 1.69
Kr 1.69	Rb 2.16 Rb^+ 1.48	Sr 1.91 Sr^{++} 1.13	In 1.50 In^{3+} 0.81	Sn 1.41 Sn^{4+} 0.71	Sb 1.41 Sb^{5+} 0.62	Te 1.37 $Te^=$ 2.21	I 1.33 I^- 2.16	Xe 1.90
X 1.90	Cs 2.35 Cs^+ 1.69	Ba 1.98 Ba^{++} 1.35	Tl 1.55 Tl^+ 1.40	Pb 1.54 Pb^{++} 1.17	Bi 1.52 Bi^{3+} 1.16			

A positive ion is smaller than the neutral atom, because electrons in the outer energy level have been removed. The addition of electrons to an atom to form a negative ion results in a larger ion. All values are in Å units.

tial is combined with a nonmetal having a high electron affinity. In general this is found to be true. However, the formation of such a compound involves other factors as well. The ionization potential and electron affinity are determined for gaseous atoms and ions, the formation of which may involve other energy consuming processes. For example, chlorine with an electron affinity of 83.3 kcal/mole should be more reactive than fluorine with an electron affinity of 79.5 kcal/mole. However, 20 more kcal are required to dissociate a mole of Cl_2. Thus, the formation of two moles of F^- ions from a mole of F_2 releases more energy (approximately 12 kcal) than the formation of two moles of Cl^- ions from a mole of Cl_2. Factors such as this make predictions other than qualitative imprudent.

Covalent bonds

There are many molecules which are held together by forces such that no electrons are completely transferred from one atom to another. This sharing of electrons is called the *covalent bond*. It results whenever the total energy of the system is reduced as two atoms are brought together. The bond strength is proportional to the magnitude of the reduction. Three typical cases are illustrated in Fig. 7.3.

There is no lowering of the energy in case *a* as the atoms are brought together. This is what one would predict from a consideration of simple electrostatic forces whereby one electron cloud repels the other. This represents an unstable antibonding situation where two atoms come together without bond formation. An example of this case occurs when two helium atoms collide without the formation of a He_2 molecule.

In case *b*, there are attractive forces of sufficient strength to form a weak bond. In case *c*, the forces of attraction are much greater than the repulsive forces, and a stable molecule is formed. The minimum in each curve r_e represents the equilibrium nuclear separation and is the bond length in the unexcited molecule. Case *b* shows the weakly bonded situation wherein the bond is easily broken by the addition of a small amount of energy. Case *c* is the one of great interest at this point. This represents the bringing together of two hydrogen atoms to form H_2. Molecule formation takes place very readily; a great amount of energy is given off.

$$H + H \rightarrow H_2 + 103.2 \text{ kcal/mole}$$

This means that 103.2 kcal must be put into the system to break up a mole of H_2 molecules into two moles of hydrogen atoms.

Covalent bonding in diatomic molecules

In simplified terms, a chemical bond is the result of the interaction of two electrons called an electron pair. For relatively simple bonds such as those found in diatomic molecules, a bond is said

Fig. 7.3

Energy of the System As Two Atoms Are Brought Together.

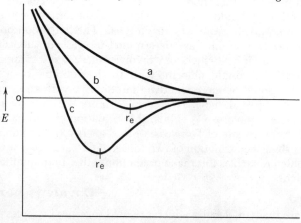

INTERNUCLEAR SEPARATION, $r \longrightarrow$

H· + H· ⟶ H:H or H——H
Dot structure

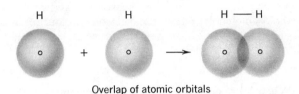

Overlap of atomic orbitals

PROBABILITY OF FINDING AN ELECTRON

H   H

H   H

Probability distribution curves

Fig. 7.4

Methods of Pictorially Representing the Chemical Bond in H_2. Dot Structure: A pair of dots represents a single bond. Overlap of Atomic Orbitals: The greater the overlap of orbitals, the stronger is the bond due to the greater probability of finding an electron between the nuclei. Probability Distribution Curves: left, probability of finding an electron in a plane containing the internuclear axis for H_2; right, contour for constant probability.

to occur when the probability of finding the electrons between the nuclei is relatively large. If this probability is zero, there is no bond and one has an antibonding situation.

Not all electrons about a given nucleus enter into bond formation. Some electrons remain rather closely associated with the parent nucleus even in a very stable molecule. Certain trends in the availability of electrons for bond formation are observed and are used to make predictions about bond formation in a diatomic molecule.

(1) Electrons in filled energy levels usually do not enter into a chemical bond. For example, of the three electrons in lithium ($1s^2 2s$), only the $2s$ electron is energetically available for bond formation. The $1s$ electrons are too tightly held to the nucleus for bonding. Thus a single bond is predicted in a covalent molecule such as Li_2.

(2) Electrons in half-filled orbitals tend to form bonds readily. For example, fluorine with the electron configuration, $1s^2 2s^2 2p_z^2$ $2p_y^2 2p_x$, forms a single bond involving the electron in the $2p_x$ orbital with other atoms having a single electron in an orbital. Thus, there is a single bond in the F_2 molecule. Multiple bonds of this type are possible, if there are two or more half-filled orbitals. Three pairs of electrons are shared by the two nitrogen atoms in the N_2 molecule, where the electron configuration of the atoms is $1s^2 2s^2 2p_x 2p_y 2p_z$. This type of bond is called a triple bond.

BOND POLARITY

When both nuclei in a diatomic molecule are the same (homo-nuclear), the electron probability distribution is symmetric about the nuclei. If the nuclei are different (heteronuclear), the probability distribution is distorted and the bond is said to be polarized. Since the electrons are attracted more strongly toward one nucleus, this portion of the molecule becomes negative with respect to the portion around the other nucleus. Atoms of each element have a different power to attract electrons. This electron attracting power, called the *electronegativity*, is expressed on an arbitrary scale which is independent of the particular chemical combination. Many attempts have been made to devise a scale using readily measured quantities. The most widely accepted electronegativity scale is that proposed by Linus Pauling and given in Fig. 7.6.

The electronegativities of the atoms in a homonuclear diatomic molecule are equal. This represents a pure covalent bond since there is no distortion of the electron distribution. An ionic bond may be considered as a bond with an extreme distortion of the electron distribution so that there is a negligible probability of finding the electron about the positive cation. Many heteronuclear molecules are intermediate cases which may be described as having a degree of ionic character. The Pauling Electronegativity Scale is used to calculate the degree of ionic character in a bond. From this viewpoint, there is no sharp delineation between an

Fig. 7.5

Electron Probability Distribution in H_2 and HF. The H_2 molecule is non-polar because each nucleus exerts equal attraction for the electrons. HF is polar because electrons more often are found about the fluorine due to its greater attraction. Thus, the hydrogen end is more positive.

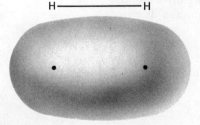

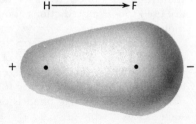

H 2.1																	
Li 1.0	Be 1.5											B 2.0	C 2.5	N 3.0	O 3.5	F 4.0	
Na 0.9	Mg 1.2											Al 1.5	Si 1.8	P 2.1	S 2.5	Cl 3.0	
K 0.8	Ca 1.0	Sc 1.3	Ti 1.5	V 1.6	Cr 1.6	Mn 1.5	Fe 1.8	Co 1.8	Ni 1.8	Cu 1.9	Zn 1.6	Ga 1.6	Ge 1.8	As 2.0	Se 2.4	Br 2.8	
Rb 0.8	Sr 1.0	Y 1.2	Zr 1.4	Nb 1.6	Mo 1.8	Tc 1.9	Ru 2.2	Rh 2.2	Pd 2.2	Ag 1.9	Cd 1.7	In 1.7	Sn 1.8	Sb 1.9	Te 2.1	I 2.5	
Cs 0.7	Ba 0.9	La 1.1	Hf 1.3	Ta 1.5	W 1.7	Re 1.9	Os 2.2	Ir 2.2	Pt 2.2	Au 2.4	Hg 1.9	Tl 1.8	Pb 1.8	Bi 1.9	Po 2.0	At 2.2	

Fig. 7.6

Pauling Electronegativity Scale. Fluorine has an electronegativity of 4.0 units; all other elements have been assigned lower values.

ionic bond and a covalent bond, although an electronegativity difference of about 1.7 represents 50% ionic character. It is convenient to classify compounds as ionic or covalent on the basis of the differences in the electronegativity of the atoms. Compounds with electronegativities greater than 1.7 are arbitrarily considered ionic compounds.

The magnitude of the polarization of a bond may be estimated from experimentally measured values, if one considers the molecule to be a bar with a positive charge on one end and a negative charge on the other. The measured values for HCl gas are such that the same polarity is obtained by transferring 0.17 electron from the hydrogen end to the chlorine end of the bar. This is referred to as 17% ionic character in HCl and reflects the greater electronegativity of Cl which has a value of 3.0 compared to 2.1 for hydrogen. A 90% ionic character is calculated for a gaseous CsF molecule using electronegativity data, although there is no doubt that crystalline and liquid CsF actually consist of Cs^+ and F^- ions, with no covalent CsF molecules.

Hydrogen bonding

The HF molecule is very polar. As a result there is a strong attraction between the negative fluorine end of one molecule and the positive hydrogen end of another molecule. The weak bond that results, which involves a hydrogen atom and is not as strong as the usual chemical bond, is called a *hydrogen bond*.

The effects of hydrogen bonding are readily observed in the properties of liquids and solids as illustrated by the boiling points of HI, HBr, HCl, and HF in Table 7.1. Generally, the boiling points of liquids increase with increasing molecular weight. HF, which on the basis of molecular weight should be the lowest boiling, is found to have the highest boiling point of the hydrogen halides. The hydrogen bonding results in the formation of large aggregations of HF molecules which have the effect of a large molecular weight. An alternate viewpoint is that the increased temperature is necessary to provide the energy needed by the HF molecules to overcome the hydrogen bond in the liquid and escape into the vapor.

Table 7.1

Boiling Points of
the Hydrogen Halides

HF	19.9°C
HCl	−85.1°C
HBr	−66.8°C
HI	−35.4°C

Hydrogen bonding is unique to hydrogen compounds, since the positive nucleus is substantially unshielded by any electron cloud distortion. Such distortion of an analogous lithium compound would expose the $1s$ electrons about the Li nucleus. These $1s$ electrons would repel the negative portion of another molecule.

Hydrogen bonding is limited to compounds in which the hydrogen is bonded to an atom with a high electronegativity—usually oxygen, nitrogen, or fluorine. Thus, any hydrogen bonding effects in HCl, for example, are too small to be detected because of the small electronegativity difference. In addition, even if hydrogen is bonded to an atom with a large electronegativity, no hydrogen bonds are formed if the molecule is symmetric. For example, the hydrogen bonds in ammonia (NH_3) are very strong, since the hydrogens are not symmetrically arranged about the nitrogen (see page 141); but no hydrogen bonds form with the symmetric NH_4^+ ion.

A very important example of hydrogen bonding is found in water. At very low temperatures the H_2O molecules are oriented so that a hydrogen atom on one water molecule is hydrogen bonded to one of the pairs of unbonded electrons of oxygen in another water molecule. This leads to a very open three-dimensional arrangement of H_2O molecules. As heat is applied to ice, some hydrogen bonds are broken while others are being formed. As the temperature increases, the number of broken hydrogen bonds increases. At 0°C, enough of the hydrogen bonds have broken so that groups of H_2O molecules move easily and melting occurs. Since the ordering of molecules has been reduced, the liquid is more dense than the ice. Hydrogen bonds continue to break as the liquid is heated. This further reduces the ordering of the molecules and results in an increase in density. However, the molecules are also moving more rapidly in a larger volume, which tends to decrease the density. Thus, two opposing effects are occurring as the liquid water is heated. At 4°C the combined effects are at a maximum, and water reaches its greatest density.

Above 4°C density decreases as the thermal motion becomes more important.

Polyatomic molecular bonding

The bonding in many polyatomic molecules may be described in terms of electron pair bonds using the principles developed for diatomic molecules. The electrons making up the bond are thought to be localized, or most probably found, between two atoms in the molecule.

The simple electron pair bond explanation is not adequate for molecules in which there are insufficient electrons to form the required pairs. The bonding in many of these molecules is explained in terms of non-localized bonds. Electrons in a non-localized bond are associated with the entire molecule rather than with two atoms in the molecule. The formation of these non-localized bonds increases the stability of the molecule.

Bonding in other polyatomic molecules is described in terms of a localized electron pair bond, but one atom is considered to have contributed both electrons to the bond. The donor ion must have all orbitals filled, while the acceptor species must have an unfilled orbital available. This type of bonding is important in the formation of complex ions (Chapter XVIII). The nature of this type of coordination bonding will become more apparent during the discussion of hybrid orbitals in the following sections.

THE sp HYBRID ORBITAL

The observed geometrical arrangement of the atoms in many polyatomic molecules is not predicted on the basis of overlapping simple atomic orbitals. A discussion of simple polyatomic molecules such as $BeCl_2$, BF_3, and CH_4 illustrates the difficulties en-

Fig. 7.7

Melting of Ice. Hydrogen bonding in the solid (right) causes a great deal of open space. As heat energy is added, hydrogen bonds are broken. Soon the structure collapses, forming a higher density liquid (left). With further heating clusters of H_2O molecules in the liquid break up.

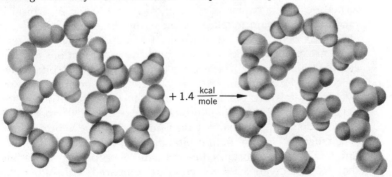

$+ 1.4 \frac{kcal}{mole} \longrightarrow$

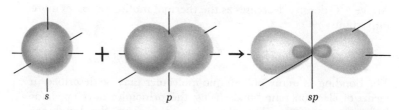

Fig. 7.8

Formation of sp Hybrid Orbitals from s and p Orbitals. Each sp orbital consists of a large lobe and a smaller one.

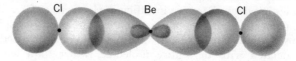

Fig. 7.9

Overlap of $Cl(3p_x)$ Orbitals with $Be(sp)^2$ Hybrids to Form $BeCl_2$. An electron in each sp hybrid orbital of beryllium forms a bond with an electron in the 3p orbital of chlorine. An overlap of orbitals is shown here.

countered as well as the modifications required to attain agreement between theory and experiment.

On the basis of the electron configuration of beryllium ($1s^2 2s^2$), one would predict that beryllium would form no stable compounds. It is found experimentally that beryllium occurs in the $+2$ oxidation state in many compounds. If these are ionic compounds, as is the case for calcium, the $+2$ oxidation state is the result of the loss of the two $2s$ electrons. However, the beryllium salts are covalently bonded. Furthermore, spectroscopic studies show that $BeCl_2$ is a linear molecule in the form Cl–Be–Cl.

In the development of the hybridization theory it is necessary to make the hypothesis that the energy levels about the beryllium atom in the bonded state are no longer the same as those for the free atom as described by the ground state electron configuration. First it is assumed that the $1s$ energy level is not affected by the bonding and remains a very low energy level. Therefore, two of the four electrons in beryllium occupy the $1s$ orbital. During bond formation in the course of a chemical reaction, the $2s$ orbital is modified and is said to take on some of the character of the higher energy $2p$ orbital. In other words, two new orbitals or energy levels are created, which are described by wave functions that are combinations of a $2p$ orbital wave function and a $2s$ orbital wave function. The resultant hybrids are called sp orbitals. The sp hybrid orbitals are particularly suited to the description of the $BeCl_2$ structure, since two sp orbitals are oriented $180°$ apart. The cross section of the probability distribution for an sp hybrid orbital is sketched in Fig. 7.8. Both orbitals are identical except for orientation. There is a substantial increase in the probability of finding the electron in an axial direction as compared with either the

2s or 2p orbitals. Thus the *sp* hybrids are said to be more directional. The shape of the orbital is independent of the *n* quantum
level; the value of *n* determines the size.

Once the two *sp* orbitals are formed, one of the two remaining
beryllium electrons occupies each orbital. The electron in the unfilled 3p level of chlorine then forms a covalent bond with each of
these *sp* electrons. This bond is illustrated as an overlap of orbitals
as shown in Fig. 7.9 which shows the formation of $BeCl_2$. The
sp hybrid orbitals are useful in the explanation of the bonding in
many other linear molecules.

THE sp^2 HYBRID ORBITAL

Boron trifloride illustrates the bonding in the Group IIIA covalent
compounds. The hybridization of the orbitals about boron must
be consistent with the observations that all of the atoms in BF_3 lie
in the same plane and that the F–B–F bond angle is 120°. If two
of the 2p orbitals are combined with the single 2s orbital, the three
resultant hybrid orbitals are in the same plane and 120° apart as
shown in Fig. 7.10. These three hybrid orbitals are called the

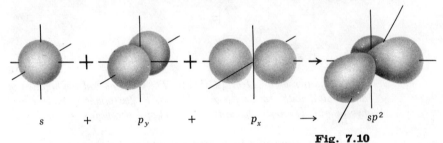

s $+$ p_y $+$ p_x $\longrightarrow$ sp^2

Fig. 7.10

Formation of sp^2 Orbitals from One s and Two p Orbitals.

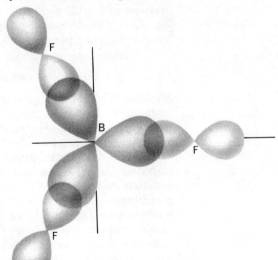

Fig. 7.11

*Overlap of $F(2p_x)$ Orbitals with
$B(2sp^2)$ Orbitals to Form BF_3. The
bonds in BF_3 result from the interaction of the electron in each sp^2
hybrid orbital of boron with the
electron in the $2p_x$ orbital of fluorine.*

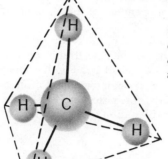

Fig. 7.12

The Structure of Methane (CH₄). The H atoms are located at the corners of the tetrahedron. The bond angle made by each H–C–H group is 109.5°.

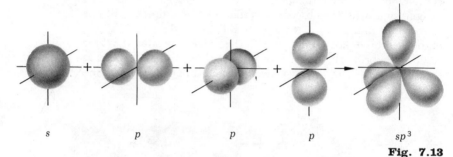

| s | p | p | p | sp³ |

Fig. 7.13

The Formation of sp³ Hybrid Orbitals. The mathematical combination of an s orbital with the three p orbitals leads to the formation of four new hybrid orbitals directed towards the corners of a tetrahedron.

sp^2 orbitals, each of which contains one of the three boron electrons that are in the $n = 2$ energy level. Each of the sp^2 orbitals overlaps with a $2p$ orbital of fluorine to form BF₃ as shown in Fig. 7.11. The sp^2 hybrid orbitals are useful in the discussion of bonding in many planar molecules similar to BF₃.

THE TETRAHEDRAL OR sp^3 HYBRID ORBITAL

Methane (CH₄) provides an example of one of the most commonly encountered hybrid orbitals, the tetrahedral or sp^3. The four hydrogens are found to be equally spaced about the carbon atom at the corners of a tetrahedron as shown in Fig. 7.12.

On the basis of the ground state electronic configuration of carbon ($1s^2 2s^2 2p^2$) one would not predict a carbon atom to bond with four other atoms. When the character of the three $2p$ orbitals is mathematically combined with the $2s$ orbital character, the result is four hybrid orbitals tetrahedrally arranged about the carbon atom as shown in Fig. 7.13. One of the four electrons in the $n = 2$ level occupies each of these sp^3 orbitals. When the $1s$ electrons of the hydrogens overlap with these sp^3 orbitals, a tetrahedral molecule of CH₄ results.

The tetrahedral arrangement of bonds about the carbon atom plays an important role in the structure of organic compounds (see Chapter XIX). In addition, tetrahedral orbitals are invoked to explain the structures of many other molecules.

The structure of NH_3 and similar nitrogen compounds usually is discussed in terms of tetrahedral orbitals. The ammonia molecule has a pyramidal structure with the hydrogens forming a triangular base and the nitrogen forming the apex. The H–N–H bond angle is 106.75°. If there are four tetrahedral orbitals about the nitrogen and five electrons in the $n = 2$ level, one of the sp^3 orbitals must be filled. The remaining three singly occupied orbitals form bonds with the hydrogen atoms. The electrons in the filled orbital are called *lone-pair electrons.*

The lone-pair electrons occupy a greater volume, since there is no distorting effect supplied by the hydrogens. This squeezes the H–N–H bonds close together reducing the bond angle from the tetrahedral angle of 109.5° to the observed 106.75°. When the NH_3 molecule becomes a symmetrical NH_4^+ ion, the H–N–H bond angle returns to 109.5°.

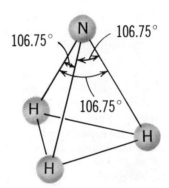

Fig. 7.14

Structure of Ammonia NH_3.

Fig. 7.15

Tetrahedral Orbitals about the Nitrogen Atom in NH_3. One orbital is filled with two electrons called the lone-pair electrons. These cause a distortion of the bond angle from that of the tetrahedron.

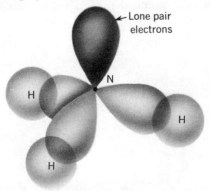

142

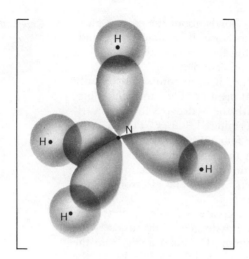

Fig. 7.16
Structure of the Ammonium Ion NH₄⁺. The symmetry supplied by the addition. of another proton returns the H–N–H bond angle to 109.5°.

A similar effect is noted for water, in which six electrons are thought to occupy four tetrahedral orbitals about oxygen. The result is the formation of two sets of lone-pair electrons and a reduction to an observed H–O–H bond angle of 104.5°. The tetrahedral angle is observed in ice at low temperatures where strong hydrogen bonds are found involving the lone-pair electrons.

Lone-pair electrons may be donated to form a bond with a molecule or ion that has a vacant orbital. For example, the bonds in the BF_3 molecule in effect make use of the $2s$ and two of the $2p$ orbitals. Thus one of the $2p$ orbitals remains unused. The NH_3 molecule readily combines with BF_3, making use of the lone-pair electrons. Similar behavior of donating a pair of electrons is shown by an F^- ion interacting with BF_3 to form BF_4^- which is a tetrahedral species.

FINAL COMMENTS ON HYBRIDIZATION

From the preceding discussion it would appear that it is possible to remove electrons from atoms, store them, hybridize the orbitals, put the electrons back into the orbitals and then form a bond. This is merely a mathematical artifact to aid in the prediction of

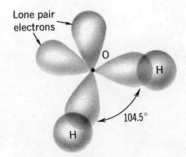

Fig. 7.17
Structure of the Water Molecule.

chemical reactions, for it is impossible to locate the electrons experimentally. No one knows what the behavior of the electrons is during the course of a chemical reaction. All that can be said is that the state of the electrons in a chemical bond is such that when hybridization theory is used, calculations can be made that predict the observed results reasonably well.

The formation of a hybrid orbital or hybrid energy state requires the use of energy. Since hybrid orbitals are rather directional, the resulting bonds are very stable. Thus, the energy expended by the system in the formation of the hybrid orbitals is more than recovered in the energy released by the formation of the stable bond.

The tetrahedral orbitals represent the maximum amount of p character that can be introduced into any hybrid orbital, since there are only three p orbitals available in any one n quantum level. In the $n = 3$ and in higher levels, it is possible to have d orbitals entering into the hybridization. One finds that both PCl_3 and PCl_5 exist, while only NCl_3 is found. The explanation of the structure of the PCl_5 molecules requires the introduction of some d orbital character into the hybrid. Since d orbitals do not exist for the $n = 2$ level, nitrogen does not exhibit the same behavior.

Metallic bonding

A few generalizations about the bonding between atoms in metals may be made, but no simple theory has been developed to explain all of the observed properties. Outer shell electrons are thought to be the only electrons used in the bonding. For most metals, this means that there are one to three electrons available per atom to form the bonds with neighboring atoms. Since each atom is surrounded by eight to twelve atoms in most metals, the bonds between the atoms cannot be described as electron pairs. Rather, the bonding effects of the electrons are spread out over several atoms leading to weak bonds and soft, ductile solids. The effect of more bonding electrons per atom is illustrated in the comparison

Fig. 7.18

Formation of the BF_3–NH_3 Compound. The approach of the NH_3 molecule causes a transformation of the BF_3 molecule from a planar to a tetrahedral arrangement. The lone pair electrons of NH_3 provide the bond.

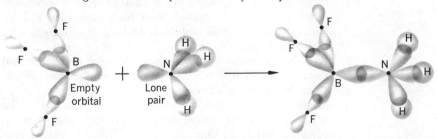

144

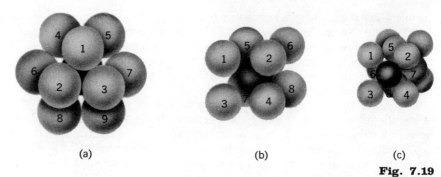

(a)   (b)   (c)

Fig. 7.19

Three Common Arrangements of Atoms in a Metal. (a) Nine of the twelve near-neighbor atoms are shown for a structure common to magnesium, zinc, and others; (b) eight near-neighbor atoms are shown in a structure common to the alkali metals; and (c) four atoms in the plane in front of the central atom are not shown in this structure typical of copper, gold, silver, and others. Shading identifies the central atom.

of sodium and magnesium. Magnesium with two bonding electrons per atom is much harder than sodium with only one bonding electron per atom.

The electrical properties of metals are explained in simple terms of a rather rigid framework of metal nuclei and filled electron shells. The outer-shell electrons are held loosely in this framework and move rather easily under the influence of an electrical field to conduct electrical current. This "sea of electrons" model has several shortcomings; more sophisticated models have been proposed but are beyond the scope of this text.

SIGNIFICANT TERMS AND CONCEPTS IN CHAPTER VII:
Ionic bonding, covalent bonding, polar molecule, electronegativity, hydrogen bonds, non-localized bonds, hybrid orbitals, lone-pair electrons, tetrahedral hybrid orbitals, geometric structures of molecules, metallic bonds.

Review questions

7.1. Rank the following four types of solids in order of increasing melting point: (a) covalent with high molecular weight; (b) covalent with low molecular weight; (c) covalent with hydrogen bonds; (d) ionic.

7.2. Plot the successive ionization potentials for potassium and calcium (see Table 6.3). What is the explanation of the sharp break in each curve?

7.3. Predict which orbitals are involved in the bonding of the following covalent compounds. (a) Cl_2 (b) BeI_2 (c) $AlCl_3$ (d) SiF_4 (e) PF_3 (f) O_2.

7.4. Predict the geometric arrangement of the nuclei in each of the molecules in question 7.3. answer: (a) linear.

7.5. Using the Pauling Electronegativity Scale, classify the following as ionic or covalent compounds. (a) BCl_3 (b) $BaCl_2$ (c) GaI_3 (d) HF (e) InSb (f) Na_2.

7.6. The boiling points of the Group VA hydrides are: NH_3 $-33°C$, PH_3 $-87°C$, AsH_3 $-55°C$, SbH_3 $-17°C$. Explain this trend.

7.7. The boiling points of the Group IVA hydrides are: CH_4 $-161°C$, SiH_4 $-112°C$, GeH_4 $-90°C$. Explain this trend. Why does it differ from that for the Group VA hydrides given in question 7.6?

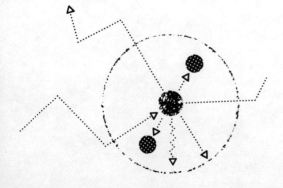

The electrons, which determine most of the chemical properties of an atom, are arranged about a small, positively charged nucleus. Most of the atomic mass is concentrated in this nuclear volume of 10^{-36} to 10^{-39} cm³. The structure and properties of this small but important portion of matter are considered in this chapter.

Nuclear composition

In simplified terms the nucleus is composed of protons and neutrons. The nuclear charge is due to the positively charged protons. The atomic number is equal to the number of protons in the nucleus as well as to the number of electrons about the nucleus of a neutral atom.

The neutron has no charge. Its function in the nucleus appears to be as some type of "glue" that holds the positively charged protons within the small nuclear volume. The number of protons and neutrons are about equal in the stable nuclei of the lightweight elements. In the heavier elements, where there are more proton–proton repulsions to overcome, the number of neutrons per proton increases. When there are 84 or more protons in the nucleus, the nucleus is relatively unstable at all neutron–proton ratios.

The protons and neutrons (under the general term, *nucleons*) make up most of the mass of the atom. The neutron mass of 1.008665 atomic mass units is slightly greater than the proton mass of 1.007276 amu. The mass of a nucleus approximates but does not equal the sum of the neutron and proton masses in it, for reasons discussed later in this chapter. However, the sum of the number of protons and the number of neutrons is equal to the mass number of an atom. The *mass number* is the whole number nearest the actual atomic mass (in amu) and is indicated as a superscript before the atomic symbol or as an integer after the elemental name. The *atomic mass* is the mass of the atom relative to a mass of exactly twelve for the commonly occurring carbon atoms. Thus, most hydrogen atoms have a mass of 1.007825 amu and are designated as ^1H or hydrogen-1.

The number of neutrons for a given number of protons may vary; thus, atoms of the same element may have different masses. These are called *isotopes*. Some elements have many isotopes; others have few, if any, that occur naturally. For example, about one of 5000 hydrogen atoms has a mass of 2.01410 amu. This heavy hydrogen with a mass number of 2 has one proton and one neutron in the nucleus and is given the special name, deuterium. A hydrogen isotope with one proton and two neutrons called tritium is produced artificially.

The existence of naturally occurring isotopes becomes important in the determination of atomic weights. The atomic weight of an element is the average of the masses of the atoms in a natural sample. For example, 98.89% of the carbon atoms in nature have a mass of 12.00000 amu and 1.11% have a mass of

13.00335 amu. The atomic weight of carbon is the weighted average of the masses of ^{12}C and ^{13}C.

Carbon-12 contribution = (0.9889)(12.0000) = 11.8668
Carbon-13 contribution = (0.0111)(13.00335) = 0.1443

Atomic weight of carbon 12.0111

The atomic weight listed for the elements is the average of the natural isotopes. The mass number of the best-known isotope is listed in parentheses for those elements which do not have any stable natural isotopes. Thorium and uranium are two exceptions to this general rule, since some isotopes of these elements are relatively stable and occur in nature. Thus, it is possible to obtain samples of these elements for which the atomic weight does not change over a long period of time.

Within the last few years the atomic physicist has discovered many sub-atomic particles. No attempt shall be made to list them all here, since 32 particles recently have been detected, and more are being found all the time. As yet no satisfactory relationship among these mesons, pions, muons, and so on has been developed. There is some question as to whether these exist within the nucleus or result from its fragmentation. Physicists are attempting to determine the relationships among all of these particles and what role, if any, they play in holding the nucleus together.

Radioactivity

Early interest in the nucleus developed even before the concept of a nucleus within the atom was introduced. Henri Becquerel, a French scientist, accidentally left a crystal of potassium uranyl sulfate wrapped in a piece of photographic paper in a dark drawer. Much to his surprise, the paper darkened as if it had been exposed to light. Thus, in 1896 scientists concluded that certain inorganic salts, particularly those containing uranium, emit radiation naturally. At first this radiation was thought to be X rays. Later it became evident that radiation involved not only very strong X rays but streams of particles as well.

Fig. 8.1
Henri Becquerel

For a few years after the discovery of these particles, much effort was devoted to their characterization. Little attention was paid to their source until Ernest Rutherford proposed the nuclear atom. Then it was suggested that the radiations come from the nucleus. The phenomenon of radiation or emission from the nucleus is known as *radioactivity*. Early investigators found that there are three types of natural radiation, called alpha (α), beta (β), and gamma (γ) rays. The terminology persists despite the fact that we now know gamma rays are the only true rays.

The alpha particle

The alpha "ray" is deflected to a very small extent by a magnetic field. This indicates that it is a heavy, charged particle. Although a relatively thin piece of material absorbs alpha particles, there is a certain minimum thickness necessary to absorb all the alpha particles. Anything less than this critical thickness stops almost no alpha particles; anything more than this thickness is unnecessary. This type of behavior is characteristic of a group of particles having the same energy. A few alpha-emitting nuclei emit alpha particles with two or three characteristic energies.

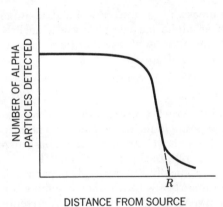

Fig. 8.2

Absorption of Alpha Particles. Until they have traveled a critical distance, very few alpha particles are absorbed. Then all particles are absorbed within a very short distance.

The distance traveled by an alpha particle depends upon its energy and the density of the absorbing medium. Alpha particles travel several centimeters in air but only a few microns in aluminum before being absorbed.

The behavior of alpha particles is very similar to that of helium nuclei. That alpha particles are helium nuclei was shown in an experiment in which an alpha-emitting substance was enclosed in a thin-walled glass tube surrounded by another heavy-walled container. The air in the outer jacket was removed. After a period

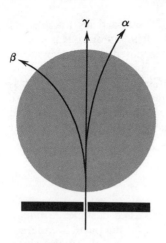

Fig. 8.3

Effect of a Magnetic Field on α, β, *and* γ *Radiations. Heavy alpha particles are deflected slightly by a magnetic field; beta particles are deflected strongly in the opposite direction; and gamma radiation is not affected.*

of time, the gas which had collected in the outer jacket was excited by an electrical discharge. The appearance of the spectrum of helium in the discharge proved that helium nuclei had been emitted and had passed through the thin inner wall into the outer jacket, where the alpha particles picked up electrons to become helium atoms.

Since helium has a mass number of 4 and an atomic number of 2, emission of an alpha particle produces a nucleus two atomic numbers and four mass numbers lower than the starting nucleus.

$$^{238}_{92}U \rightarrow \alpha + ^{234}_{90}Th$$

The beta particle

The path of a beta "ray" is strongly deflected by a magnetic field in a direction opposite to the deflection for an alpha particle. This is indicative of a lightweight, negatively charged particle. The penetrating power of a beta particle is much greater than that of an alpha particle. The absorption of a beta particle beam falls off throughout an absorber with a rather indefinite absorber thickness. The somewhat indefinite thickness representing complete beta absorption is much greater than that for the alpha particles. The falling off of beta intensity with thickness is due to the fact that the beta particle beam is made up of particles with many different energies. A particular source of beta particles has a characteristic distribution of energies of the form shown in Fig. 8.5. Beta emitters are characterized by the maximum energy E_{max} of their beta particles.

In addition to the beta particle, the nucleus emits a neutrino. The neutrino is a particle of infinitely small mass and has an energy equal to the difference between the actual beta energy and the energy equal to or greater than the maximum energy E_{max}. A beta-emitting nucleus always emits a neutrino along with the beta particle. A neutrino is very difficult to detect because of its properties. It is only recently that experimenters have been able to confirm the existence of this particle.

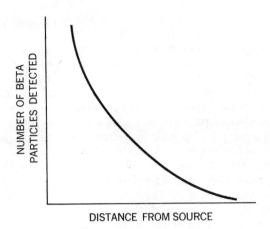

Fig. 8.4

Absorption of Beta Particles. Compare with Fig. 8.2.

Early workers had difficulty characterizing the beta particle. Its charge, penetration, and other properties appear to be those of an electron. However, the mass of the beta particle appeared to be significantly greater than the mass of an electron. The difficulty was resolved when a correction was made for the increase in mass that results when a particle travels at high speeds. The beta particle is recognized as an electron traveling at speeds up to nine tenths the speed of light and originating from the nucleus.

The atomic number of the nucleus is increased by one when a beta particle is emitted. The mass number is unchanged because of the very small mass of the beta particle.

$$^{234}_{90}\text{Th} \rightarrow \beta^- + ^{234}_{91}\text{Pa}$$

Fig. 8.5

Beta Energy Distribution.

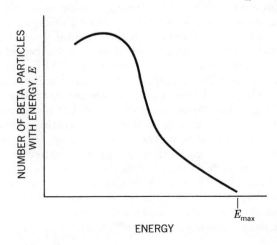

Gamma radiation

Gamma rays are unaffected by a magnetic field. This fact, in addition to other evidence, shows gamma rays to be electromagnetic radiation similar to light rather than to particles. Gamma rays have wavelengths of 700 Å or less, whereas red light wavelengths are about 7000 Å. Since the energy of light is inversely related to wavelength, gamma rays are very energetic. They are very penetrating due to their high energy and their non-particle nature, since loss of energy by collision of particles is not possible.

Gamma rays are closely related to X rays. In general, gamma rays are more energetic. The difference is in the origin of the radiation. Visible light originates when the outer electrons of an atom drop from an excited state to a lower energy state. X rays are emitted when an electron from a higher energy level drops into a vacancy in the $1s$, $2s$, or $2p$ level. The vacancy is due to the ejection of the lower level electron. Gamma rays are emitted as a nucleus goes from one energy level to another. There may be several characteristic gamma rays emitted from an excited nucleus representing several transitions between energy levels in the nucleus.

Since gamma radiation results from the emission of excess energy by the nucleus, the mass number and the atomic number are unaffected. Gamma radiation accompanies practically all particle emissions from the nucleus and may occur without particle emission.

Natural radioactivity

Alpha particles, beta particles, and gamma rays are the only types of nuclear emissions or decay found in naturally occurring isotopes. The nucleus resulting from an emission may not be stable and may undergo further transformation. Since only alpha emission results in a change in mass number, the mass numbers of the isotopes in a series differ only by some multiple of four.

Four radioactive decay series are observed to occur naturally. The first of these to be found was the uranium series. All of the isotopes in the series are characterized by mass numbers of $4n + 2$, where n is an integer. The series begins with ^{238}U and ends with the stable isotope ^{206}Pb. The thorium series, beginning with ^{232}Th, consists of elements whose mass numbers are represented by $4n$. A branching of the chain occurs at ^{212}Bi. About two thirds of the nuclei first emit a beta, then an alpha. The remaining nuclei first emit an alpha, then a beta. The actinium series, beginning with ^{235}U, is made up of nuclei with mass numbers represented by $4n + 3$. The name arises from the error on the part of early workers who thought actinium-227 was the first member of the series. The neptunium series, corresponding to mass numbers of $4n + 1$, is not found in nature, since all of these isotopes originally present in the earth have decayed to stable ^{209}Bi. The series has been prepared artificially, and the decay scheme given in Table 8.1 has been found.

Very few naturally occurring isotopes other than those involved in the decay chains are radioactive. The naturally occurring radioisotopes for elements with atomic numbers less than 80 are listed in Table 8.2. The extent to which these isotopes occur is listed as the natural abundance.

The neutron

Naturally occurring nuclei can be converted to other nuclei by subjecting them to bombardment by alpha particles, beta particles, or gamma rays. Many of these man-made isotopes are un-

Table 8.1

Natural Radioactive Decay Series

Uranium series		Thorium series	Actinium series	Neptunium series
	(Historical Terms)			
^{238}U	U-I	^{232}Th	^{235}U	^{241}Pu
β ↓		β ↓	β ↓	α ↓
^{234}Th	UX₁	^{238}Ra	^{231}Th	^{241}Am
α ↓		α ↓	α ↓	β ↓
^{234}Pa	UX₂	^{238}Ac	^{231}Pa	^{237}Np
α ↓		α ↓	β ↓	β ↓
^{234}U	U-II	^{228}Th	^{227}Ac	^{233}Pa
β ↓		β ↓	α ↓	α ↓
^{230}Th	Ionium	^{224}Ra	^{227}Th	^{233}U
β ↓		β ↓	β ↓	β ↓
^{226}Ra	Radium	^{220}Rn	^{223}Ra	^{229}Th
β ↓		β ↓	β ↓	β ↓
^{222}Rn	Ra Emanation	^{216}Po	^{219}Rn	^{225}Ra
β ↓		β ↓	β ↓	α ↓
^{218}Po	RaA	^{212}Pb	^{215}Po	^{225}Ac
β ↓		α ↓	β ↓	β ↓
^{214}Pb	RaB	^{212}Bi	^{211}Pb	^{221}Fr
α ↓		2/3β / \ 1/3α	α ↓	β ↓
^{214}Bi	RaC		^{211}Bi	^{217}At
α ↓		^{212}Po ^{208}Tl	β ↓	β ↓
^{214}Po	RaC	α \ / β	^{207}Tl	^{213}Bi
β ↓			α ↓	α ↓
^{210}Pb	RaD	^{208}Pb	^{207}Pb	^{213}Po
α ↓				β ↓
^{210}Bi	RaE			^{209}Pb
α ↓				α ↓
^{210}Po	RaF			^{209}Bi
β ↓				
^{206}Pb	RaG			

Element	Mass number	Natural abundance (%)	Mode of decay	Half life** (years)
Potassium	40	0.0118	β^-	1.3×10^9
Vanadium	50	0.24	β^-	6.0×10^{15}
Rubidium	87	27.85	β^-	5.2×10^{10}
Indium	115	95.72	β^-	$5. \times 10^{14}$
Tellurium	123	0.87	E.C.*	1.2×10^{13}
Lanthanum	138	0.089	β^-	1.1×10^{11}
Cerium	142	11.07	α	5.0×10^{15}
Neodymium	144	23.85	α	2.4×10^{15}
Samarium	147	14.97	α	1.08×10^{11}
	148	11.24	α	1.2×10^{13}
	149	13.83	α	$4. \times 10^{14}$
Gadolinium	152	0.20	α	1.1×10^{14}
Dysprosium	156	0.052	α	2.0×10^{14}
Lutetium	176	2.59	β^-	2.2×10^{10}
Hafnium	174	0.18	α	2.0×10^{15}
Rhenium	187	62.93	β^-	$5. \times 10^{10}$
Platinum	190	0.0127	α	$7. \times 10^{11}$

*E.C. = Electron capture. (See page 155.)
**For a definition of half life see page 159.

stable and emit other particles that are useful for the preparation of other nuclei.

The most important of these particles is the neutron. Since it is a neutral particle, there are no electrostatic forces to be overcome before the neutron penetrates the nucleus. Neutron capture results in a nucleus that is one mass number larger. This isotope may or may not radiate other particles. Neutron capture almost always is accompanied by gamma radiation.

The earliest method used to obtain laboratory amounts of neutrons is the bombardment of ^{9}Be with alpha particles. When an alpha particle is captured by a ^{9}Be nucleus, an unstable combination is made; decay to ^{12}C and a neutron occurs almost immediately. This neutron source is made by mixing metallic beryllium with an alpha emitter such as radon gas, powdered radium, or polonium. The entire source is carefully sealed. The method is still in use. Large numbers of neutrons are available inside a nuclear pile, since neutrons are given off during the nuclear reactions within the pile.

The positron

The positron is unique in that its existence was postulated by P. A. M. Dirac in 1930 as a result of calculations on the structure of matter. The answer indicated there were two particles. One was the electron; the other had exactly the same properties as the electron, but it was positively charged. Carl D. Anderson first observed the positron in 1932.

In addition to being emitted by certain nuclei, positrons may be formed as the result of pair production. When a high energy gamma ray passes near a heavy nucleus, the gamma ray is converted to a positron, β^+, and a beta particle, β^-. Conversely, a β^+ and an electron may combine and be converted into two or three gamma rays.

Other decay mechanisms

Protons may be ejected from the nucleus resulting in a nucleus of one less mass number and one less atomic number.

K electron capture. Some artificial radioisotope nuclei absorb an electron from the $1s$ energy level. The resultant nucleus is one atomic number smaller than the original nucleus. X rays are emitted as electrons in higher energy levels fill the lower energy levels.

Nuclear equations

Just as one may write an equation for a chemical reaction, it is possible to write equations for reactions involving nuclei. Two simple rules must be followed.

(1) The sum of the atomic numbers of the reactants must equal the sum of the atomic number of the products.

(2) The sum of the mass numbers of the reactants must equal the sum of the mass numbers of the products.

When writing nuclear equations, it is conventional to write the atomic number as a subscript before the atomic symbol to emphasize the first rule. Effective mass numbers and atomic numbers are assigned to the radioparticles. They are shown in Table 8.3.

Table 8.3

*Effective
Mass and Atomic Numbers
of Radioparticles*

Particle	Symbol	Effective atomic number	Effective mass number
alpha	α	2	4
beta	β^-	-1	0
neutron	n	0	1
positron	β^+	$+1$	0
proton	p	$+1$	1
electron	e	-1	0
gamma	γ	0	0

The decay of ^{14}C by beta emission is shown as

$$^{14}_{6}C \rightarrow X + {}^{0}_{-1}\beta^-.$$

In order to achieve balance, X must have a mass of 14 and an atomic number of 7. Therefore, $X = {}^{14}_{7}N$ and:

$$^{14}_{6}C \rightarrow {}^{14}_{7}N + \beta^-.$$

A shorthand notation has been developed for describing the reactions involving a bombarding particle and a radioisotope product. The reactant nucleus is followed by parentheses containing the bombarding particle(s), a comma, and the emitted particle(s). The parentheses are followed by the product nucleus. The equation

$$^{7}_{3}Li + {}^{1}_{1}p \rightarrow {}^{1}_{0}n + {}^{7}_{4}Be$$

is shortened to ^{7}Li (p,n)^{7}Be. This notation is not used for radioactive decay process, since no bombarding particle is used.

Example 8.1 Balance the following radiochemical equations.

(a) $^{238}_{92}U \rightarrow X + \alpha$

(b) $^{239}_{94}Pu + \alpha \rightarrow X + n$

(c) $^{27}_{13}Al + {}^{14}_{7}N \rightarrow 2p + 2\alpha + X$

Answers:
(a) Mass number of $X = 238 - 4 = 234$
    atomic number of $X = 92 - 2 = 90$ (Th)

$$^{238}_{92}U \rightarrow {}^{234}_{90}X + \alpha$$

(b) Mass number of $X = 239 + 4 - 1 = 242$
    atomic number of $X = 94 + 2 - 0 = 96$ (Cm)

$$^{239}_{94}Pu + \alpha \rightarrow {}^{242}_{96}X + n$$

shortened form: ^{239}Pu $(\alpha,n)^{242}Cm$

(c) Mass number of $X = 27 + 14 - 2(1) - 2(4) = 31$
    atomic number of $X = 13 + 7 - 2(1) - 2(2) = 14$ (Si)

$$^{27}_{13}Al + {}^{14}_{7}N \rightarrow 2p + 2\alpha + {}^{31}_{14}X$$

shortened form: $^{27}Al(^{14}N, 2p2\alpha)^{31}Si$

Detection and measurement of radiation

The earliest device used to measure radioactive decay was the *gold electroscope*. The thin gold leaves of the electroscope are separated by charging them with static electricity. Radioparticles ionize the gas between the leaves permitting the charge to leak off and the leaves to come closer together. The rate at which the leaves come together is a measure of the rate of emission of particles by the radionuclide. The same principles are in operation in the modern pocket dosimeter which consists of a movable quartz

Fig. 8.6

*Gold Electroscope. Application of a
static electricity charge to the knob
causes separation of the thin gold
leaves. Radiation entering the chamber ionizes the air, permitting the
charge to leak from the leaves.*

fiber and a fixed plate. The fiber is set to the zero of the scale by
charging plate and fiber with a definite charge. As the charge
leaks off due to passage of radioparticles, the quartz fiber moves
across a calibrated scale.

Another method of measurement is the darkening of photographic film. The amount of darkening is proportional to the
amount of radiation to which the film has been exposed, provided
that the total radiation is relatively small. Present-day applications are found in film badges which are worn by personnel exposed to radiation in the course of their work. By the use of films
of appropriate sensitivity and selected absorbing covers, it is
possible to relate the film darkening to the amount of radiation
received.

The *Geiger-Müller* tube consists of a central wire which acts as an
anode (positive electrode) and a conducting tube which acts as the
cathode. The outer tube is metal or glass with a conducting film.
The tube is filled with a gas such as argon at low pressure. During
operation the direct current voltage on the anode is slowly increased until the potential difference is enough to cause the positive ions formed by radiation to travel to the cathode and the
electrons to move to the anode. Ionization continues down the
wire until a great amplification occurs. The amplification then is
recorded as a pulse by an associated electronic device known as a
scaler. At low voltages only the largest pulses are recorded; as
voltage increases, the amplification increases and more pulses are
recorded. Soon an increase in voltage causes no significant increase in the number of pulses, because the amplification is great
enough for all pulses to be recorded. This point is known as the
G–M plateau. The tube usually is operated within this voltage
range. If the voltage is increased too high, the tube arcs, or breaks
into continual discharge.

Thin-walled G–M tubes detect beta particles most efficiently.
Gamma rays tend to pass through the tube without causing much
ionization in the short gas length, and alpha particles are absorbed

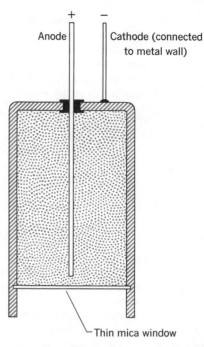

+   –

Anode   Cathode (connected
to metal wall)

Thin mica window

Fig. 8.7

Sketch of a Geiger-Müller Tube. Most efficient for detecting beta particles which enter through the window.

by the walls of the tube. It is possible to construct a G–M tube in such a way that the alpha emitter can be placed inside the tube.

Scintillation counters were developed originally as efficient gamma ray detectors. Improved scintillation techniques are used for detecting alpha and beta particles as well. Because of this versatility, use of scintillation counting has become widespread.

As the gamma ray travels through the scintillator medium, electrons are removed from its atoms. The electrons, which have considerable energy, excite electrons in other atoms. The electrons in this second group emit light as they return to the ground state. The flashes of light, the number of which depends upon the energy of the gamma ray, are counted by a photomultiplier tube. The current produced by the photomultiplier is proportional to the light intensity. Thus, it is possible to determine the energy of a gamma ray.

The rate of decay—half life

Radiation detectors measure the emissions from a large number of nuclei. The number of emissions in any given time period depends upon the number of unstable nuclei present. There is a certain probability that a given nucleus will decay within the time period. Thus, radioactive decay is a statistical phenomenon; a given nucleus may disintegrate within the next micro-second, or it may not disintegrate in the next million years. The probability of this, and consequently the rate of decay, is unaffected by chemical combination or temperature.

The number of nuclei n present after a length of time t has elapsed is given by the expression

$$\log n = \log n_0 - 0.4343 \, kt,$$

where n_0 is the number of nuclei present at the beginning of the time interval and k is the *decay constant*. It is convenient to characterize an isotope in terms of its half life. The *half life* is defined as the length of time required for one half of a given number of radioactive nuclei to disintegrate. By rearranging the above expression,

$$t_{1/2} = \frac{2.303}{k} \log \frac{n_0}{1/2 \; n_0} = \frac{2.303}{k} \log 2 = \frac{0.693}{k}.$$

Since the number of particles being emitted is dependent upon the number of radioactive nuclei present, the half life is determined by finding the length of time required for the rate of decay to be reduced by one half. During each half life, one half of the nuclei present at the beginning of the half life period disintegrates. At the end of one half life there is one half of the original number; at the end of two half lives there is one fourth of the original; at the

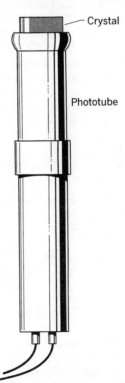

Crystal

Phototube

Fig. 8.8
Scintillation Counter.

end of three half lives there is one eighth of the original, and so on. Eventually, the number of nuclei becomes too small to behave statistically, and the half life becomes meaningless. However, this point is far beyond the limits of detectability.

Activity is usually measured in terms of the number of pulses recorded by the detector in a given length of time. Most commonly, activity is expressed in counts per minute. Unless extreme care is used in the counter design and sample placement, the counter only records a small fraction of the total number of disintegrations. As long as detector and sample are held in the same relative position, this fraction is constant for all measurements.

Background

If a counter is turned on in the absence of a sample, some activity is detected. This activity, or background, arises from cosmic radiation, traces of contamination in the laboratory, and natural radioisotopes which are present. A very common natural source is ^{40}K which is present in the clay used for bricks. Background may be reduced by using heavy lead shields to cover the detectors. Cosmic radiation is impossible to eliminate completely so a background must be subtracted from all readings. Corrected readings are used for half life determinations.

Example 8.2 Phosphorus-32 has a half life of fourteen days. How many days will it take for the activity of a ^{32}P containing sample to drop from 80000 counts per minute (cpm) to 160 cpm?

Two methods may be used. The first is usable only when dealing with an integral number of half lives. $80000 \xrightarrow{1} 40000 \xrightarrow{2} 20000 \xrightarrow{3} 10000 \xrightarrow{4} 5000 \xrightarrow{5} 2500 \xrightarrow{6} 1250 \xrightarrow{7} 625 \xrightarrow{8} 312 \xrightarrow{9} 156$. Nine half lives are required or 9×14 days $= 126$ days (an approximate answer).

The second method is usable in all cases. First, the decay constant is calculated.

$$t_{1/2} = \frac{0.693}{k},$$

$$k = \frac{0.693}{14 \text{ days}} = \frac{0.0495}{\text{day}}.$$

The value is used in the relation,

$$\log n = \log n_0 - 0.4343\, kt,$$
$$\log 160 = \log 80000 - 0.4343\, (0.0495)t,$$
$$2.204 = 4.903 - 0.0215t,$$
$$t = \frac{4.903 - 2.204}{0.0215} = 125.5 \text{ days (an exact answer).}$$

Units of activity

It is necessary to be able to correlate the disintegration rates between different samples and different emissions. The absolute disintegration rate for a particular sample may be obtained from

the observed rate by the use of standard samples. Certain units have been adopted to indicate the disintegration rate. Three of the common units are:
(a) The curie (c)
The curie is defined as that amount of material which undergoes 3.7×10^{10} disintegrations per second.
(b) The rutherford (rd)
The rutherford is the absolute unit of radioactive decay recommended by the National Bureau of Standards. It is the amount of material that undergoes 10^6 disintegrations per second.
(c) the roentgen (r)
The curie and rutherford are applicable primarily to alpha and beta decay. Gamma radiation usually is measured in terms of roentgens per hour at one meter (rhm, pronounced "rum"). The roentgen is defined as that quantity of X or gamma radiation such that 1.61×10^{12} ion pairs (a β^- and a β^+) are produced in a gram of dry air. This corresponds to absorption of 86 ergs of energy by one gram of dry air. Dosage rates are given in terms of roentgens per unit time.

Nuclear energetics and transmutation

Binding energy

The mass of an isotope is measured relative to a mass of exactly 12 amu for the ^{12}C isotope. Although the mass number is equal to the sum of the number of protons and the number of neutrons, the isotopic mass is not equal to the sum of the masses of the electrons, protons, and neutrons that make up the atom. For example, the sum of the masses of two electrons, two protons, and two neutrons is greater than the mass of ^4He:

2 H masses (including electrons)	2.01565 amu
2 n masses	2.01733 amu
total mass of the parts	4.03298 amu
^4He mass	4.00260 amu
Mass defect	0.03038 amu

The difference in the masses, or the mass defect, represents the increased stability of the nucleus compared to individual particles. This stability is called the *binding energy*. The energy equivalent of the mass is given by the well-known relationship, $E = mc^2$, developed by Albert Einstein who first postulated that mass and energy are interconvertible. In the Einstein equation, E is the energy, m is the amount of mass gained or lost, and c is the velocity of light in a vacuum (3×10^{10} cm/sec). Substitution of appropriate values in this relationship shows that 931 million electron volts (MeV) or 3.57×10^{-11} calories are produced when 1 amu is converted to energy. Thus, the binding energy of the ^4He

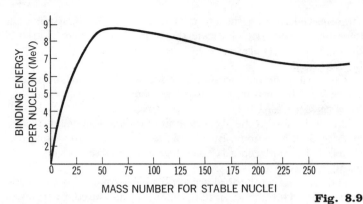

Fig. 8.9

Binding Energy per Nucleon as a Function of Mass Number for Stable Nuclei.

nucleus is $(931 \text{ MeV/amu})(0.03038 \text{ amu}) = 28.3 \text{ MeV}$. In other words, 28.3 MeV of energy would be liberated if two protons and two neutrons were forced together to form a ^{4}He nucleus (an alpha particle), since the ^{4}He nucleus is more stable than the free particles.

When calculating the binding energy, it is necessary to count the electrons as well as the protons and neutrons. Atomic masses of ^{1}H and ^{4}He are used in the above calculation to maintain a balance of two electrons. The same result is obtained if the proton mass (1.007276 amu) and the alpha particle mass (4.0015 amu) are used instead of the ^{1}H mass (1.007825 amu) and the ^{4}He mass (4.00260 amu). Except for the proton and alpha particle, atomic masses usually are listed.

The binding energy per nucleon in ^{4}He is $\dfrac{28.3 \text{ MeV}}{4 \text{ nucleons}} = 7.1$

MeV/nucleon. This value is somewhat lower than the binding energy per nucleon for many other stable nuclei. For most stable nuclei the binding energy per nucleon is 8.0 to 8.5 MeV. The higher value extends over a wide range of mass numbers in the middle portion of the periodic table. Figure 8.9 is a sketch of the binding energy per nucleon as a function of mass number.

The values of the binding energy per nucleon for a few nuclei such as ^{4}He, ^{12}C, and ^{16}O lie well above the curve, indicating the very stable nature of these nuclei. The instability of the heavy radioactive nuclei is explained partially in terms of this curve. The binding energy per nucleon for the heavy nuclei is less than that for the lighter nuclei. The emission of an alpha particle reduces the mass of the nucleus. The emission is favored, since the nucleons in the lighter nucleus have a higher binding energy and represent a lower energy state relative to the heavy nucleus.

Fission

If a heavy nucleus splits into two parts, energy is released since the binding energy per nucleon in the resultant nuclei is somewhat greater. This process, called *fission*, was observed for the first time in 1934 by Enrico Fermi, although it was not until 1939 that it was described correctly. The early fission reactions resulted from the bombardment of uranium with neutrons.

It is known now that the uranium-235 isotope is fissionable by neutrons. The process is the capture of a slow, or thermal, neutron by the ^{235}U nucleus which then splits into nuclei with mass numbers in the range about 90 and 140. There are no fixed elements that result from fission of a ^{235}U nucleus. Usually many elements are found in the fission products. Many of the fission products are unstable and emit alpha and subatomic particles and gamma rays. In addition, two or three neutrons are given off during the fission process. These neutrons cause further fissions if captured. If the reacting mass of the uranium is too small, neutrons escape from the mass without causing fission. If the reacting mass is large enough, the neutrons are slowed down and captured with more fission resulting. If one of the neutrons from every fission causes another fission, the fission rate remains constant. The reacting mass required to just sustain the fission reaction is known as the *critical mass*. The size of the critical mass may be reduced by surrounding it with neutron reflectors. Graphite is an excellent neutron reflector. In addition, the graphite slows the neutrons without absorbing them. Thus graphite is frequently placed about the uranium as a moderator. Water is a good moderator also.

If the size, shape, and moderator of the fissionable material are such that more than one neutron per fission is captured, the fission rate increases. If this build-up in the fission rate takes place rap-

Fig. 8.10

Fission of Uranium-235. Capture of a slow neutron by ^{235}U results in the formation of two new nuclei and two to three neutrons. Neutrons are slowed by a moderator. Some neutrons may be lost from the mass of the material; others are absorbed by ^{235}U to continue the reaction. Step 1—increase in reaction rate; Step 2—steady reaction rate.

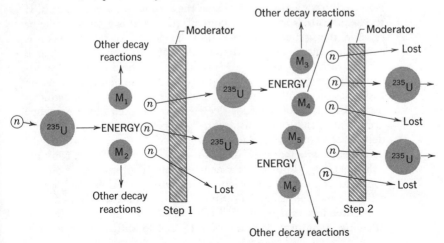

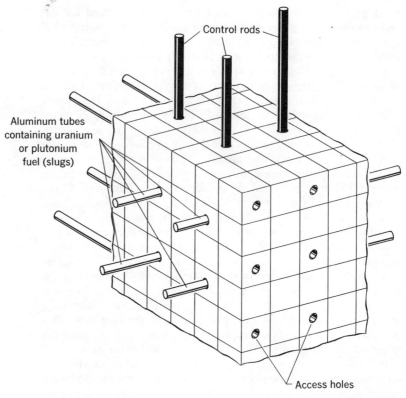

Control rods

Aluminum tubes
containing uranium
or plutonium
fuel (slugs)

Access holes

Fig. 8.11

Diagram of a Nuclear Reactor. Graphite blocks serve as the moderator for neutrons. Fuel elements are inserted in one set of holes. Neutron-absorbing control rods limit the number of neutrons available for the chain reaction. Heavy concrete shielding is not shown.

idly, a tremendous amount of energy is released. This process was achieved first on July 16, 1945, in the form of an atomic bomb. If the fission rate is kept under control, the result is a nuclear pile or reactor, the first of which was built in 1942. The rate of fission is controlled by using rods that readily absorb neutrons. When a certain rate (or power level) is reached, it is held constant by inserting these control rods to a point where one neutron from one fission causes another atom to fission. The power level is reduced by putting the control rods deeper into the pile. Since neutrons are being produced constantly, a nuclear reactor has a high density of neutrons available.

The early reactors used uranium enriched with ^{235}U. Uranium-235 makes up about 0.7 per cent in natural uranium. The most spectacular method of enriching uranium in ^{235}U is the gaseous diffusion method using UF_6. Since the molecular weight of $^{235}UF_6$ is slightly less than that of $^{238}UF_6$, it diffuses more rapidly. By allowing a natural mixture of UF_6 gas to diffuse over a long enough path, the product contains substantially more ^{235}U and is useful for a sustained or chain reaction.

Other nuclei are fissionable. The use of plutonium-239, prepared by the bombardment of ^{238}U with neutrons, is increasing. Uranium-233 prepared from ^{232}Th is used also.

Fusion

Figure 8.9 shows that the binding energy in the lightweight elements is somewhat less than that in the heavier elements. The formation of a heavier nucleus from two lightweight nuclei therefore results in the release of energy. As we have seen, the formation of a helium-4 nucleus from two protons and two neutrons results in 28.3 MeV of energy being released. This is 6.51×10^8 kcal for the formation of a mole of helium.

Other combinations of nuclei are more practical for a fusion reaction. The fusion of two deuterium nuclei or of a deuterium and a tritium nucleus is feasible. Uncontrolled fusion reactions occur in the hydrogen bomb. The tremendous energies come from the binding energy increase in the formation of heavier nuclei. Since the product nuclei are stable, no radioactivity results. The major obstacle for the practical use of the fusion reaction is the repulsion between nuclei that must be overcome. In the hydrogen bomb the reacting nuclei are given sufficient kinetic energy by the use of an atomic bomb trigger. In the laboratory high temperatures must be created while maintaining a high density of the gaseous reactants. As yet, no prolonged controlled fusion reaction has been reported, although some fusions over a short period of time have been observed.

Nuclear fusion is thought to be the source of the energy in our sun. Although ^{12}C, ^{13}N, and ^{15}O are involved in the process, the net overall reaction is

$$4p \rightarrow {}^4He + 2\beta^+ + energy$$

Synthetic elements

With the understanding of the nucleus and the nuclear particles and the development of instrumentation for their control and detection, it has become possible to create many new nuclei. Not only have new isotopes of naturally occurring elements been prepared, but several elements that do not occur in nature have been prepared.

Space was left for elements numbered 43, 61, 85, and 87 in the periodic tables of the 1930's. In 1939, francium-223 was found to be a part of a branching of the actinium ($4n + 3$) series. Because it has a half life of 22 minutes, no substantial build-up of it can occur. By use of nuclear reactions several other francium isotopes have been prepared, and some of its chemical properties have been studied. All of these isotopes are short lived.

Table 8.4

The Trans-uranium Elements

Atomic Number	Name	Important isotopes			Longest-lived isotope			Number of Isotopes Identified (1966)	Source of Name
		Mass No.	Mode of decay	Half life	Mass No.	Mode of decay	Half life		
93	Neptunium	Np-237	α	2.14×10^6 yr	Np-237	α	2.14×10^6 yr	12	The planet Neptune which lies beyond Uranus in the solar system.
94	Plutonium	Pu-239	α	24,360 yr	Pu-244	α	7.6×10^7 yr	15	The planet Pluto which lies beyond Neptune.
		Pu-242	α	3.79×10^5 yr					
95	Americium	Am-241	α	458 yr	Am-243	α	7650 yr	10	Analogous to its lanthanide homolog, europium.
		Am-243	α	7650 yr					
96	Curium	Cm-242	α	163 days	Cm-247	α	1.67×10^7 yr	14	In honor of Marie and Pierre Curie.
		Cm-244	α	18.1 yr					
97	Berkelium	Bk-247	α	$\sim 10^4$ yr	Bk-247	α	$\sim 10^4$ yr	9	The city where it was discovered.
		Bk-249	β^-	314 days					
98	Californium	Cf-249	α	360 yr	Cf-251	α	800 yr	11	The state and university where it was first prepared.
		Cf-252	α	2.55 yr					
99	Einsteinium				Es-254	α	480 days	11	In honor of Albert Einstein.
100	Fermium				Fm-257	α	94 days	11	In honor of Enrico Fermi.
101	Mendelevium				Md-257	E.C.	3 hr	3	In honor of D. I. Mendeleev.
102	Nobelium				No-254	α	~ 50 sec	3	In honor of Alfred Nobel.*
103	Lawrencium				Lw-256	?	45 sec	2	In honor of E. O. Lawrence.**

E.C. = electron capture

*Name not yet confirmed.
**Lr also used as symbol.

Element 43 (technetium) and element 61 (promethium) do not occur in nature. Technetium is a product of uranium fission. It may be produced also by bombardment of molybdenum with deuterium nuclei (deuterons) and the subsequent ejection of a neutron. Undetectable traces of technetium should appear in nature as a result of spontaneous fission. All known technetium isotopes are radioactive; the longest half life is 2.6×10^6 years for ^{97}Tc. Promethium was found in the fission products of uranium during World War II. The longest-lived isotope ^{145}Pm has a half life of 18 years.

Element 85 (astatine) is available only by nuclear transformation. All isotopes are radioactive; the longest half life is 8.3 hours for ^{210}At. The chemistry of astatine shows a continuation of the trends found in the halogens.

Prior to 1940, the existence of elements with atomic numbers above 92 was unknown and unpredicted. With a plentiful supply of neutrons in high concentration available in the nuclear piles, eleven elements above uranium have been synthesized. The properties of these elements, the trans-uranium elements, are very similar to the lanthanides. Now it is recognized that actinium, thorium, protactinium, uranium, and the trans-uranium elements make up the actinide series which is very much like the lanthanide series.

The first of the trans-uranium elements to be prepared was neptunium. It is now available as a byproduct of the operation of nuclear reactors. Plutonium is now recognized as occurring in very low (one part in 10^{11}) concentrations in some pitchblende ores. Plutonium-239 produced in a nuclear reactor is used to fuel other reactors, since it undergoes fission readily upon neutron capture. Elements 95 (americium) through 100 (fermium) are most readily prepared by the successive absorption of neutrons in a reactor and the emission of a beta particle when the nucleus reaches a high degree of instability. Since most of the curium-245 and -247 nuclei undergo spontaneous fission rather than neutron capture, the yield of berkelium and californium is very small. Due to the short half life of the californium nuclei an accumulation of it is not possible. Einsteinium and fermium can be produced only in trace quantities because of their short half lives. Mendelevium is prepared in a cyclotron where one alpha particle at a time is accelerated and directed at an einsteinium target.

$$^{253}\text{Es}(\alpha,\text{n})^{256}\text{Md}$$

Typically, the target contains about 10^{-12} grams of einsteinium.

The degree of sophistication of preparative techniques is shown by the bombardment of curium targets with carbon nuclei to produce nobelium,

$$^{244}\text{Cm}(^{12}\text{C},4\text{n})^{252}\text{No}$$

and californium targets with boron nuclei to produce lawrencium.

$$^{252}\text{Cf}(^{10}\text{B},5\text{n})^{257}\text{Lw}$$

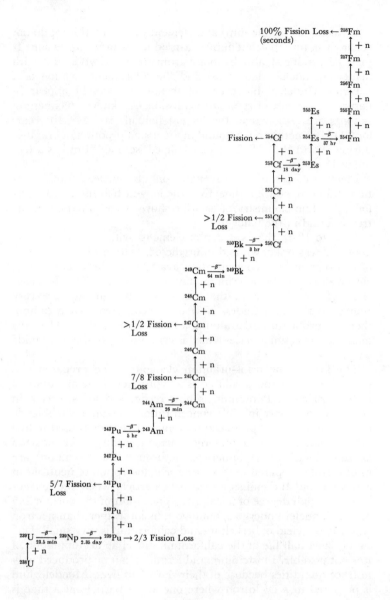

Fig. 8.12

Neutron Capture Chain. Many of the trans-uranium elements are prepared in a nuclear pile. Because of the high density of neutrons in the pile, there is successive capture of neutrons by the nuclei. If a ^{238}U sample is exposed to the neutron flux for a long period of time, all of the isotopes shown here along with the fission products would be found. The large fission losses along the chain severely limit the yield of the higher atomic numbers. The chain terminates with ^{258}Fm since essentially all of these nuclei fission in a matter of seconds. New elements are formed by beta particle emission when the nuclei become too unstable. The half life for the beta decay is given.

Due to the instability of the boron–californium intermediate, only a few atoms of lawrencium are available at any one time. If the lawrencium atoms could be stablized long enough to reach a ground state electronic configuration, the 5*f* energy level would be filled and the actinide series would be complete.

There are unconfirmed reports from the U.S.S.R. of the preparation of element 104 with mass number 260 and a half life of 0.3 second by the bombardment of plutonium-242 with neon-22 nuclei. It is thought that element 104 would be placed in Group IVB of the periodic table. Due to the extreme instability of the nuclei, the ground state electron configuration is never reached. Unless nuclei with more than 104 protons develop an unexpected stability, it is unlikely that many more elements will be synthesized and detected.

Applications
Radiochemical dating

The occurrence of long-lived isotopes in nature permits the determination of the age of objects, if the half life and decay scheme of the isotopes are known. If the present and original amounts of a radioisotope are known, it is possible to calculate the length of time an object has existed. Some of the following methods have been used.

AGE-OF-THE-EARTH MEASUREMENTS

Uranium-238 decays to stable lead-206 with the emission of eight alpha particles. The alpha particles pick up electrons readily to form helium gas. If the uranium-bearing rock is fine grained so as to prevent the escape of helium, the amount of helium in the rock is indicative of the amount of uranium-238 that has decayed. From the known half life of uranium-238 (4.5×10^9 years) one can determine the age of the rock from the ratio of the remaining ^{238}U to that which has decayed. Since the decay of thorium-232 produces helium, it is necessary to measure and correct for the ^{232}Th content. The ^{206}Pb content may also be used to determine the amount of ^{238}U that has decayed, provided that all of the isotope is the result of the decay and that none of the lead has been leached out by exposure to the atmosphere. From the results of the studies of these and other long-lived isotope decay schemes, the age of the earth is calculated to be 2×10^9 to 4×10^9 years.

CARBON-14

Carbon-14 is not useful for determining the age of the earth, since its half life of 5730 years is too short. This isotope is particularly useful for dating old organic materials such as those found in archeological excavations. Cosmic rays produce neutrons which undergo a (n,p) reaction with nitrogen-14 of the atmosphere to produce carbon-14. The assumption is that the ^{14}C content of the atmosphere has been constant over the last several thousand years. Living material, such as a tree, maintains an equilibrium concentration of ^{14}C with the $^{14}CO_2$ of the atmosphere. When the organism dies, the ^{14}C decays without being replenished from the atmosphere. The ^{14}C content is thus a function of the time elapsed since the organism died. The techniques of carbon-14 dating have been developed to the point that very small samples can be analyzed very accurately. Ages up to about 50,000 years can be measured.

TRITIUM DATING

Tritium with a half life of 12.26 years is useful for measurement of ages up to 30 years. Tritium occurs in the atmosphere as the result of a $^{14}N(n,^3H)^{12}C$ reaction. The neutrons are produced by cosmic radiation. Usually the tritium content of water is measured. Corrections must be applied for amount of rainfall and latitude, since cosmic radiation varies with latitude.

Tracers

It is assumed that all isotopes of an element undergo the same chemical reactions. Detection of stable or radioactive isotopes is easier and much more sensitive than most other analytical techniques. If the course of a particular compound in a reaction or in an organism is to be followed, the compound is tagged by incorporating into it a readily detectable isotope of which little or none occurs in the natural material. By careful attention to mounting and counting the sample, relative rather than absolute values provide the desired answers. Some of the commonly used tracer isotopes are listed in Table 8.5. Stable isotopes are measured using a mass spectrograph.

Deuterium and tritium are useful not only for tracing hydrogen through a reaction but for detailing molecular geometry and changes in chemical properties caused by changes in mass. The changes in properties are usually relatively small and are primarily changes in reaction rates. For example, electrolysis of ordinary water produces a residue that is richer in deuterium, since the hydrogen-1 comes off five times faster than deuterium. While natural water contains one part deuterium to 5000 parts hydrogen, the gas to come off first contains one part deuterium in 25,000 parts hydrogen. By repetition of the electrolysis process, it is possible to produce 99.5% D_2O.

Phosphorus-32 is used in agricultural research to follow the utilization of phosphate by plants. Among the applications of iodine-131 is the diagnosis and treatment of thyroid disorders. Small doses of ^{131}I in a NaI solution are given to the patient. If the amount of radioiodine taken up by the thyroid is high, the overactive gland is partially destroyed by massive, but controlled, doses of ^{131}I solutions.

Health physics and fallout

Exposure of humans to radioactive sources results in ionization in the tissues. If the amount of damage is not very extensive, the body replaces the damaged tissue and eliminates the toxic products. Ionization in the reproductive organs may cause mutations, which unfortunately are usually regressive. Because of the possible genetic damage, the U.S. Atomic Energy Commission limits exposure of personnel to 50 milliroentgens per week spread over the entire body. There is thought to be a margin of safety in this limit.

Mankind has always been subject to radiation due to cosmic rays, radioactive minerals in the earth, traces of radon in the air, and ^{14}C and ^{40}K in the body. Natural radioactivity leads to an exposure of 0.14 to 0.16 roentgens per year, which has caused some mutations in living organisms.

Each of the emissions has its particular biological danger. Alpha particles cause extensive damage but have a very short path length. Any thin layer of protection such as skin or clothing absorbs alpha particles. The primary danger is the ingestion of an alpha emitter, leading to damage to internal organs.

The beta particle causes less damage per unit length than the alpha, but the beta is more penetrating. Because of this penetration into the body, beta particles are a more serious health problem. Special protection, such as a few centimeters of aluminum, is required for working with a beta emitter.

Gamma radiation is the most penetrating and the greatest health hazard. While the damage per unit path length is small, it may occur in the vital organs deep within the body. The ions

Table 8.5

Isotopes Commonly Used in Tracer Work

Element	Tracer Isotope	Characteristic
Hydrogen	^{2}H (deuterium)	stable
	^{3}H (tritium)	β^-, 12.3 years
Carbon	^{13}C	stable
	^{14}C	β^-, 5730 years
Nitrogen	^{15}N	stable
Oxygen	^{18}O	stable
Phosphorus	^{32}P	β^-, 14.3 days
Sulfur	^{34}S	stable
	^{35}S	β^-, 86.7 days
Chlorine	^{36}Cl	β^-, 3×10^5 years
Iodine	^{128}I	β^-, 25 minutes
	^{131}I	β^-, 8 days

formed by the gamma ray cause additional damage; there may be spots of severe damage along the gamma path. Most of the gamma rays pass through the body with little loss of energy. Heavy shielding, such as several feet of concrete or several inches of lead, is needed to absorb and protect against the gamma rays.

Neutrons cause ionization and are readily absorbed by the body at a moderate penetration. Protection is provided by graphite "mirrors" and water absorption. Since lead is transparent to neutrons, lead, graphite, and water shields are necessary to protect against both neutrons and the gamma radiation associated with them.

The half life of a radioactive isotope is important in health considerations. As a general rule, an active sample is considered safe after ten half lives. A short lived isotope disappears quickly and requires shielding for a short time. If such an isotope does get into the body, the damage does not continue for very long. If the emitter is used in an insoluble form, it is passed through the body with only moderate damage to the intestinal tract.

In the explosion of a nuclear device, many radioisotopes are formed by the fission process. It should be noted that a thermonuclear or hydrogen bomb is a clean bomb in that no radioisotopes are formed in the fusion reaction; but a dirty (radioisotope-producing) atomic or fission bomb is required as a trigger. Dust and other debris may become radioactive due to exposure to the emissions from the blast products. This material is pulled up into the upper atmosphere to return slowly as fallout in rain or dust. The farther above the earth a bomb is exploded, the less dust is pulled into the atmosphere.

The two most serious health hazards in the fallout are strontium-90 and cesium-137. Strontium-90 is a moderately strong beta emitter that is chemically similar to calcium. It is deposited in the bone structure where the beta particles destroy the red-blood-cell-producing bone marrow. Since the half life is 28.8 years, ^{90}Sr causes damage as long as it is in the body.

Cesium-137 is a beta emitter of about the same energy as strontium-90. Since it is chemically similar to sodium, it becomes widely scattered throughout the body. The 30-year half life is a biological problem as long as it is in the body. Fortunately, it is not as readily retained by the body as is ^{90}Sr.

Nature has provided a discrimination pattern that is favorable to the human organism with respect to these isotopes. When strontium-90 falls on a pasture, it is taken up by the grass but in the ratio to calcium that is less than that on the ground. The cow eats this grass and discriminates against this isotope in the milk production. Man drinks the milk and again there is discrimination against retaining the isotope in the body. The result is that the strontium-90 content of the bone is much less than that predicted on the basis of the ^{90}Sr content of the original fallout. The primary danger is that young children take in much more calcium than an adult and along with it much more strontium-90.

SIGNIFICANT TERMS AND CONCEPTS IN CHAPTER VIII:

Neutron, nucleon, atomic mass, mass number, isotope, alpha particle, beta particle, gamma ray, neutrino, positron, pair production, electron capture, nuclear equations, effective mass and atomic numbers of radioparticles, detection of radioactivity, half life, background, curie, rutherford, roentgen, mass defect, binding energy, fission, fusion, critical mass, tracers, radiation hazards and protection.

Review questions

8.1. The atomic mass of boron-10 is 10.013. Its mass number is 10. The atomic weight of boron is 10.81. Explain how these values are related.

8.2. How are the number of protons and the number of neutrons related to the mass number and to the atomic number?

8.3. How many protons and neutrons are in the nucleus of each of the following isotopes? What is the ratio of neutrons to protons in each? (These are the most abundant isotopes of the elements listed.) ^{4}He, ^{24}Mg, ^{48}Ti, ^{74}Ge, ^{98}Mo, ^{130}Te, ^{152}Sm, ^{180}Hf, ^{208}Pb, ^{238}U.

8.4. What is the charge and mass number of a (a) proton, (b) neutron, (c) alpha particle, (d) beta particle, (e) positron?

8.5. What isotopes of radium should be found in mineral ores on the basis of Table 8.1?

8.6. Balance the following nuclear equations:
(a) ^{234}Pa $\rightarrow \beta^- + $ ____   (e) ^{238}U $+ ^{12}$C $\rightarrow ^{246}$Cf $+ $ ____
(b) ^{58}Co $\rightarrow ^{56}$Fe $+ $ ____   (f) ^{6}Li $+ $ n $\rightarrow \alpha + $ ____
(c) ^{24}Mg $+ \alpha \rightarrow $ n $+ $ ____   (g) ^{27}Al $+ \alpha \rightarrow ^{30}$P $+ $ ____
(d) $\alpha + ^{14}$N $\rightarrow $ p $+ $ ____

8.7. Write balanced equations for the following:
(a) ^{127}I (n,____)^{128}I   (e) ^{198}Hg(____,2n)^{197}Hg
(b) ^{9}Be(____,n)^{8}Be   (f) ^{235}U(____,p2n)^{236}Np
(c) Beta decay of ^{131}Te   (g) ^{59}Co $+ $ ____ $\rightarrow ^{61}$Co $+ ^1$H
(d) Positron decay of ^{71}As   (h) ^{10}B $+ $ ____ $\rightarrow ^{13}$N $+ ^{11}$B

8.8. Write the equations in question 8.7 (g) and (h) in shorthand notation.

8.9. Why does fission not occur for elements such as iron, cobalt, and nickel?

8.10. Would the fusion of copper atoms produce any energy? Why?

8.11. What characteristics are desirable for a tracer isotope?

Problems

Isotopic masses (in amu) that may be needed to work the following problems.

p 1.007276, α 4.00150, β^- 0.000549, n 1.008665

p 1.007276, α 4.00150, β̄ 0.00054
n 1.008665

The following values include the electrons.

^{1}H 1.007825, ^{4}He 4.00260, ^{14}N 14.00307, ^{2}H 2.01410,
^{9}Be 9.01219, ^{17}O 16.99913, ^{238}U 238.0508

8.12. The half life of ^{32}P is fourteen days. What is the activity of a ^{32}P sample 84 days after it gave a reading of 10,000 counts per minute?   answer: 156 cpm

8.13. How long does it take for the activity of a ^{90}Sr sample to reach 10 disintegrations per minute, if the present activity is 10,240 dis/min? The half life is 28.8 years.

8.14. One rutherford of ^{24}Na has an activity of approximately one millirutherford in how many hours? (Half life = 15 hours)

8.15. One curie of ^{80}Br is equivalent to how many rutherfords? (Half life ^{80}Br = 18 min)

8.16. Calculate the energy (in MeV) released in the following reactions. (a) ^{9}Be$(\alpha,n)^{12}$C, (b) ^{14}N$(\alpha,p)^{17}$O, (c) The annihilation of a β^+ and a β^-, (d) The fusion of two deuterium nuclei to form a helium-4 nucleus.

answer: (a) 5.71 MeV

8.17. Calculate the approximate mass of ^{234}Th knowing that ^{238}U emits a 4.19 MeV alpha particle.

8.18. Calculate the weight in grams of: (a) a neutron (b) a proton (c) an atom of ^{12}C.   answer: (a) 1.675×10^{-24} g

8.19. Calculate the density of the hydrogen-1 nucleus if its radius is 1.2×10^{-13} cm.

8.20. Calculate the atomic weight of the following elements for which the indicated isotopic distribution exists.

    (a)   19.78% ^{10}B 10.01294 amu
          80.22% ^{11}B 11.00931 amu
    (b)   78.70% ^{24}Mg 23.98504 amu
          10.13% ^{25}Mg 24.98584 amu
          11.17% ^{26}Mg 25.98259 amu
    (c)   7.42% ^{6}Li 6.01512 amu
          92.58% ^{7}Li 7.01600 amu

answer: (a) 10.812 amu

nine
the noble gases

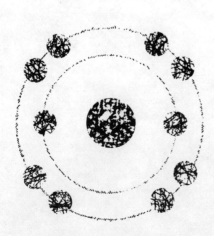

From the time of their discovery during the first decade of the twentieth century until 1962, the elements of Group VIIIA were referred to as the *inert gases*, because they apparently lacked any chemical reactivity. Many chemists felt that the s^2p^6 electron configuration was so stable that there was no possibility of chemical combination. In the time since the first preparation of compounds of these elements a greater effort has been made to understand the relationship between the electron configuration of an element and the compounds it forms. The discovery that the inert gases do form compounds necessitated a change in the group name. *Noble gases* seemed more descriptive of the elements' apparent magnanimity toward chemical reaction.

Discovery and occurrence

Although argon was first observed by Sir Henry Cavendish in 1785, it was not recognized as an element until 1894. Cavendish repeatedly passed a spark through a sample of air and oxygen. After absorbing the excess oxygen and the spark product (NO_2), he found that less than 1/120 of the original air remained. In 1894, Lord Rayleigh found the density of nitrogen obtained from air (1.2572 g/l at S.T.P.) to be slightly greater than the density of nitrogen obtained from decomposition of ammonium nitrate (1.2506 g/l at S.T.P.). He concluded that there must be a gas heavier than nitrogen in the atmosphere. Later Sir William Ramsey repeated the Rayleigh experiment and proved that argon was present by its emission spectrum.

Helium was discovered in the atmosphere of the sun. The spectral lines of helium were found during a solar eclipse in 1868. The element, in fact, derives its name from the Greek word for sun—*helios*. Ramsey was able to detect the presence of helium as a trace element in the earth's atmosphere. It is also trapped in uranium ores where its existence can be demonstrated by spectroscopic means.

Between 1894 and 1908, Ramsey and his co-workers were able to isolate all of the noble gases—helium, neon, argon, krypton, xenon, and radon—from the atmosphere. Large volumes of liquid air were carefully evaporated. The emission spectrum of each portion of the gas was examined. By following the intensity of the spectral lines it was possible to concentrate and isolate each of the noble gases. Ramsey is the only person who isolated a whole family of elements. The noble gases were discovered primarily because Cavendish would not ignore the small bubble of gas remaining from his experiment and because Rayleigh thought the density difference of five parts per 1000 was not experimental error. The eight to ten milliliters of gas remaining after the nitrogen and oxygen have been removed from a liter of air contain a whole family of elements that are vital to industry, to the laboratory, and to the theoretician. The noble gas content of the atmosphere is shown in Table 9.1.

Table 9.1

Properties of the Noble Gases

Name	Symbol	Atmospheric content (% by volume)	Melting points (°K)	Melting points (°C)	Boiling points (°K)	Boiling points (°C)
Helium	He	5.24×10^{-4}	——	——	4	−269
Neon	Ne	1.82×10^{-3}	24	−249	27	−246
Argon	Ar	0.934	84	−189	87	−186
Krypton	Kr	1.14×10^{-3}	116	−157	120	−153
Xenon	Xe	8.7×10^{-6}	161	−112	167	−108
Radon	Ra	(unstable)	202	−71	211	−62

Helium is a constituent of some natural gas wells in the United States. It is necessary to extract the helium by gaseous diffusion or by liquefaction of the other gases. Since both methods are expensive, only gas wells containing relatively high concentrations of helium are stripped of this valuable resource. Due to its low density and inertness, helium is a very valuable, but limited resource. Therefore, in the United States the government maintains control of helium storage and use.

The other noble gases are obtained from the atmosphere. Air is liquefied and allowed to warm slowly. Neon is found in the lower boiling nitrogen fraction. The others are found in the oxygen fraction. Argon is removed from the oxygen fraction by very careful distillation. Since the boiling points are separated by only three degrees, the last traces of oxygen in the argon are removed by burning the gas with hydrogen or by passing the gas over hot copper. Neon, krypton, and xenon are separated by selective adsorption on activated charcoal. These gases are not available in large quantities. All radon is the result of radium decay and is found in conjunction with radium ores. All radon isotopes are radioactive and short lived.

Physical properties

All of the noble gases are monatomic, with relatively low boiling points (Table 9.1). All of the noble gases except helium solidify two to seven degrees below the boiling point. The low melting points indicate that the forces of attraction between molecules are very weak, since little energy in the form of heat is needed to overcome the forces holding the solid together. The intermolecular forces in the liquid are very weak, and very little more energy is required to cause the molecules to vaporize. The increase in boiling points with increasing atomic weight is as predicted, since more energy is required to attain the necessary velocity to remove a heavy molecule from the surface of a liquid.

Helium is a most interesting element. It may be solidified at 0.96°K by the application of 20 atmospheres of pressure. As yet, solid helium has not been formed at atmospheric pressure. Naturally occurring helium contains about 10^{-4} atom per cent ^{3}He; the rest is ^{4}He. Helium-3 also results from the beta decay of tritium and other nuclear reactions. Helium-3 is a stable isotope and when liquefied behaves as a normal liquid.

Fig. 9.1

Behavior of Liquid Helium. Helium in its superfluid phase (temperature, −271°C) creeps up the walls of its container, provided the temperature above the container is higher than that of the liquid. In this picture, liquid helium "falls down" the outside of the container and collects in drops at the bottom.

Liquid helium-4 has some very unusual properties. It condenses at 4.12°K as the normal liquid known as He-I. At atmospheric pressure and 2.178°K a unique transition from one liquid phase to another liquid phase takes place. This transition to He-II is very sudden and is known as the lambda point. Helium-II is like no other known liquid. There is essentially no electrical resistance. The thermal conductivity is many hundred times that of copper. Upon cooling He-II expands. The surface tension and viscosity are so low that the liquid flows up and over the top of the container, leading some to say that He-II flows uphill. The films formed by the liquid are very thin. As yet no satisfactory explanation is available for these properties.

Chemical properties

The noble gases are characterized by their chemical inertness. Noble gas atoms can be trapped within crystal lattices when certain liquids are frozen under high noble gas pressure. These enclosure compounds are stable for many years under careful storage. If the crystal is dissolved or melted, the gas escapes. Since ice crystallizes with a rather open framework, noble gas atoms are easily trapped, thus forming noble gas hydrates. These enclosure compounds are not true compounds in the sense that chemical bonds are formed. The formation of such enclosure compounds is not restricted to the noble gases.

The first true noble gas compound to be prepared was xenon hexafluoroplatinate ($XePtF_6$). This compound is ionic and is prepared easily by mixing xenon and platinum hexafluoride vapor. Within four months of the announcement of the preparation of $XePtF_6$, a covalent compound, XeF_4, was prepared.

Fig. 9.2

Crystals of Xenon Tetrafluoride. Crystals were grown at room temperature.

When xenon gas is heated to 400°C with five times as much fluorine gas in a nickel container, all of the xenon is converted to XeF_4 within one hour. This simple reaction could have been carried out earlier, if the techniques for handling fluorine had been developed and if xenon were not so rare. The estimated maximum daily production of xenon in the United States is 138 moles. Even this small amount has not been entirely recovered because of the lack of need.

Xenon tetrafluoride is a colorless crystalline material that melts at 90°C. Its vapor pressure of 3 torr at room temperature permits formation of rather large crystals by sublimation. The molecule is thought to consist of four fluorine atoms at the corners of a square with the xenon atom in the middle of the plane.

With this breakthrough, many other noble gas compounds have been prepared and studied. By the addition of traces of oxygen, oxyfluorides such as $XeOF_3$ and $XeOF_4$ have been prepared. XeF_2 is a stable white solid with a vapor pressure higher than that of XeF_4. XeF_2 is a linear molecule which reacts with additional fluorine to form XeF_4. XeF_6 results when a large excess of fluorine is used. It is a colorless solid with a vapor pressure slightly higher than that of XeF_4.

If XeF_4 or XeF_6 is added to water, not all of the available xenon escapes. The solution is very reactive, suggesting the presence

Fig. 9.3

Structures of the Xenon Fluorides. The nuclei in XeF_2 lie in a straight line. In XeF_4 all of the nuclei are in a plane with the xenon atom in the center. Four of the six fluorine atoms in XeF_6 are in the same plane as the xenon atom; the other two fluorine atoms are located directly above and below the xenon.

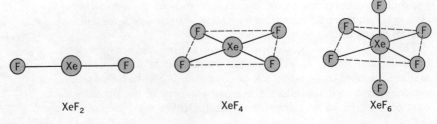

XeF_2 XeF_4 XeF_6

of $Xe(OH)_6$. Hydrogen reacts with all of the xenon fluorides to form xenon and HF.

Xenon trioxide (XeO_3) has been prepared and found to be explosive. It is thought that traces of XeO_3 in XeF_4 have accounted for the reports of explosive XeF_4.

Radon fluorides have been prepared under conditions similar to those used to prepare XeF_4. The product has a very low vapor pressure, and a temperature of 250°C is required to sublime it in a vacuum. Because of this and the radioactivity problem, radon fluoride has not been analyzed.

Krypton and fluorine react only in the presence of a source of energy such as an electric arc. The colorless crystals of KrF_4 are stable at −78°C for several days but are less stable than XeF_4 at room temperatures. KrF_2 has been reported, but it must be kept at −78°C. The rubidium hexafluoride of xenon is prepared in the same manner as $XePtF_6$. Neither RbF_6 nor PtF_6 react with krypton.

Uses

Helium is used extensively in filling weather balloons and the balloons used in space explorations. Although hydrogen has half the density, helium does not have the explosive danger. The welding industry uses large quantities as a protective atmosphere, particularly when working with very reactive elements. Helium rather than hydrogen, must be used in producing metals, such as titanium and vanadium, which absorb hydrogen. Divers frequently use a mixture of 80% helium–20% oxygen. Helium is irreplaceable in the laboratory to attain temperatures of the order of 1°K. It is very useful in a gas thermometer at low temperatures.

Neon is primarily used in gas discharge tubes commonly known as neon signs. The neon discharge produces the characteristic red light.

Argon is often used as a substitute for helium in protective atmospheres. It is used extensively in the filling of ordinary light

Fig. 9.4

Neil Bartlett, the British-born chemist who created the first noble gas compound. He is now at Princeton University.

bulbs. The presence of a gas in the bulb reduces the filament temperature, resulting in longer bulb life. The efficiencies of gases used in this way increase with molecular weight. Krypton and xenon would be most efficient but are too rare and expensive. Nitrogen is not suitable as a filling gas, because it reacts with the tungsten filament. Argon is sometimes used in "neon" lights to obtain special color effects.

Krypton and xenon have limited use in special electronic tubes. Krypton is also used for special effects in "neon" lights. Radon, being radioactive, finds use primarily in cancer treatment.

SIGNIFICANT TERMS AND CONCEPTS IN CHAPTER IX:

Relationship of structure and boiling point and melting point, physical properties, formation of noble gas compounds, uses of the noble gases.

Review questions

9.1. What is the characteristic outer shell electron configuration for the noble gases?

9.2. Write equations for the following:
   (a) The preparation of xenon tetrafluoride
   (b) The preparation of krypton difluoride
   (c) The formation of XeF_6 from XeF_4 and fluorine
   (d) The hydrolysis of xenon hexafluoride

9.3. Why is the preparation of HeF_4 not expected?

9.4. What is the density of argon at S.T.P.?

9.5. What was the percentage of argon in the atmospheric nitrogen samples used by Lord Rayleigh? Assume all of the excess weight is due to argon.

ten

the active metals

Metals are characterized by the ease with which they lose electrons and by their high thermal and electrical conductivity. The active metals are those elements with the most metallic properties. The most active metals are those of Group IA—lithium, sodium, potassium, rubidium, and cesium—the alkali metals. The Group IIA or alkaline earth metals—beryllium, magnesium, calcium, strontium, and barium—are the next most active group. The metallic character of each group increases with increasing atomic number. The chemistry of the alkali metals is the least complex of the metals in that almost all of their compounds involve the +1 ion. The alkaline earth metals are denser and harder than the corresponding alkali metals and are somewhat less active chemically. Covalent and ionic compounds of the alkaline earths are in the +2 oxidation state.

Discovery and occurrence

The salts of sodium, potassium, magnesium, and calcium are rather common and have been known for many years. Impure samples of elemental sodium, potassium, magnesium, calcium, strontium, and barium were prepared by Sir Humphry Davy in 1807–1808 using the then newly discovered voltaic pile to electrolyze fused (melted) salts of the elements. Davy used the same method to prepare lithium metal in 1817. Beryllium was prepared about ten years later in Germany. Cesium and rubidium were identified by their spectra in 1860 and 1861; they were the first elements to be identified spectroscopically. Radium, a radioactive product in the decay of uranium, was isolated from pitchblende by the Curies in 1898. Francium does not occur in nature and was not prepared until 1939.

All of these metals are found chemically combined in nature due to their reactivity. The common minerals containing these elements are given in Table 10.1. In addition, sea water contains enough magnesium ion to make recovery feasible. The minerals of the most important members of this group (sodium, potassium, magnesium, and calcium) are found throughout the world. Usable amounts of the other minerals occur rarely.

Preparation

Since the alkali metals react vigorously with oxygen and water vapor, procedures must be taken to provide a protective atmosphere during their preparation. Thus, it is not feasible to prepare any of these metals on a laboratory scale.

All of the alkali metals are prepared commercially by electrolysis of fused salts, usually the chloride. Mixed chlorides may be used to lower the melting point and operating temperature, as is the case when KCl is added to LiCl in the manufacture of lithium. Because few natural sources of the alkali metals are chloride salts, special techniques are required to convert the ore to chloride. Removal of interfering metal ions is necessary in many cases. For example, magnesium ions are precipitated as magnesium hydroxide from a solution of carnallite. The remaining solution is evaporated to form KOH which usually is used in the electrolysis cell.

Electrolysis and chemical reduction are used in the preparation of the alkaline earth metals. Once the beryllium salts are separated from the aluminum salts always found with beryllium ores, magnesium metal is added to a melt of $(NH_4)_2BeF_4$ to obtain beryllium metal. The beryllium occurs as small pellets inside a solid mass of MgF_2. The beryllium is removed, and the pellets are powdered and pressed into blocks under high pressure and temperature.

About 85 per cent of the world's magnesium is produced by electrolysis of a $MgCl_2$–fused salt melt. The remainder is produced by the reduction of magnesium oxide with silicon in the form of ferrosilicon, $Si(Fe)$. In general, sea water serves as the source of magnesium for the electrolytic processes, while dolomite is used in the chemical reduction. Sea water contains about 1300 parts per million Mg^{++} ion or roughly 12 billion pounds of magnesium per cubic mile. Since there are about 331 million cubic miles of ocean water on the earth, the quantity of available magnesium is considerable.

A slurry consisting of lime (CaO) and a small amount of lye $(NaOH)$ is added to large tanks of sea water in the first step of the recovery of magnesium. A precipitate of $Mg(OH)_2$ forms as a result of the relative solubilities of $Mg(OH)_2$ and $Ca(OH)_2$. Neither of the hydroxides is considered water soluble. However, the solubility of $Mg(OH)_2$ $(1.6 \times 10^{-4}$ moles/l$)$ is much less than that of $Ca(OH)_2$ $(2.5 \times 10^{-2}$ moles/l$)$. Thus Mg^{++} ions in solution precipitate in the presence of the OH^- ions from $Ca(OH)_2$ with the result that Ca^{++} ions go into solution as the precipitate forms. After $Mg(OH)_2$ is recovered by decantation and filtration, it is dissolved in HCl. A series of purification steps removes NaCl and $CaSO_4$ impurities, and the solution then is evaporated to recover $MgCl_2 \cdot 6H_2O$ crystals. Further heating to 450°C results

Fig. 10.1
Sir Humphry Davy

Fig. 10.2

Settling Basins. Sea water is mixed with lime and sodium hydroxide as it is pumped into these tanks. $Mg(OH)_2$ settles out. The tanks are about 500 feet in diameter.

in a solid corresponding to $MgCl_2 \cdot 1\frac{1}{2}H_2O$. This product is fed into the electrolysis cell where it is dissolved in a fused salt bath of NaCl, $MgCl_2$, and $CaCl_2$ at 700–720°C. At this temperature the remaining water is removed rapidly. During electrolysis, magnesium metal and chlorine gas are formed. The chlorine is converted to HCl and returned to the process.

In the ferrosilicon process, a mixture of MgO and CaO is formed by heating dolomite. This is mixed with ferrosilicon and formed into pellets. The pellets are heated to 1150°C in an electric furnace under reduced pressures. Magnesium vaporizes out of the pellets as the reaction proceeds and is condensed to provide a high purity (99.98%) product. CaO combines with SiO_2 to form a calcium silicate slag.

$$MgCO_3 \cdot CaCO_3 \xrightarrow{\Delta} MgO \cdot CaO + 2CO_2\uparrow$$
$$MgO \cdot CaO + FeSi \xrightarrow{\Delta} Mg\uparrow + \text{calcium and iron silicates}$$

The usual method of calcium preparation prior to World War II was the electrolysis of molten calcium chloride. The calcium deposit is removed from melt as fast as it is formed to prevent reaction with the container. The increased demands of the war brought the development of a reduction process using aluminum. Limestone is decomposed to calcium oxide by heating and is then reduced with aluminum. Calcium is distilled from the reaction mixture under a vacuum. Strontium and barium are produced by the same aluminum reduction method.

$$CaCO_3 \xrightarrow{\Delta} CaO + CO_2\uparrow$$
$$3CaO + 2Al \xrightarrow{\Delta} 3Ca\uparrow + Al_2O_3$$

Table 10.1
Some Minerals Containing the Active Metals

Metal	Mineral	Major deposits
Lithium	Lepidolite, $KLiAl(OHF)_2AlSi_3O_9$; Spodumene, $Li_2O \cdot Al_2O_3 \cdot 4SiO_2$	South Dakota
Sodium	Halite, common salt, $NaCl$ Chile saltpeter, $NaNO_3$ Cryolite, Na_3AlF_6	Salt mines and sea water Chile Greenland
Potassium	Sylvite, KCl	Utah, New Mexico, and Germany
	Carnallite, $KCl \cdot MgCl_2 \cdot 6H_2O$	New Mexico and Germany
	Feldspar, $KAlSi_3O_8$ Mica, $KH_2Al_3(SiO_4)_3$ among other compositions Orthoclase, $K_2Al_2Si_6O_{10}$	
Rubidium	Impurity in sodium and potassium minerals	
Cesium	Pollucite, $2Cs_2O \cdot 2Al_2O_3 \cdot 9SiO_3 \cdot H_2O$ Impurity in sodium and potassium minerals	South Dakota
Beryllium	Beryl, $Be_3Al_2(SiO_3)_6$ Bertrandite, $4BeO \cdot 2SiO_2$ Phenacite, Be_2SiO_4	Brazil, North Carolina Rocky Mountain region Rocky Mountain region
Magnesium	Dolomite, $MgCO_3 \cdot CaCO_3$ Carnallite, $KCl \cdot MgCl_2 \cdot 6H_2O$	New Mexico and Germany
	Magnesite, $MgCO_3$ Asbestos, $CaMg_3(SiO_3)_4$ Epsomite (Epsom salts) $MgSO_4 \cdot 7H_2O$ Periclase, MgO	England
Calcium	Marble, limestone, chalk, calcite, aragonite, Iceland spar, $CaCO_3$ Gypsum, Alabaster, $CaSO_4 \cdot 2H_2O$ Phosphate rock, $Ca_3(PO_4)_2$ Fluorspar, Fluorite, CaF_2	
Strontium	Strontianite, $SrCO_3$ Celestite, $SrSO_4$	
Barium	Witherite, $BaCO_3$ Barite, $BaSO_4$	

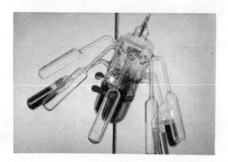

Fig. 10.3

Sample of Cesium Metal. Cesium must be kept under vacuum or in argon gas, as it burns rapidly when exposed to air and explodes when in contact with water.

Physical properties

The alkali metals are soft, low melting metals with relatively low densities. As is seen in Table 10.2, the densities increase with increasing atomic number as would be expected. Surprisingly, the melting point and boiling point trends are in the opposite direction. The low ionization potentials indicate that the single s electron is held loosely by the atom, with the attractive force between the nucleus and the outer electron decreasing with atomic size. This loosely held electron also accounts for the low density of the alkali metals. The electron gives the atom a large volume as can be appreciated from the comparison of atomic radii (with the outer s electron) and the ionic radii (without the outer s electron). This may account for the unexpected trend in melting and boiling points. For example, the large volume of the cesium atom may result in a reduction of the interaction of the electrons of one atom with the protons of the neighboring atom.

When freshly cut, the alkali metals have a silvery sheen that soon disappears as an oxide film (or nitride film in the case of

Table 10.2

Physical Properties of the Alkali Metals

	Density at 20°C (g/cc)	Melting point (°C)	Boiling point (°C)	First ionization potential (eV)	Atomic radius (Å)	Ionic radius (Å)
Li	0.53	181	1347	5.36	1.22	0.60
Na	0.97	98	883	5.12	1.57	0.95
K	0.86	64	764	4.32	2.02	1.33
Rb	1.53	39	679	4.16	2.16	1.48
Cs	1.87	29	690	3.87	2.35	1.69

Table 10.3
Physical Properties of the Alkaline Earths

	Density at 20°C (g/cc)	Melting point (°C)	Boiling point (°C)	First ionization potential (eV)	Atomic radius (Å)	Ionic radius* (Å)
Be	1.85	1283	2474	9.28	0.90	0.31
Mg	1.74	650	1105	7.61	1.36	0.65
Ca	1.55	851	1487	6.09	1.74	0.99
Sr	2.58	770	1384	5.67	1.91	1.13
Ba	3.60	710	1638	5.19	1.98	1.35

* The ionic radii are those for the +2 ion.

lithium) forms. This film forms even when the metals are stored under oil, due to the traces of moisture in the oil.

With the exception of beryllium, the physical properties of the alkaline earth metals, as shown in Table 10.3, are somewhat as expected. The alkaline earth metals also have a silvery metallic luster when freshly cut or prepared. Calcium, strontium, and barium form a coating of the oxide and nitride upon standing in air. Beryllium and magnesium quickly form a thin layer of the oxide that protects the metal against further attack by oxygen.

The ionization potentials indicate that the outer *s* electrons are more tightly held than those in the alkali metals. This tighter bonding results in smaller atoms and harder, more dense metals. A comparison of the values for calcium and potassium given in Table 10.4 is illustrative of this behavior.

Salts of the alkali metals and alkaline earths impart characteristic colors to a flame and provide a convenient method of identification. The energy levels for the electrons in these atoms are such that visible light is emitted by the electrons after they are excited in a flame. The following characteristic colors are observed: Lithium—red, sodium—intense yellow, potassium—pale violet, rubidium—dark red, cesium—sky blue, calcium—brick

Table 10.4
Comparison of Some Properties of Potassium and Calcium

	K	Ca
first ionization potential	4.32 eV	6.09 eV
atomic radius	2.02 Å	1.74 Å
density	0.86 g/cc	1.55 g/cc
Brinell hardness number*	0.037	42

* The Brinell number is the ratio of the load on the sphere (kg) to the area of the indentation made by the sphere (mm²).

red, strontium—crimson red, barium—green. Beryllium, magnesium, and cesium salts emit no visible light in a flame.

Chemical properties of the alkali metals

With the exception of a few lithium compounds, the alkali metals do not form covalent compounds. The alkali metals exist as the $+1$ ion in compounds, the result of the loss of the outer s electron.

In many ways lithium behaves more like an alkaline earth than an alkali metal. Some of these properties may be explained by the small size of the lithium ion.

The following summarizes the chemistry of the alkali metals.

(1) Reaction with oxygen (excess)

$$4Li + O_2 \rightarrow 2Li_2O$$

(very slow reaction below 100°C in dry O_2; cf. Mg)

$$2Na + O_2 \rightarrow Na_2O_2 \quad (Na_2O \text{ in limited } O_2)$$

$$M + O_2 \rightarrow MO_2 \ (M = K, Rb, Cs; O_2^- = superoxide)$$

The trend from oxide and peroxide to superoxide reflects the increasing activity of the alkali metals. Even in limited oxygen, K, Rb, and Cs readily form the peroxide. Characteristically, Li_2O_2 is very difficult to prepare. When the peroxides and superoxides are added to water, oxygen is liberated, and a basic solution is formed.

(2) Reaction with hydrogen

$$2M + H_2 \xrightarrow{\text{heat}} 2MH$$

All the alkali metals form ionic hydrides; the ease of formation and stability is greatest for Li and least for Cs. Hydrogen is formed when these hydrides are added to water. There is no doubt that hydrogen exists as H^- in the hydrides.

(3) Reaction with the halogens (Group VIIA)

$$2M + X_2 \rightarrow 2MX$$

This reaction proceeds vigorously for alkali metals and all of the halogens (represented by X). It is usually more practical to prepare them by the neutralization of the hydroxide with the hydrogen halide.

$$MOH + HX \rightarrow MX + H_2O$$

The properties of lithium halides parallel those of magnesium halides. Lithium fluoride is essentially insoluble in water. Other lithium halides are very hygroscopic, usually crystallizing as the dihydrate. The halides of the other alkali metals are water soluble and non-hygroscopic.

(4) Reaction with sulfur

$$2M + S \xrightarrow{\text{heat}} M_2S$$

It is necessary to heat the mixture to initiate the reaction. A slight excess of metal insures that M_2S is the only product. With excess sulfur, the polysulfides (e.g., M_2S_2) are formed. All of the monosulfides are hygroscopic and react with water to form H_2S.

(5) Reaction with nitrogen

$$6Li + N_2 \rightarrow 2Li_3N$$

Only lithium reacts with nitrogen to form the nitride, which reflects its chemical similarity to magnesium and calcium. It is possible to prepare the nitrides of the other metals indirectly. The nitrides are compounds with the N^{3+} ion present in the solid. Ammonia is formed upon the addition of water.

$$M_3N + 3H_2O \rightarrow 3MOH + NH_3$$

(6) Reaction with water

$$2M + 2H_2O \rightarrow 2MOH + H_2$$

The vigor with which the alkali metals react with water increases with increasing atomic number. Lithium liberates hydrogen at a moderate rate. Potassium liberates hydrogen at such a rate that the heat of the reaction almost always causes the hydrogen to ignite when the reaction is carried out in air. Rubidium and cesium react vigorously with traces of water.

Compounds of the alkali metals

Alkali metal hydroxides

Sodium and potassium hydroxides are common industrial chemicals. Sodium hydroxide is a product of the electrolysis of concentrated brine (NaCl) solutions which are readily available from sea water. Hydrogen and chlorine are the other products of the electrolysis. The NaOH concentrates at the bottom of the cell where it is drained off periodically and evaporated to dryness. Potassium hydroxide is produced commercially in the same manner using KCl. In the laboratory, the alkali hydroxides are prepared by exposure of the metal to water vapor with provision for the hydrogen to escape from the reaction vessel. Since the hydroxides are hygroscopic, the product is dehydrated by heating, although the monohydrate is very difficult to decompose. The alkali hydroxides readily react with CO_2 in the atmosphere to produce carbonates. Commercial NaOH or KOH contains five to ten per cent water and carbonate as a result of exposure to air during manufacture.

Solutions of the alkali hydroxides also absorb carbon dioxide from the air.

$$2OH^- + CO_2 \rightarrow CO_3^= + H_2O$$

When basic solutions are used for analysis, it is necessary to protect the solution from CO_2. The preparation of carbonate-free base is difficult, owing to the presence of CO_2 in water and absorbed CO_2 in the solid. Since Na_2CO_3 is insoluble in concentrated NaOH, a saturated solution of NaOH pellets is prepared. After the carbonate precipitate has settled and has been removed from this viscous solution, the purified NaOH solution is diluted with freshly boiled distilled water to make the desired concentration. Since none of the other alkali carbonates are insoluble in saturated hydroxide solutions, carbonate-free solutions of the hydroxides of the other alkali metals are prepared by reacting the metal with CO_2-free water.

Except for LiOH, the alkali metal hydroxides are stable upon heating. LiOH decomposes to Li_2O and H_2O when heated. LiOH is the least soluble of the group, reflecting its similarity to the alkaline earths.

Alkali metal carbonates

The carbonates may be prepared in the laboratory by exposure of the hydroxide to the atmosphere. A similar procedure is used commercially to prepare every alkali metal carbonate except Na_2CO_3. It is difficult to get exactly the right amount of CO_2 and hydroxide for the normal carbonate in either the production plant or the laboratory. The usual practice is to use a deficiency of CO_2; the resulting hydrogen carbonate impurity is decomposed with heat.

$$2MHCO_3 \xrightarrow{\Delta} M_2CO_3 + CO_2 + H_2O$$

Great quantities of sodium carbonate are produced annually by the *Solvay process* which is based on the limited solubility of sodium hydrogen carbonate in water. The process is economical in that brine and limestone are the only raw materials consumed in the reaction. The Solvay process consists of the following steps:

(a) Ammonia is passed into the brine solution until the solution is saturated. A slightly basic solution results.

$$NH_3 + H_2O \rightarrow NH_4^+ + OH^-$$

(b) Carbon dioxide, generated by heating limestone, is passed into the solution. The solubility of the CO_2 as the HCO_3^- ion, is enhanced by the presence of the weak base. If the solution were a strong base, $CO_3^=$ would result from the neutralization of the HCO_3^-.

$$CO_2 + OH^- \rightarrow HCO_3^-$$

(c) Due to the high concentration of HCO_3^-, the not too soluble $NaHCO_3$ precipitates. The $NaHCO_3$ is filtered, dried, and then heated to the point of decomposition.

$$2NaHCO_3 \xrightarrow{heat} Na_2CO_3 + CO_2\uparrow + H_2O$$

The CO_2 is returned to the process for further use.

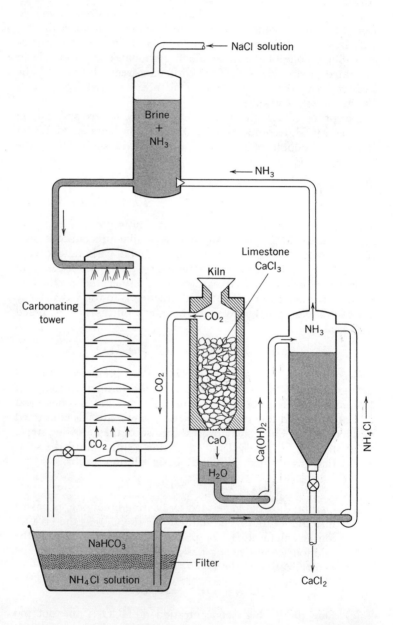

Fig. 10.4

The Solvay Process. In principle, only limestone and brine need to be added to the process which produces $NaHCO_3$ with $CaCl_2$ as a by-product. Ammonia is cycled through the reaction chambers; only operational losses need to be replaced.

(d) After the $NaHCO_3$ precipitates, the solution contains NH_4^+ and Cl^- ions. Boiling this solution with the lime (CaO), produced upon heating the limestone, regenerates ammonia.

$$2NH_4^+ + CaO \rightarrow Ca^{++} + H_2O + 2NH_3\uparrow$$

The ammonia, which is the most expensive part of the process, is continually regenerated for recycling in the reaction. The chloride salt of sodium is used because of the ready availability of brine.

The overall reaction for the Solvay process may be expressed as

$$2Na^+ + CaCO_3 \rightarrow Ca^{++} + Na_2CO_3$$

When sodium carbonate is precipitated from water, the decahydrate $Na_2CO_3 \cdot 10H_2O$ is formed. The decahydrate is known as washing soda, as it was once a common component of washing powders. Since the water vapor pressure of this hydrate is greater than the vapor pressure of water in the atmosphere, it decomposes to the heptahydrate which in turn loses water to form the anhydrous carbonate. Loss of water to the atmosphere is known as *efflorescence*.

$$Na_2CO_3 \cdot 10H_2O \rightarrow Na_2CO_3 \cdot 7H_2O + 3H_2O \rightarrow$$
$$Na_2CO_3 + 10H_2O$$

The hydrogen carbonate ion may behave as either an acid or a base.

$$HCO_3^- + H^+ \rightarrow H_2O + CO_2\uparrow$$
$$HCO_3^- + OH^- \rightarrow H_2O + CO_3^=$$

The first of these reactions has a practical application in cooking. Baking soda (or bicarbonate of soda) is added to an acid such as vinegar to produce a "light" bakery product.

All of the alkali metal carbonates except Li_2CO_3 are stable with heating. Li_2CO_3 decomposes to the oxide and CO_2, like the alkaline earth carbonates.

Chemical properties of the alkaline earths

The alkaline earths have a $+2$ oxidation state in all cases. The compounds of beryllium are covalent. Magnesium forms covalent and ionic compounds, while calcium, strontium, and barium form ionic compounds only. The latter three elements have a very similar chemistry. As is observed in almost all of the "A" groups of the periodic table, the first member is more like the next group chemically. This relationship is stronger for beryllium and aluminum than for lithium and magnesium.

The chemistries of beryllium and aluminum are almost identical. Since beryllium does not occur except in the presence of a large excess of aluminum silicates, it is difficult to effect a separation of pure beryllium compounds. Present techniques make use of the much greater solubility of $(NH_4)_2BeF_4$ over $(NH_4)_3AlF_6$ in water.

Beryllium salts uniformly crystallize from aqueous solution with four waters of hydration. The other alkaline earth ions are larger and have six water molecules associated with them. The bond between beryllium and the oxygen of the water molecules is quite strong. Heating the hydrates of beryllium salts yields beryllium oxide instead of the anhydrous salt. Heating magnesium salt hydrates produces a mixture of MgO and the anhydrous salt. All of the other alkaline earth salt hydrates form water vapor and the salt upon heating.

All of the metals react with acid to liberate hydrogen. In addition, beryllium reacts with concentrated base to form hydrogen and the beryllate ion $Be(OH)_4^=$.

The reactions of the alkaline earths are summarized below.
(1) Reaction with oxygen (excess)

$$2M + O_2 \xrightarrow{\text{heat}} 2MO$$

Beryllium must be powdered before it will form the oxide upon heating. Barium forms the peroxide (BaO_2) at reaction temperatures below 800°C. Beryllium and magnesium form a very thin (probably a few molecules thick) layer of oxide which protects the metal from further attack. None of the other oxides are protective. Beryllium oxide protection ends at about 850°C, when the layer of oxide begins to flake.

The oxides are characterized by their very high melting points: BeO, 2550°C; MgO, 2900°C; CaO, 2600°C; SrO, 2415°C; BaO, 1923°C. There are many high-temperature thermal and electrical insulating applications for MgO and BeO.
(2) Reaction with hydrogen

$$M + H_2 \xrightarrow{\text{heat}} MH_2 \ (M \neq Be, Mg)$$

Temperatures of 1000°C are required for BaH_2 formation, while calcium and strontium react with hydrogen at 300 to 400°C. These hydrides are ionic solids which characteristically liberate hydrogen when reacted with water.
(3) Reactions with the halogens

$$2M + X_2 \xrightarrow{\text{heat}} 2MX$$

This direct combination of the elements proceeds readily upon heating. The usual method of preparing the halides is to react the oxide with the hydrogen halide. It is necessary to use anhydrous oxide and halides to prepare the beryllium halides, since the hydrated halides decompose readily upon heating.

$$BeX_2 \cdot 4H_2O \xrightarrow{\Delta} BeO + 2HX + 3H_2O$$

The beryllium halides are covalent compounds with relatively low melting points as can be seen in Table 10.5. The magnesium

Table 10.5

Melting Points of the Alkaline Earth Halides (°C)

BeF_2	542	MgF_2	1263	CaF_2	1418	SrF_2	1400	BaF_2	1320
$BeCl_2$	400	$MgCl_2$	714	$CaCl_2$	782	$SrCl_2$	872	$BaCl_2$	960
$BeBr_2$	488	$MgBr_2$	711	$CaBr_2$	760	$SrBr_2$	653	$BaBr_2$	847
BeI_2	480	MgI_2	650	CaI_2	740	SrI_2	515	BaI_2	711

halides have some covalent character, while the rest of the halides are ionic. Fused beryllium halides are not conductors of electricity, a fact which gives further proof of their covalent character.

With the exception of BeF_2, all of the fluorides are rather insoluble in water; all other halides are very water soluble.

Calcium chloride has a great affinity for water and is valuable as an inexpensive desiccant (drying agent). It readily forms a low freezing point solution with water which makes it useful for melting ice on streets and highways.

(4) Reactions with sulfur

$$M + S \rightarrow MS$$

With the exception of covalent BeS, the sulfides react with water to form HS^-, H_2S, and OH^-.

$$S^= + H_2O \rightarrow HS^- + OH^-$$
$$HS^- + H_2O \rightarrow H_2S + OH^-$$

(5) Reactions with nitrogen

$$3M + N_2 \xrightarrow{\Delta} M_3N_2$$

All of the alkaline earths react readily with nitrogen when heated. When the metals are burned in air, some nitride is formed along with the oxide. Appreciable amounts of Mg_3N_2 form when a magnesium ribbon is burned. Lesser amounts of Ba_3N_2 form when barium is burned in air. All of the nitrides are ionic and typically decompose to NH_3 and hydroxides when placed in water.

(6) Reactions with water

$$M + 2H_2O \rightarrow M(OH)_2 + H_2\uparrow \quad (M \neq Be)$$

Barium, strontium, and calcium react with cold water with decreasing vigor. Magnesium must be heated before it will react with steam. Beryllium is stable even in superheated steam.

Compounds of the alkaline earths

Alkaline earth hydroxides

These hydroxides are prepared best by hydrating the oxide. Neither the oxides nor the hydroxides are very soluble in water, and the hydration process is relatively slow. Solubility increases as the metal ion size increases (Table 10.6).

With exception of $Be(OH)_2$, the hydroxides are strong bases within the limits of their solubility. $Ba(OH)_2$ is the only hydroxide that is sufficiently soluble for making standard base solutions. Such solutions have the additional advantage that any $BaCO_3$ formed immediately precipitates.

Table 10.6

Solubilities of
Alkaline Earth Hydroxides
at 20°C (moles per liter)

$Be(OH)_2$	5×10^{-9}
$Mg(OH)_2$	3×10^{-4}
$Ca(OH)_2$	2.2×10^{-2}
$Sr(OH)_2$	6.5×10^{-2}
$Ba(OH)_2$	2.2×10^{-1}

All of the hydroxides decompose to oxides and water upon heating. $Ba(OH)_2$ is the only member of the group that is stable to the melting point.

Beryllium hydroxide is amphoteric. It dissolves in acids, and also forms the beryllate ion in concentrated strong base.

$$Be(OH)_2 + 2H^+ \rightarrow Be^{++} + 2H_2O$$
$$Be(OH)_2 + 2OH^- \rightarrow Be(OH)_4^=$$

Alkaline earth carbonates

The Group IIA carbonates are insoluble in water, and as a result $MgCO_3$ and $CaCO_3$ are commonly found in nature. Calcium carbonate is very widespread in many physical forms such as limestone, chalk, and marble. All of these carbonates decompose upon heating to form oxides and CO_2. Beryllium carbonate is stable only when kept in an atmosphere of CO_2.

The carbonates dissolve in water that is saturated with CO_2 with the formation of the soluble hydrogen carbonate.

$$MgCO_3 + CO_2 + H_2O \rightarrow Mg^{++} + 2HCO_3^-$$

Rainwater seeping through the earth slowly dissolves $MgCO_3$ and $CaCO_3$ deposits to create caves and to form temporary hard water. As with any carbonate, CO_2 is evolved when acid reacts with the Group IIA carbonates.

Limestone ($CaCO_3$) is a very important mineral. It is a valuable industrial source of CO_2 which is obtained by strong heating.

$$CaCO_3 \xrightarrow{heat} CaO + CO_2\uparrow$$

Lime (CaO) is widely used. When lime is added to water, calcium hydroxide forms in a process known as *slaking*. In the building industry lime is used in plaster, cement, and mortar. A thick paste of sand, water, and lime (or slaked lime) is allowed to set or harden as the water evaporates and the hydroxide is deposited. A second and much slower hardening stage is the result of absorption of CO_2 from the air to form the carbonate.

$$Ca(OH)_2 + CO_2 \rightarrow CaCO_3 + H_2O$$

If this stage is made to proceed very slowly by keeping the material moist, large crystals are formed. A very slow third stage is the formation of a network of calcium silicate structures in the solid.

A sensitive test for the presence of CO_2 involves the use of lime water (a dilute solution of $Ca(OH)_2$ prepared from CaO) to form a $CaCO_3$ precipitate.

Alkaline earth sulfates

Magnesium sulfate is best known in the form of Epsom salts, $MgSO_4 \cdot 7H_2O$. The anhydrous sulfate cannot be prepared, since a mixture of oxide and sulfate is formed upon heating. When gypsum, $CaSO_4 \cdot 2H_2O$, is heated, the hemihydrate is formed.

$$2CaSO_4 \cdot 2H_2O \rightleftarrows (CaSO_4)_2 \cdot H_2O + H_2O$$

The hemihydrate is known more familiarly as plaster of Paris. When water is added to plaster of Paris, the above reaction is reversed and a mass of gypsum crystals is formed. If $CaSO_4 \cdot 2H_2O$ is heated above 300°C, the resulting anhydrous sulfate reacts very slowly with water. If the dehydration is carried out between 120 and 300°C, the resulting $CaSO_4$ readily reforms the hydrate in the presence of water vapor. This product is used extensively as a desiccant under the trade name, "Drierite." It is much more efficient as a desiccant than $CaCl_2$. Heating the dihydrate to temperatures below 120°C results only in hemihydrate formation.

The solubility of the Group IIA sulfates in water decreases from the quite soluble $BeSO_4$ and $MgSO_4$ to the very insoluble $BaSO_4$. Because of its low solubility, $BaSO_4$ is used as a means of determining the amount of sulfate in a solution quantitatively. By adding sufficient Ba^{++} ion, it is possible to precipitate all but an insignificant amount of the sulfate from a solution.

Uses of the alkaline earth metals

Beryllium and magnesium are often used when lightweight structural materials are required. The fabrication of magnesium and magnesium alloy frames and panels is quite routine. The manufacturing and fabricating processes for beryllium have not been developed to the point where ductile, non-brittle beryllium metal parts can be made on a large scale. Despite the problems of high temperature protection of the surface and of its high toxicity, beryllium fabrication will be improved, because this metal has the lowest density of any metal that can be fabricated. Beryllium metal now is used extensively in nuclear reactors as a neutron reflector or moderator. The other metals have limited commercial use as metals. Calcium salts are widely used. Barium salts have some use, while strontium salts have very limited commercial value.

Hard water

Hard water contains dissolved magnesium or calcium ions. Hard water is objectionable, since these ions react with soaps to form insoluble magnesium or calcium salts. The precipitate is difficult to remove and is a waste of soap. Another objection is the fact that hard water forms scales composed of calcium carbonate, the "insoluble" form of calcium sulfate, and basic magnesium salts, on boilers.

Hardness in water may be classified into two types, temporary and permanent, depending upon the anion present. Temporary hardness is due to the presence of the hydrogen carbonate ion and is removed by heating.

$$Ca(HCO_3)_2 \xrightarrow{\Delta} CaCO_3\downarrow + CO_2\uparrow + H_2O$$

It is also possible to remove temporary hardness on a large scale by adding lime equivalent to the HCO_3^- ions present and sodium carbonate equivalent to the Mg^{++} and Ca^{++} ions present, as these equations show.

$$CaO + H_2O \rightarrow Ca^{++} + 2OH^-$$
$$HCO_3^- + Ca^{++} + OH^- \rightarrow CaCO_3\downarrow + H_2O$$

Permanent hard water consists of the sulfates and chlorides of magnesium and calcium and is removed or softened by slow filtration through zeolite, a hydrated sodium aluminum silicate. The sodium ion of the zeolite is replaced by the calcium, magnesium, or other $+2$ ions.

$$2NaH_6AlSiO_7 + Ca^{++} \rightleftarrows Ca(H_6AlSiO_7)_2 + 2Na^+$$

Eventually most of the sodium ions are replaced, and the efficiency of the ion exchange is reduced. The zeolite is regenerated by passing a concentrated sodium chloride solution through the column which reverses the reaction. Many problems of soap in hard water have been overcome by the use of detergents, which do not produce precipitates with calcium or magnesium ions.

SIGNIFICANT TERMS AND CONCEPTS IN CHAPTER X:
Preparation, physical properties, chemical properties, the similarity of lithium and magnesium, the similarity of beryllium and aluminum, properties of the hydroxides, carbonates, and alkaline earth sulfates, removal of hardness from water.

Review questions

10.1. Give three chemical reactions in which lithium exhibits properties that are more similar to those of magnesium than to those of sodium.

10.2. Compare the products of the reactions of potassium and calcium with oxygen, sulfur, nitrogen, water, chlorine, and hydrogen.

10.3. Compare the behavior of $NaOH$ and $Mg(OH)_2$ when heated and when exposed to CO_2.

10.4. Compare the behavior of Na_2CO_3 and $CaCO_3$ when heated and when HCl is added.

10.5. Give two reactions that distinguish between beryllium and magnesium metal.

10.6. Give a test that distinguishes between each of the following pairs of substances. Give the equation for the reaction (if any) as well as the predicted observation.

(a) K_2CO_3 and Mg_2CO_3 (d) Na_2CO_3 and $BaCO_3$
(b) BeO and MgO (e) Na_2S and Na_2SO_4
(c) $BaCl_2$ and $MgCl_2$ (f) $NaHCO_3$ and Na_2CO_3
   answer: (a) Heat both compounds.

$MgCO_3$ gives off CO_2. $MgCO_3 \xrightarrow{\Delta} MgO + CO_2$

K_2CO_3 is stable. $K_2CO_3 \xrightarrow{\Delta} N.R.$

10.7. Give equations for the following.
(a) Preparation of beryllium metal from $(NH_4)_2BeF_4$
(b) Preparation of H_2S from sulfur, calcium, and water
(c) Preparation of NH_3 from lithium, air, and water
(d) Preparation of a small amount of solid Na_2CO_3 from sodium, air, and water
(e) Preparation of a $KHCO_3$ solution from K_2CO_3 and other common reagents

10.8. Compare the method of softening temporary hard water with that for permanent hard water.

chemical equilibrium

In this chapter we consider two topics basic to the quantitative study of a chemical reaction. Chemical equilibrium deals with how far a reaction proceeds with no reference as to how long it will take. Chemical kinetics deals with how a reaction proceeds and how long it takes for a given amount of material to react.

Chemical kinetics

A chemical reaction proceeds as the result of the collisions of molecules, atoms, or ions. Most reactions do not proceed directly by collisions of the species written in the overall chemical equation; rather they proceed by a series of intermediate steps involving intermediate species. It is found that the *rate of a chemical reaction* (the amount of product produced per unit of time) usually increases with an increase in the concentration of the reactants. The exact relationship between the overall reaction rate, which reflects the rates of the intermediate steps, and the reactant concentrations must be determined experimentally.

Rate equations

The rate of reaction for each step may be expressed as a simple rate equation. The rate at which the simple reaction step

$$A + B \rightarrow product$$

proceeds depends upon the concentration of A and B, since at higher concentrations the number of collisions between molecules of A and molecules of B are increased. The rate equation for this step is

rate of loss of A = rate of loss of B
$$= \text{rate of formation of product} = k[A][B]$$

The brackets indicate that the concentrations of A and B are to be expressed in moles per liter, and k is a proportionality constant known as the specific rate constant.

The series of reaction steps that make up the overall reaction constitute the mechanism of the reaction. The overall reaction rate is measured experimentally. Then a series of possible reaction steps are postulated so that the combination of the simple rate equations yields the overall rate equation. The choice of reaction steps is seldom unique. Certain possibilities can be eliminated by varying the concentration of reactants. It is possible to identify an intermediate species in some reactions. This is a great aid in selecting the correct mechanism.

The reaction of hydrogen and iodine to form hydrogen iodide is an example of a simple reaction mechanism. Experimentally, the rate of the reaction

$$H_2 + I_2 \rightarrow 2HI$$

is found to be

rate of HI formation = $k[H_2][I_2]$

During the first step of one proposed mechanism, I_2 molecules dissociate into atoms which then react with the H_2 molecules to form HI.

$$I_2 \rightarrow 2I$$
$$2I + H_2 \rightarrow 2HI$$

The rate of the second step depends upon the concentration of I atoms which in turn depends upon the I_2 concentration. Therefore, the rate of formation of HI in the second step depends upon the concentration of I_2 and H_2 in the system.

A comparison of the reaction of H_2 and I_2 with that of H_2 and Br_2 illustrates the need for experimental studies. The observed rate equation is much more complex for HBr than for HI.

$$\text{rate of HBr formation} = \frac{k[H_2][Br_2]^{1/2}}{1 + \dfrac{k'[HBr]}{[Br_2]}}$$

The following set of reaction steps are consistent with the observed behavior of the reaction.

$$Br_2 \rightarrow 2Br$$
$$Br + H_2 \rightarrow HBr + H$$
$$H + Br_2 \rightarrow HBr + Br$$
$$H + HBr \rightarrow H_2 + Br$$
$$Br + Br \rightarrow Br_2$$

Alternative steps may be proposed that lead to the same rate equation.

Energy relationships

Not every collision results in a chemical reaction, since the species involved must have sufficient energy to break and re-form bonds. The minimum energy which the colliding species must have for a reaction to take place is called the *activation energy*. The species that come together form a grouping called an activated complex. If there is sufficient energy in the complex, it may break apart as the product species. If it does not have sufficient energy, the complex breaks apart into the reactant species. The mean lifetime of the activated complex is estimated to be 10^{-14} seconds or less.

When the energy of the products is less than that of the reactants, the system should go spontaneously to the lower energy state. This is found to occur for few reactions. For example, no water molecules are formed if a mixture of hydrogen and oxygen gas is allowed to stand at room temperature for an exceedingly long time (it would be only slightly incorrect to say "forever"), although water is a much more stable combination of hydrogen and oxygen than is the gaseous mixture. If some energy, such as a spark or flame, is introduced into the mixture, the reaction pro-

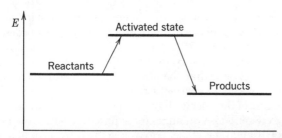

Fig. 11.1

Energy Relationships During a Chemical Reaction. If the reactant species come together with sufficient energy to reach the activated state, product molecules may be formed by bond rearrangement. Diagram shows an exothermic reaction in which the products are more stable than the reactants. Energy released by the formation of products keeps the reaction going. In an endothermic reaction energy must be supplied to keep the reaction going, as the products are less stable than the reactants.

ceeds at an explosive rate. This behavior is explained by a consideration of the activated state and activation energy. Before the introduction of the energy, the H_2 and O_2 molecules do not have sufficient energy to reach the activated state for at least one of the steps in the reaction. The flame or spark supplies the necessary energy to a few of the molecules which then react. Since the product molecule is so stable, much energy is given off at its formation, usually as kinetic energy to the water molecules. This energy is transferred by collisions to other H_2 and O_2 molecules which then have sufficient energy to react. The process proceeds very rapidly once sufficient energy has been introduced to overcome the initial activation energy barrier.

It is possible to increase the rate of some chemical reactions by the addition of a *catalyst*, a substance which changes the rate of a chemical reaction but is not consumed by it. Usually it is desirable for the rate of the reaction to be increased, although it is necessary to slow some reactions with negative catalysts or *inhibitors*. Catalysts are classified as homogeneous and heterogeneous. A *homogeneous catalyst* is a substance that is introduced into the reaction mixture and is in the same phase. Acids are typical examples of homogeneous catalysts in that many reactions in solution proceed more rapidly in the presence of hydrogen ions. A *heterogeneous catalyst* is a substance that is some phase other than that of the reaction mixture. Solids very frequently are used as heterogeneous catalysts for gaseous reactions, apparently serving as a site for the reaction to occur. The mechanism of catalytic action is not well understood, although it is thought that the catalyst provides a reaction pathway which requires a lower activation energy.

It is observed that the rate for many reactions is roughly doubled for every ten-degree rise in temperature. An increase of ten per cent in the rate can be attributed to the increase in collision frequency due to the increased velocity of the reacting species.

The increase in the average kinetic energy accounts for an additional ten to fifteen per cent increase in the rate. In order to account for the remaining 75 to 80 per cent of the observed reaction rate increase, it is necessary to recall that not all molecules have the same energy and that the absolute temperature is a measure of the average kinetic energy of the molecules (Fig. 3.4). Only a small fraction of the species have sufficiently high kinetic energy to undergo reaction. With an increase in temperature the number of species with high kinetic energy is increased by a small amount. However, this corresponds to a large percentage increase in the number of energetically reactive species. For example, 0.001% of the molecules may have sufficient kinetic energy to pass through the activated state at 25°C. This percentage need be increased only to 0.002% at 35°C to have twice as many molecules passing through the activated state. A great deal fewer than 0.001% of the molecules in most reactions have sufficient kinetic energy to react. Therefore, even fewer molecules need to be excited for the 100% increase in the number of energetically available molecules.

Chemical equilibria

A discussion of chemical equilibria cannot be undertaken completely apart from consideration of the chemical equation (Chapter IV). A study of chemical equilibrium tells how much product is obtained from a given amount of reactants. There need not be 100 per cent conversion of reactants into products. There are many reactions which never reach this degree of completion before the reaction apparently stops. The chemical equation shows the molar ratio, or *stoichiometry*, for the number of moles that do undergo reaction.

Up to this point in our discussion, each step of a reaction has been considered as proceeding in only one direction. It is also possible for the product species to collide with sufficient energy to reach the activated state and to return to reactants. This is the reverse reaction. The probability of the reverse reaction taking place increases as the concentration of product molecules increases.

Concepts of chemical equilibrium are demonstrated by the simple reaction of hydrogen gas and iodine vapor to form hydrogen iodide gas.

$$H_2 + I_2 \rightarrow 2HI$$

The rate of this forward reaction r_f is

$$r_f = k_f[H_2][I_2],$$

where k_f is the specific rate constant for the forward reaction, $[H_2]$ is the concentration of hydrogen in moles per liter, and $[I_2]$ is the concentration of I_2 molecules in moles per liter.

A sample of hydrogen iodide is found to decompose to the elements in a reverse reaction.

$$2HI \rightarrow H_2 + I_2$$

The rate of this reverse reaction r_r is

$$r_r = k_r \, [HI][HI] = k_r \, [HI]^2,$$

where k_r is the specific rate constant for the reverse reaction.

If one mixes hydrogen and iodine in a container, there is no reverse reaction initially, since $[HI] = 0$. As the reaction proceeds, the forward reaction rate r_f decreases as H_2 and I_2 are consumed and the concentration of these molecules is reduced (Fig. 11.2). At the same time, the concentration of HI molecules is increasing because of the forward reaction. As HI is formed, the rate of the reverse reaction r_r increases due to the increase in the concentration of HI. The rate of decomposition of HI continues to increase, until the rate of decomposition is equal to the rate of formation. Since HI is being formed by the forward reaction as fast as it is being consumed, the concentration of HI remains constant. Similarly, the concentrations of H_2 and I_2 in the system are constant.

A system is in a state of *chemical equilibrium* when the rate of the forward reaction is equal to the rate of the reverse reaction.

$$r_f = r_r$$

In the case of the formation of HI

$$k_f[H_2]_{eq}[I_2]_{eq} = k_r[HI]^2_{eq}, \qquad (11.1)$$

where the subscript eq indicates equilibrium concentrations. Rearranging equation 11.1 yields

$$\frac{k_f}{k_r} = \frac{[HI]^2_{eq}}{[H_2]_{eq}[I_2]_{eq}} \qquad (11.2)$$

Since k_f and k_r are specific rate constants for the reaction and are independent of concentrations, the left-hand side of equation 11.2 is a constant K_{eq} called the equilibrium constant.

Fig. 11.2

Reaction Rates As a Function of Time. The forward rate of the reaction drops as reactants are consumed; the reverse rate increases as products are formed. When the rates become equal, the system is at equilibrium. After this point no change in rates or concentrations occurs.

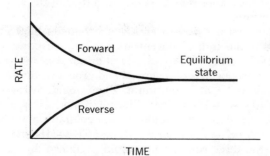

$$K_{eq} = \frac{k_f}{k_r} = \frac{[HI]^2_{eq}}{[H_2]_{eq}[I_2]_{eq}} \qquad (11.3)$$

Equilibrium constant

It is found that (11.3) is applicable to all equilibrium reactions. In other words, the equilibrium constant K_{eq} is applicable to any system where the rate of the forward reaction is equal to the rate of the reverse reaction and is independent of the reaction kinetics. Thus for the general reaction

$$aA + bB \rightleftarrows gG + hH$$

the equilibrium constant expression is

$$K_{eq} = \frac{[G]^g[H]^h}{[A]^a[B]^b}, \qquad (11.4)$$

where the concentrations of all species are the molar concentrations at equilibrium although the *eq* subscripts are not indicated. Note that the coefficients in the chemical equation appear as the power of the molar concentrations in the equilibrium constant expression. The brackets indicate concentrations in moles per liter. (11.4) is basic to a study of equilibrium. There are many specialized applications which modify this fundamental expression, but all are based upon it.

Tests for equilibrium

The fundamental criterion for determining whether a system is at equilibrium is that the forward reaction rate equal the reverse reaction rate. Certain tests may be applied to determine if a reaction is at equilibrium.

One test is that the concentrations of all species in the system do not vary. If the concentrations are not constant with time, the system cannot be at equilibrium. However, invariance of concentration does not assure that the system is at equilibrium. The rate of reaction may be so slow that concentration changes are not observed. For example, the concentrations in a container of H_2, O_2, and water vapor remain constant, although the system is not at equilibrium.

A second test is the invariance of the value of the equilibrium constant, if the initial concentration of the reacting species is varied. If the same value of the equilibrium constant is attained for several proportions of reactants and products, the systems are considered to be at equilibrium. One would discover that a H_2-O_2-H_2O system is not at equilibrium if more H_2 is added. The new concentration of H_2 would remain constant, and a different value would be obtained for K_{eq}. In the H_2-I_2-HI system various ratios of the three components would be mixed and allowed to react. The concentration of each component would be measured after no variance is observed in the concentrations. These values would be used to calculate K_{eq}. If the same value of K_{eq} is obtained for all ratios, this is the equilibrium constant value at the temperature of the reaction. Thus, any mixture of H_2, I_2, and HI which yields that value of K_{eq} is at equilibrium.

Factors affecting chemical equilibrium

The value of the equilibrium constant K_{eq} changes *only* with temperature. However, other factors may change the position of the equilibrium. The direction of this equilibrium shift can be predicted from LeChatelier's Principle which states that if a stress is applied to a system at equilibrium, the equilibrium concentrations change in such a way as to relieve that stress.

One stress that can be placed upon a system at equilibrium is the addition or removal of a component of the system. The addition of one component shifts the equilibrium toward formation of components on the other side of equation. Conversely, the removal of a component shifts the equilibrium in the direction of producing more of that component. For example, if Cl_2 gas is added to a container where the equilibrium

$$\text{Heat} + PCl_5 \rightleftarrows PCl_3 + Cl_2$$

exists, the reverse reaction rate increases due to the increase in Cl_2 concentration. PCl_3 is consumed as more PCl_5 is formed. The result is that the equilibrium is shifted toward more PCl_5, while the equilibrium remains constant.

This principle finds application in the preparation of ammonia by the reaction

$$N_2 + 3H_2 \rightleftarrows 2NH_3$$

For temperatures at which the rate of ammonia formation is appreciable, the equilibrium constant is rather small. The reaction is made commercially feasible by constantly removing ammonia, while unreacted nitrogen and hydrogen are recycled for further reaction.

Another stress that can be applied to an equilibrium system is pressure. The effect on reactions in solid or liquid phases is slight, but gas phase reactions are very sensitive to pressure changes. An increase in the pressure on a gas results in a decrease of the volume. The smaller volume favors a decrease in the number of molecules in the system. Thus, a pressure increase which is accompanied by a decrease in volume causes the equilibrium to shift in the direction of the fewer number of moles. In the decomposition of PCl_5 a pressure increase favors PCl_5 formation, since one mole of PCl_5 is formed from two moles of product. The formation of ammonia is favored by a pressure increase, since there are two moles of product against four moles of reactants. It should be noted that the concentration of all molecules increases when there is a volume decrease resulting from a pressure increase, although the concentration of the favored species increases more than that of the other molecules.

The pressure in a container may be increased by the addition of a gas while the volume remains constant. If the gas does not enter into the reaction and can be considered inert, the addition has no effect on the equilibrium. If the gas is a product or reactant, this has the same effect as an increase in concentration.

Table 11.1

Thermal Dissociation of Iodine at $2000°K*$ $I_2(g) \rightleftarrows 2I(g)$

Total pressure =	1 atm	2 atm	10 atm
I	1.5×10^{-4} M	2.4×10^{-4} M	6.4×10^{-4} M
I_2	1.0×10^{-4}	2.6×10^{-4}	18.6×10^{-4}
K_{eq}	2.2×10^{-4}	2.2×10^{-4}	2.2×10^{-4}

* The effect of pressure on the equilibrium constant and on the concentrations of atoms and molecules is readily seen in this Table. An application of LeChatelier's Principle predicts a shift toward more I_2 molecules as the pressure is increased. An increase in pressure from one to two atmospheres results in a 60 per cent increase in the concentration of the atoms compared to a 160 per cent increase in the molecular concentration. With a tenfold increase in pressure, atomic concentration is increased by a factor of four; the favored molecular concentration is increased by a factor of almost 19. The value of the equilibrium constant is the same at all pressures.

Heat may be considered as a component of the system when predicting the effects of temperature changes on an equilibrium. A temperature increase is the result of adding heat to the system. If the reaction is exothermic (produces heat), a temperature increase favors the formation of more reactants. The formation of products is favored in an endothermic reaction following a rise in temperature. The value of the equilibrium constant as well as the position of equilibrium changes with a change in temperature. If the formation of products is favored by the temperature change, the value of the equilibrium constant is increased. Similarly, the value of K_{eq} is decreased when the reactants are favored by the temperature change. Additional data are needed to determine the magnitude of the change quantitatively. Consider the dissociation of I_2 molecule, which is an endothermic reaction.

$$heat + I_2 \rightleftarrows 2I$$

An increase in temperature shifts the equilibrium toward I atoms. Since $K_{eq} = \dfrac{[I]^2}{[I_2]}$, an increase in the value of $[I]$ and a decrease in the value of $[I_2]$ results in a larger value of K_{eq}.

Example 11.1 Hydrogen iodide is 11.5% dissociated to H_2 and I_2 at 125°C and 69% dissociated at 225°C. The concentration of HI at a pressure of 1 atmosphere is 0.030 mole per liter at 125°C and 0.024 mole per liter at 225°C.

(a) Predict whether the value of K_{eq} increases or decreases in going from 125°C to 225°C if the reaction is

$$\text{heat} + 2HI \rightleftharpoons H_2 + I_2$$

Since heat appears as a reactant in this equation, the addition of heat causes a shift to form more H_2 and I_2. This conclusion is borne out by the increase in the percentage dissociation. Since $K_{eq} = [H_2][I_2]/[HI]^2$, an increase in the concentration of H_2 and I_2 and a decrease in the HI concentration results in a larger value for K_{eq}.

(b) Calculate K_{eq} at both temperatures at a pressure of 1 atm. Compare results with the prediction made in part (a).

Initial concentration at 125°C: [HI] = 0.030 moles per liter

$$[H_2] = [I_2] = 0$$

$$\text{amount of HI decomposed} = (0.030)(11.5\%)$$
$$= 3.45 \times 10^{-3} \text{ moles/liter}$$

$$\text{amount of } H_2 \text{ formed} = \text{amount of } I_2 \text{ formed}$$
$$= (3.45 \times 10^{-3} \text{ moles HI/liter})\left(\frac{1 \text{ mole } H_2}{2 \text{ moles HI}}\right)$$
$$= 1.72 \times 10^{-3} \text{ moles/liter}$$

Equilibrium concentrations:

$$[HI] = 0.030 - 0.003 = 0.027 \ M$$
$$[H_2] = [I_2] = 0 + 0.00345 = 0.0034 \ M$$
$$K_{eq} = \frac{[H_2][I_2]}{[HI]^2} = \frac{(3.4 \times 10^{-3})^2}{(2.7 \times 10^{-2})^2} = 1.6 \times 10^{-2}$$

Initial concentrations at 225°C: [HI] = 0.024 mole/liter

$$[H_2] = [I_2] = 0$$

$$\text{amount of HI decomposed} = (0.024)(69\%) = 0.017 \text{ mole/liter}$$

$$\text{amount of } H_2 \text{ formed} = \text{amount of } I_2 \text{ formed}$$
$$= \left(1.7 \times 10^{-2} \ \frac{\text{mole}}{\text{liter}}\right)\left(\frac{1 \text{ mole } H_2}{2 \text{ mole HI}}\right)$$
$$= 8.5 \times 10^{-3} \text{ mole/liter}$$

Equiilbrium concentrations:

$$[HI] = 0.024 - 0.017 = 0.007 \ M$$
$$[H_2] = [I_2] = 0 + (8.5 \times 10^{-3}) = 0.0085$$
$$K_{eq} = \frac{[H_2][I_2]}{[HI]^2} = \frac{(8.5 \times 10^{-3})^2}{(7 \times 10^{-3})^2} = 1.5$$

It is predicted in part (a) that the value of K_{eq} increases with an increase in temperature. These calculations show that the value of K_{eq} increases from 0.016 at 125°C to 1.5 at 225°C.

Molecular equilibria

In discussing an equilibrium reaction there is no real distinction to be made between product and reactant molecules, since equilibrium is attained in either case. In some reactions it is possible to designate reactants and products by standard conventions. In the case of equilibria involving molecular species it is not possible to provide such a convention. Thus, it is necessary to indicate the chemical equation for which the equilibrium constant is evaluated. In making calculations involving the equilibrium constants the final answer is not affected by the form of the constant as long as all computations are made using the value of K_{eq} associated with the given equation. The H_2-I_2-HI equilibrium provides an example of the various ways of expressing the reaction and the corresponding equilibrium constants.

(a) $H_2 + I_2 \rightleftarrows 2HI$ $K_{eq} = \dfrac{[HI]^2}{[H_2][I_2]}$

(b) $2HI \rightleftarrows H_2 + I_2$ $K_{eq} = \dfrac{[H_2][I_2]}{[HI]^2} = $ reciprocal of K_{eq} in (a)

(c) $HI \rightleftarrows 1/2H_2 + 1/2I_2$

$$K_{eq} = \frac{[H_2]^{1/2}[I_2]^{1/2}}{[HI]} = \text{square root of } K_{eq} \text{ in (b)}$$

It cannot be emphasized too strongly that the magnitude of the equilibrium constant is no indication of how long it takes a reaction to reach equilibrium. A large value for K_{eq} indicates that the product side of the equation is favored; a small value for K_{eq} indicates that the reactant side of the equation is favored by the reaction. Reactions for which the value of K_{eq} is very large are said to go to completion. Reactions that do not proceed, such as the decomposition of I_2 into atoms at room temperature, can be treated as having equilibrium constants of almost zero, reflecting the near-zero concentration of products.

Experimental techniques for the study of equilibrium reactions are such that it is more convenient to measure the concentration of the substances placed into a reaction vessel and the concentration of one component at equilibrium. The equilibrium concentrations of the other substances are calculated using the chemical equation. Once the equilibrium constant is determined for a reaction, the equilibrium concentrations can be calculated if the initial concentrations are known.

Example 11.2 Four moles of N_2, 0.50 mole of H_2, and 4.0 moles of NH_3 are placed in a 5.0 liter container. At equilibrium 1.0 mole NH_3 remains. Calculate (a) the amount of N_2 and H_2 at equilibrium, (b) the equilibrium molar concentrations of N_2, H_2, and NH_3, and (c) the equilibrium constant at this temperature for the reaction $N_2 + 3H_2 \rightleftarrows 2NH_3$.

(a) Since 1.0 mole of NH_3 remains at equilibrium, 3.0 moles must have undergone reaction. The following tabulation is set up to work the problem systematically.

Equation:	N_2	$+$	$3H_2$	$\rightleftarrows$	$2NH_3$
Initial:	4.0 moles		0.5 mole		4.0 moles
Amount Reacted*	3 moles NH_3		3 moles NH_3		3.0 moles
	$\times$		$\times$		
	$\left(\dfrac{1 \text{ mole } N_2}{2 \text{ moles } NH_3}\right)$		$\left(\dfrac{3 \text{ moles } H_2}{2 \text{ moles } NH_3}\right)$		
Equilibrium:	4.0 + 1.5		0.5 + 4.5		1.0 mole
	5.5 moles		5.0 moles		1.0 mole

answers to (a) 5.5 moles N_2, 5.0 moles H_2

(b) The concentrations are expressed in moles per liter; therefore,

$$[N_2] = \frac{5.5 \text{ moles}}{5.0 \text{ liters}} = 1.1 \ M$$

$$[H_2] = \frac{5.0 \text{ moles}}{5.0 \text{ liters}} = 1.0 \ M$$

$$[NH_3] = \frac{1.0 \text{ moles}}{5.0 \text{ liters}} = 0.2 \ M$$

(c)
$$K_{eq} = \frac{[NH_3]^2}{[N_2][H_2]^3} = \frac{(0.2)^2}{(1.1)(1.0)^3} = 0.036$$

Application of equilibrium principles

The remainder of this chapter is devoted to the application of the principles of chemical equilibrium to specific types of reactions. The form of the equilibrium constant may be modified by the introduction of certain assumptions, but the underlying principles always are applicable.

GAS PHASE REACTIONS

In reactions involving gases, the partial pressures are measured. Rather than convert these partial pressure values to molar concentrations, it is more convenient to derive an equilibrium constant in terms of the partial pressures.

For example, the equilibrium constant for a gaseous reaction K_p for the reaction $PCl_5(g) \rightleftarrows PCl_3(g) + Cl_2(g)$ is

$$K_p = \frac{p_{Cl_2} p_{PCl_3}}{p_{PCl_5}},$$

where p_{Cl_2}, p_{PCl_3}, and p_{PCl_5} are the partial pressures of the gases. Unless clearly indicated otherwise, the partial pressures are expressed in atmospheres. The numerical value of K_p is not the same as that of K_{eq} in which molar concentrations are used, except for those reactions in which the number of moles on the reactant side is equal to the number of moles on the product side of the equation. Since molar concentrations are directly proportional to the partial pressure, the values of K_p and K_{eq} are related by a constant.

---

* The need for the balanced equation is apparent in this step. The values in the parentheses are obtained from the equation and provide a means of expressing the amount of NH_3 that has undergone reaction in terms of H_2 and N_2 formed.

A weak electrolyte was defined in Chapter V as a molecular substance that dissociates into ions only to a small extent in solution. The dissociation of a weak electrolyte in solution may be represented as a reaction in which equilibrium is reached when only a small percentage of the molecules have dissociated into ions. As with all equilibria, the behavior in the solution is very dynamic. Molecules are dissociating and ions are combining continually; but the equilibrium is such that most of the solute is in the molecular form.

There are very few salts that are weak electrolytes in water. Ammonium hydroxide is the only commonly encountered weak base in aqueous systems. Thus, the most common weak electrolytes are weak acids. The acid dissociation constant expression K_a is easily developed using acetic acid as a typical example. The dissociation of acetic acid in water always is written with the molecular species as the reactant.

$$HC_2H_3O_2 + H_2O \rightleftarrows H_3O^+ + C_2H_3O_2^- \qquad (11.5)$$

A molecular equilibrium constant for this reaction would be

$$K_{eq} = \frac{[H_3O^+][C_2H_3O_2^-]}{[HC_2H_3O_2][H_2O]}$$

Since the number of moles of water per liter remains nearly constant at 55.56 moles in dilute solutions, $[H_2O]$ is considered to be a constant and is incorporated into the equilibrium constant to give the acid dissociation constant, expression K_a.

$$K_a = \frac{[H_3O^+][C_2H_3O_2^-]}{[HC_2H_3O_2]} \qquad (11.6)$$

Since water does not appear in the K_a expression, the ionization equilibrium often is expressed as

$$HC_2H_3O_2 \rightleftarrows H^+ + C_2H_3O_2^- \qquad (11.7)$$

Since $[H^+]$ is identical with $[H_3O^+]$, (11.6) is commonly written as

$$K_a = \frac{[H^+][C_2H_3O_2^-]}{[HC_2H_3O_2]} \qquad (11.8)$$

The concentration of the ions always appears in the numerator of the K_a expression, while the concentration of the molecular species always appears in the denominator.

Both equilibrium expressions (11.5) and (11.7) show why a weak acid such as acetic acid may be titrated readily with a strong base such as NaOH. As the base is added, OH^- ions combine with H^+ ions in equilibrium with the molecular acid to form water. This removes the H^+ ions from the acetic acid equilibrium. As H^+ ions are removed, the reverse (combination) reaction slows down, and the number of acetic acid molecules is reduced until essentially all of the molecules have been used up. Since the dissociation

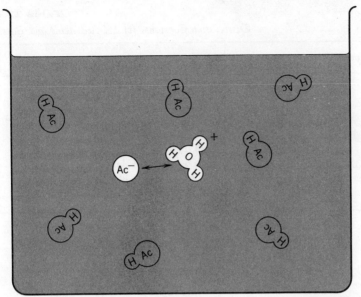

Fig. 11.3

Equilibrium in a Solution of Acetic Acid. A few molecules of acetic acid lose protons to water molecules and form $C_2H_3O_2^-$ and H_3O^+ ions. The dissociation rate is equal to the rate at which other $C_2H_3O_2^-$ and H_3O^+ ions form molecules of H_2O and $HC_2H_3O_2$.

is very rapid, there is no delay in the neutralization of the acid.

A similar discussion may be given for a weak base to obtain a base dissociation constant K_b. The properties of this constant are similar to those of the acid dissociation constant K_a. The base dissociation constant for ammonium hydroxide which undergoes the reaction $NH_4OH \rightleftarrows NH_4^+ + OH^-$ is

$$K_b = \frac{[NH_4^+][OH^-]}{[NH_4OH]}$$

A large value of K_a or K_b indicates that the acid or base is greatly dissociated, while a small value indicates a very weak electrolyte. Selected values of acid and base dissociation constants are given in Table 11.2 (page 216).

Example 11.3 Approximately 1.35% of the ammonium hydroxide in a 0.100 M solution is dissociated. Calculate the value of K_b.

Step 1. Write the equation for the reaction.

$$NH_4OH \rightleftarrows NH_4^+ + OH^-$$

Step 2. Determine the equilibrium concentrations by tabulating initial and equilibrium concentrations.

Initial concentrations: $[NH_4OH] = 0.100\ M$
$[NH_4^+] = 0$
$[OH^-] = 0$

Table 11.2

Dissociation Constants for Selected Acids and Bases

Equilibrium	K_b	Equilibrium	K_b
$NH_4OH \rightleftarrows NH_4^+ + OH^-$	1.8×10^{-5}	$H_2S \rightleftarrows H^+ + HS^-$	1.0×10^{-7}
	K_a	$HS^- \rightleftarrows H^+ + S^=$	1.3×10^{-13}
$HC_2H_3O_2 \rightleftarrows H^+ + C_2H_3O_2^-$	1.85×10^{-5}	$H_2S \rightleftarrows 2H^+ + S^=$	1.3×10^{-20}
$H_2CO_3 \rightleftarrows H^+ + HCO_3^-$	4.2×10^{-7}	$HClO \rightleftarrows H^+ + ClO^-$	3.2×10^{-8}
$HCO_3^- \rightleftarrows H^+ + CO_3^=$	4.8×10^{-11}	$H_3PO_4 \rightleftarrows H^+ + H_2PO_4^-$	7.5×10^{-3}
$HCN \rightleftarrows H^+ + CN^-$	4.0×10^{-10}	$H_2PO_4^- \rightleftarrows H^+ + HPO_4^=$	6.2×10^{-8}
$HF \rightleftarrows H^+ + F^-$	6.9×10^{-4}	$HPO_4^= \rightleftarrows H^+ + PO_4^\equiv$	1.0×10^{-12}
		$HSO_3^- \rightleftarrows H^+ + SO_3^=$	5.6×10^{-8}

$$\text{Equilibrium concentrations: } [NH_4OH] = 0.100 - (1.35\%)(0.1)$$
$$= 0.100 - 0.00135$$
$$= \sim 0.1 \ M$$
$$[NH_4^+] = 0.00135 \ M$$
$$[OH^-] = 0.00135 \ M$$

Note that $[NH_4^+] = [OH^-] =$ number of moles of NH_4OH that have dissociated, since one molecule of NH_4OH produces one NH_4^+ ion and one OH^- ion. The equilibrium concentration of NH_4OH has not been changed appreciably and is still very close to $0.1M$.

Step 3. Set up and calculate K_b.

$$K_b = \frac{[NH_4^+][OH^-]}{[NH_4OH]} = \frac{(1.35 \times 10^{-3})^2}{1 \times 10^{-1}} = 1.8 \times 10^{-5}$$

Example 11.4 What is the OH^- ion concentration in $0.020 \ M$ NH_4OH if $K_b = 1.8 \times 10^{-5}$?

$$NH_4OH \rightleftarrows NH_4^+ + OH^-$$

Initial concentrations:

$$0.020 \ M \qquad - \qquad -$$

Let $X =$ number of moles per liter of NH_4OH that dissociates. Equilibrium concentrations:

$$0.020 - X \quad X \quad X$$

$$K_b = 1.8 \times 10^{-5} = \frac{[NH_4^+][OH^-]}{[NH_4OH]} = \frac{X^2}{0.020 - X}$$

In Example 11.3, it was found that the amount of dissociation is very small compared to $0.010M$. The same assumption is made here. Let $0.020 - X \approx 0.020$.

$$\frac{X^2}{0.020} = 1.8 \times 10^{-5}$$
$$X^2 = (1.8 \times 10^{-5})(2 \times 10^{-2}) = 3.6 \times 10^{-7}$$
$$X^2 = 36 \times 10^{-8}$$
$$X = \sqrt{36 \times 10^{-8}} = 6.0 \times 10^{-4}$$
$$[OH]^- = X = 6.0 \times 10^{-4} \ M$$

Note that $(2.0 \times 10^{-2}) - (6.0 \times 10^{-4})$ is approximately 0.020 and the assumption is valid.

COMMON ION EFFECT AND BUFFERS

When the concentration of one ion involved in the dissociation of a weak acid or base is increased, the concentration of the other ion is reduced as predicted from the basic principles of chemical equilibrium. For example, the acetate ion concentration in an acetic acid solution is lowered by the addition of HCl which serves as a source of H^+ ions.

$HCl \rightarrow H^+ + Cl^-$ (strong electrolyte, complete dissociation)

$HC_2H_3O_2 \rightleftarrows H^+ + C_2H_3O_2^-$

Similarly, the addition of sodium acetate lowers the H^+ concentration since the salt completely dissociates.

$$NaC_2H_3O_2 \rightarrow Na^+ + C_2H_3O_2^-$$

The high acetate concentration shifts the equilibrium toward more molecular $HC_2H_3O_2$ and fewer H^+ ions.

Example 11.5 One-half mole of NH_4Cl is added to a liter of 0.10 M NH_4OH. What is the OH^- ion concentration, if K_b $(NH_4OH) = 1.8 \times 10^{-5}$?

$$NH_4Cl \rightarrow NH_4^+ + Cl^- \text{ (complete dissociation)}$$

$$NH_4OH \rightleftarrows NH_4^+ + OH^-$$

Initial concentration:	0.1 M	0.5 M	—
Equilibrium concentration:	0.1 − x	0.5 + x	x

where x is the amount of NH_4OH that dissociates. Assume x to be small so that $0.1 - x \approx 0.1$ and $0.5 + x \approx 0.5$.

$$K_b = 1.8 \times 10^{-5} = \frac{[NH^+][OH^-]}{[NH_4OH]} = \frac{0.5\, x}{0.1}$$

$$x = \frac{(1.8 \times 10^{-5})(1 \times 10^{-1})}{5 \times 10^{-1}} = 3.6 \times 10^{-6}\ M = [OH^-]$$

Compare this with the value of $[OH^-] = 1.35 \times 10^{-3}\ M$ for the ammonium hydroxide without the chloride (Example 11.3). The common ion has reduced the $[OH^-]$ concentration greatly.

This shifting of the equilibrium by the addition of an ion common to the equilibrium is called the *common ion effect*, which finds useful application in the preparation of buffer solutions. A *buffer* is a solution in which the H^+ ion or OH^- ion concentration is not greatly affected by the addition of small amounts of acid or base. A buffer is prepared by adding the salt of a weak acid or base to a solution of the acid or base. Thus, the molecular acid and the ion from the salt are present in high concentration relative to the concentration of the H^+ or OH^- ions. The concentration of H^+

or OH^- ions is adjusted by an appropriate ratio of ions to molecules.

A solution of acetic acid and sodium acetate behaves as a typical buffer. The expression for the hydrogen ion concentration in a buffer is given by rearranging the acid dissociation constant expression.

$$HC_2H_3O_2 \rightleftarrows H^+ + C_2H_3O_2$$

$$\frac{[H^+][C_2H_3O_2^-]}{[HC_2H_3O_2]} = K_a$$

$$[H^+] = \frac{K_a[HC_2H_3O_2]}{[C_2H_3O_2^-]} \tag{11.9}$$

In a typical acetate buffer solution the concentrations of $HC_2H_3O_2$ molecules and acetate ions are large. When a small amount of a strong acid is added, most of the additional H^+ ions combine with acetate ions. This represents a very small change in the total acetate ion and $HC_2H_3O_2$ concentrations. These small changes do not appreciably change the value of the ratio, $[HC_2H_3O_2]/[C_2H_3O_2^-]$. Thus, the change in H^+ ion concentration is very small (11.9). The addition of a small amount of OH^- ions shifts the equilibrium toward the formation of acetate ions. But again the reduction in the concentration of $HC_2H_3O_2$ and the increase in the concentration of $C_2H_3O_2^-$ ions is small compared to the original concentrations. As a result, the H^+ ion concentration is changed only slightly.

It should be emphasized that the H^+ ion concentration does not remain completely invariant upon addition of acid or base, but the change is very small compared to the change in concentration if the acid or base were to be added to an unbuffered solution. There is also a limit to the amount of acid or base that can be added to a buffered solution, before the H^+ ion concentration changes rather rapidly with additional reagent. The capacity of a buffer depends upon the initial concentrations of weak acid and salt. For example, a buffer consisting of 1.0 M acetic acid and 1.0 M $NaC_2H_3O_2$ has the same H^+ ion concentration as one prepared from 0.1 M acetic acid and 0.1 M $NaC_2H_3O_2$, but the buffering capacity of the more concentrated solution is about ten times that of the dilute solution.

The sodium acetate-acetic acid buffer system is relatively simple. More complex systems are employed to obtain higher capacities and different ranges of H^+ ion concentrations. Since living organisms are very sensitive to changes in H^+ ion concentrations, very complex buffers are found in the blood and other body fluids.

Example 11.6 What molar ratio of NH_4OH to NH_4Cl is needed to prepare a buffer with an OH^- ion concentration of 9.0×10^{-5} moles per liter?

$$[OH^-] = K_b \frac{[NH_4OH]}{[NH_4^+]}$$

$$(9.0 \times 10^{-5}) = (1.8 \times 10^{-5}) \frac{[NH_4OH]}{[NH_4^+]}$$

$$\frac{[NH_4OH]}{[NH_4^+]} = \frac{9.0 \times 10^{-5}}{1.8 \times 10^{-5}} = 5$$

5 moles NH_4OH per mole NH_4Cl.

Example 11.7 What weight of NH_4Cl must be added to 400 ml of 0.10 M NH_4OH to prepare a buffer with a OH^- ion concentration of 5.4 × 10^{-7} M?

$$[OH^-] = K_b \frac{[NH_4OH]}{[NH_4^+]}$$

$$5.4 \times 10^{-7} = 1.8 \times 10^{-5} \frac{(0.1)}{[NH_4^+]}$$

$$[NH_4^+] = \frac{1.8 \times 10^{-6}}{5.4 \times 10^{-7}} = 3.3 \ M$$

$$\text{wt } NH_4Cl = \left(\frac{3.3 \text{ moles}}{1 \text{ liter}}\right)(0.400 \ l)\left(\frac{53.5 \text{ g}}{1 \text{ mole } NH_4Cl}\right) = 70.6 \text{ g}$$

ION PRODUCT FOR WATER

The reaction of a H^+ ion with an OH^- ion to form water is considered to be an equilibrium reaction.

$$H_2O \rightleftarrows H^+ + OH^-$$

The equilibrium is strongly toward molecular water at room temperatures. The equilibrium constant expression for this reaction is the *ion product for water*, K_w.

$$K_w = [H^+][OH^-]$$

The H^+ ion concentration in pure water at 25°C is known to be 1×10^{-7} M. It is seen from the equilibrium reaction that the OH^- ion concentration is equal to that of the H^+ ion; therefore, the value of K_w at 25°C is $(1 \times 10^{-7})(1 \times 10^{-7}) = 1 \times 10^{-14}$.

The value of K_w in *any* aqueous solution at 25°C is (1×10^{-14}). Thus, if NaOH is added to water to make a solution of sodium hydroxide, the increase in the OH^- ion concentration causes a lowering of the H^+ ion concentration such that K_w remains at (1×10^{-14}). The addition of H^+ ions to form an acid solution also results in the lowering of the OH^- ion concentration. Even in the most acidic solution there are still a few OH^- ions present, just as a few H^+ ions are present in a concentrated base.

Example 11.8 Calculate (a) the H^+ concentration in 0.10 M NaOH and (b) the H^+ ion and OH^- ion concentrations in 0.0010 M HCl.

(a) Since NaOH is a strong base, it is completely dissociated.

$$[OH^-] = 0.10 \ M$$
$$K_w = 1 \times 10^{-14} = [H^+](1 \times 10^{-1})$$
$$[H^+] = 1 \times 10^{-13} \ M$$

(b) HCl is a strong acid; therefore, $[H^+] = 0.0010\ M$
$$= 1.0 \times 10^{-3}\ M$$
$$K_w = 1 \times 10^{-14} = (1 \times 10^{-3})[OH^-]$$
$$[OH^-] = 1 \times 10^{-11}\ M$$

The H^+ ion concentration in a neutral solution is equal to the OH^- ion concentration which is equal to $1 \times 10^{-7}\ M$. An acid solution is one in which the H^+ ion concentration is greater than $1 \times 10^{-7}\ M$ and the OH^- ion concentration is less than 1×10^{-7} M. A basic solution is one in which the H^+ ion concentration is less than $1 \times 10^{-7}\ M$ and the OH^- ion concentration is greater than $1 \times 10^{-7}\ M$.

*p*H *and p*OH. It is more convenient to express low concentrations of acid and base in terms of the negative logarithm of the concentration. This scale is defined as

$$pH = -\log\ [H^+] \text{ and } pOH = -\log[OH^-]$$

The *p*H of a neutral solution is 7.00; an acid solution has a *p*H less than 7.00, and a basic solution has a *p*H greater than 7.00. The sum of the *p*H and *p*OH of any aqueous solution is equal to 14.

$$K_w = [H^+][OH^-] = 1 \times 10^{-14}$$
$$\log[H^+] + \log[OH^-] = -14$$
$$-\log[H^+] - \log[OH^-] = 14$$
$$pH + pOH = 14$$

The *p*H and *p*OH scales find greatest utility in the range from 1.0 M base to 1.0 M acid. The *p* notation to indicate $-\log$ is used extensively when dealing with small numbers. The values of K_a, K_b, and K_w are often listed in terms of pK_a, pK_b, and pK_w.

Example 11.9 What are the *p*H and *p*OH of the solutions in Example 11.8?

(a) 0.10 M NaOH: *p*H = 13.00, *p*OH = 1.00
(b) 0.0010 M HCl; *p*H = 3.00, *p*OH = 11.00

HYDROLYSIS

Whenever the salt of a weak acid or base is dissolved in water, an interaction between the ions from the weak species and water takes place. The interaction is called *hydrolysis*. For example, when sodium acetate is placed in water, the salt dissociates completely to sodium ions and acetate ions. The Na^+ ions do not undergo hydrolysis, since NaOH is a strong base; no molecules are formed when the Na^+ ions and H_2O molecules come together. The acetate ions remove a proton from the water molecules to form acetic acid molecules. Since OH^- ions also are formed in this reaction, the OH^- ion concentration is greater than the uncombined H^+ ion concentration, resulting in a basic solution. This process is shown in the hydrolysis equation.

$$C_2H_3O_2^- + H_2O \rightleftarrows HC_2H_3O_2 + OH^-$$

Other examples of hydrolysis include the following.

$$CN^- + H_2O \rightleftarrows HCN + OH^-$$
(basic solution results since HCN is a weak acid)

$$NH_4^+ + H_2O \rightleftarrows NH_4OH + H^+$$
(acid solution results since NH_4OH is a weak base)

Hydrolysis of the salts of very weak acids produces very basic solutions. For example, the pH of a 1.0 M $NaC_2H_3O_2$ is approximately 9, while the pH of 1.0 M NaCN is approximately 12. The acid dissociation constants are 1.85×10^{-5} for $HC_2H_3O_2$ and 4×10^{-10} for HCN.

Hydrolysis also occurs during the neutralization of a weak acid or base, leading to a pH value other than 7.0 at the equivalence point. A salt of the weak species is being formed during the titration. The solution at the equivalence point is identical to one of the same concentration prepared from the same salt. For example, the titration of 2.0 M $HC_2H_3O_2$ with 2.0 M NaOH produces a 1.0 M $NaC_2H_3O_2$ solution at the equivalence point. The pH of this solution is approximately 9.0, reflecting the hydrolysis of the acetate ion. If more dilute acid and base are used the pH is smaller; however, it is always greater than 7.0 at the equivalence point. The pH is 7.0 at the equivalence point only in the titration of a strong acid with a strong base.

INSTABILITY CONSTANT

There are many simple ions that undergo reaction to form complex ions. A *complex ion* is a simple ion combined with one or more other ions or neutral polar molecules. All complex ions are unstable to some extent. An instability constant is used to describe this equilibrium between the complex ion and its components. A small value of the instability constant K_{Inst} indicates a stable complex, since the complex is written as the reactant. The hexathiocyanoferrate(III) ion is a typical complex ion. The equilibrium involved is

$$Fe(SCN)_6{}^{3-} \rightleftarrows Fe^{3+} + 6SCN^-$$

$$K_{Inst} = \frac{[Fe^{3+}][SCN^-]^6}{[Fe(SCN)_6{}^{3-}]}$$

The addition of thiocyanate ion (SCN^-) results in the formation of more complex, while its removal destroys the complex. The complex is destroyed also if the Fe^{3+} ion is taken up in a more stable complex or a more stable precipitate.

SOLUBILITY PRODUCT CONSTANT

When a slightly soluble salt is placed in water, only a few ions are needed in solution before the rate at which ions are leaving the solid is equal to the rate at which the ions are returning to the

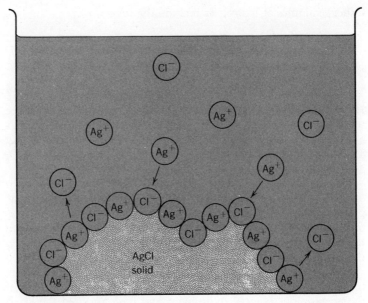

Fig. 11.4

Equilibrium in a Saturated AgCl Solution. The rate at which Ag$^+$ and Cl$^-$ ions go into solution from the surface of the solid is equal to the rate at which other Ag$^+$ and Cl$^-$ ions come out of solution. A low concentration of ions in solution is constant.

solid. This type of equilibrium differs from the weak acid dissociation in that a second phase (a solid) is present while the molecular form of the acid is dissolved in the solution.

A classic example of the equilibrium principles involved with a slightly soluble salt is provided by the dissociation of silver chloride.

$$AgCl(s) \rightleftarrows Ag^+ + Cl^-$$

The concentration of Ag$^+$ ions and Cl$^-$ ions is independent of the amount of AgCl present as long as some solid is present. The density of the solid, which is usually expressed in terms of g/cm^3, may be converted to concentration units of moles per liter by the factor $\left(\dfrac{1000 \text{ cm}^3/\text{l}}{\text{g/mole}}\right)$. Since the density is constant, the concentration of the solid is considered to be constant. Thus, the solid phase concentration does not appear in the expression for the solubility product constant K_{sp}.

$$K_{sp} = [Ag^+][Cl^-]$$

It is necessary to distinguish carefully between solubility and solubility product constant. Solubility is the weight of solid that dissolves in a given volume of water. Usually solubilities are given in grams per 100 ml, although grams per liter and moles per liter are used. The solubility product constant is the value of the appropriate product of the molar concentrations of the ions. The relationship of the molar solubility and the solubility product constant is dependent upon the ratio of cations and anions formed when the solid goes into solution.

The solubility product constant is useful for the prediction of precipitate formation. A precipitate forms in any solution when the concentration of the ions in solution is such that the value of K_{sp} is exceeded. For example, the solubility product constant for AgCl is 3×10^{-10}. A precipitate does not form when silver ion is added to a 0.01 M chloride solution until the silver ion concentration reaches 3×10^{-8} M. As soon as this concentration is reached, solid AgCl begins to form.

Example 11.10 The solubility of $BaSO_4$ is 1×10^{-5} mole per liter. Calculate K_{sp} for $BaSO_4$.

$$BaSO_4 \rightleftarrows Ba^{++} + SO_4^{=}$$

For every mole of $BaSO_4$ that dissolves, one mole Ba^{++} and one mole $SO_4^{=}$ are formed. Therefore,

$$[Ba^{++}] = [SO_4^{=}] = 1 \times 10^{-5} \ M$$
$$K_{sp} = [Ba^{++}][SO_4^{=}] = (1 \times 10^{-5})^2 = 1 \times 10^{-10}$$

Example 11.11 The solubility of $Ca_3(AsO_4)_2$ is 9.1×10^{-5} moles per liter. Calculate K_{sp} for $Ca_3(AsO_4)_2$.

Table 11.3

Solubility Product Constants for Selected Substances

Salt	K_{sp}
Barium sulfate, $BaSO_4$	1×10^{-10}
Calcium carbonate, $CaCO_3$	7×10^{-9}
Chromic hydroxide, $Cr(OH)_3$	7×10^{-31}
Cupric sulfide, CuS	4×10^{-36}
Ferric hydroxide, $Fe(OH)_3$	6×10^{-38}
Lead carbonate, $PbCO_3$	1.5×10^{-13}
chloride, $PbCl_2$	1.6×10^{-5}
iodate, $Pb(IO_3)_2$	3×10^{-13}
iodide, PbI_2	8×10^{-9}
sulfate, $PbSO_4$	1×10^{-8}
Magnesium carbonate, $MgCO_3$	4×10^{-5}
hydroxide, $Mg(OH)_2$	1.35×10^{-11}
Mercuric sulfide, HgS	1×10^{-50}
Nickel sulfide, NiS	1×10^{-22}
Silver bromide, AgBr	5×10^{-13}
chromate, Ag_2CrO_4	9×10^{-12}
chloride, AgCl	3×10^{-10}
iodide, AgI	8×10^{-17}
sulfide, Ag_2S	2×10^{-49}
Stannous hydroxide, $Sn(OH)_2$	3×10^{-27}

$$Ca_3(AsO_4)_2(s) \rightleftarrows \quad 3\ Ca^{++} \quad + \quad 2AsO_4{}^{3-}$$

9.1 $\times$ 10^{-5} mole dissolves $\rightarrow$ 3 (9.1 $\times$ 10^{-5}) 2 (9.1 $\times$ 10^{-5})
in one liter

$$\rightarrow 2.73 \times 10^{-4}\ M \quad 1.82 \times 10^{-4}\ M$$

$$K_{sp} = [Ca^{++}]^3\ [AsO_4{}^{3-}]^2$$
$$= (2.7 \times 10^{-4})^3\ (1.8 \times 10^{-4})^2 = 6.4 \times 10^{-19}$$

A comparison of this problem with Example 11.10 indicates the difficulty of assigning a direct relationship between solubility and K_{sp}. Although the molar solubility of $Ca_3(AsO_4)_2$ is nine times greater than that of $BaSO_4$, the K_{sp} of $Ca_3(AsO_4)_2$ is 10^8 times smaller than the K_{sp} of $BaSO_4$. The K_{sp} values reflect the fact that each $BaSO_4$ forms one cation and one anion while each $Ca_3(AsO_4)_2$ forms three cations and two anions.

Example 11.12 What is the maximum concentration of arsenate ion that can exist in a 0.01 M $CaCl_2$ solution without the formation of a precipitate? The value of K_{sp} calculated in Example 11.11 is 6.4 $\times$ 10^{-19}.

$$K_{sp} = [Ca^{++}]^3[AsO_4{}^{3-}]^2 = 6.4 \times 10^{-19}$$
$$(1 \times 10^{-2})^3[AsO_4{}^{3-}]^2 = 6.4 \times 10^{-19}$$
$$[AsO_4{}^{3-}]^2 = \frac{6.4 \times 10^{-19}}{1 \times 10^{-6}} = 6.4 \times 10^{-13} = 64 \times 10^{-14}$$
$$[AsO_4{}^{3-}] = 8 \times 10^{-7}\ M$$

Note that the concentration of Ca^{++} ions is not tripled, nor is the $AsO_4{}^{3-}$ ion concentration doubled in this problem. In Example 11.11, the source of the ions is the solid salt, and it is necessary to multiply the solubility by 2 and 3. In this problem, since the ions come from another source, multiplication is not necessary, although one works with the cube of the Ca^{++} ion concentration and the square of the $AsO_4{}^{3-}$ ion concentration.

Example 11.13 The K_{sp} for $Mg(OH)_2$ is 1.35 $\times$ 10^{-11}. Calculate the maximum concentration of Mg^{++} ions that can be in a solution with a pH of 10 without the formation of a precipitate.

$$Mg(OH)_2 \rightleftarrows Mg^{++} + 2OH^-$$
$$K_{sp} = [Mg^{++}][OH^-]^2 = 1.35 \times 10^{-11}$$
$$pOH = 14.0 - pH = 4.0$$
$$[OH^-] = 1 \times 10^{-4}\ M$$
$$[Mg^{++}](1 \times 10^{-4})^2 = 1.35 \times 10^{-11}$$
$$[Mg^{++}] = \frac{1.35 \times 10^{-11}}{1 \times 10^{-8}} = 1.35 \times 10^{-3}\ \text{moles/liter}$$

Example 11.14 The K_{sp} for $PbCl_2$ is 1.6 $\times$ 10^{-5}. Does $PbCl_2$ precipitate if 10 ml of 0.020 M HCl are added to 10 ml of 0.060 M $Pb(NO_3)_2$?

Answer: An ion product K_{ip} is calculated for the actual concentrations. If the value of K_{ip} exceeds the value of K_{sp}, a precipitate forms. A correction for the volume change must be made before K_{ip} is calculated.

$$\text{Concentration of Cl}^- \text{ in solution} = \frac{\left(\dfrac{0.02 \text{ mole}}{1 \text{ liter}}\right)(0.010 \text{ l})}{(0.020 \text{ l})}$$

$$= 0.010 \; M$$

$$\text{Concentration of Pb}^{++} \text{ in solution} = \frac{\left(\dfrac{0.060 \text{ mole}}{1 \text{ liter}}\right)(0.010 \text{ l})}{(0.020 \text{ l})}$$

$$= 0.030 \; M$$

$$\text{PbCl}_2 \text{ (s)} \rightleftarrows \text{Pb}^{++} + 2\text{Cl}^-$$

$$
\begin{aligned}
K_{ip} = [\text{Pb}^{++}]_{\text{initial}} \, [\text{Cl}^-]^2_{\text{initial}} &= (0.030)(0.010)^2 \\
&= (3.0 \times 10^{-2})(1.0 \times 10^{-2})^2 \\
&= 3.0 \times 10^{-6}
\end{aligned}
$$

This value of K_{ip} is less than K_{sp} for PbCl$_2$. Therefore, no PbCl$_2$ precipitates from this solution.

Many metal ions hydrolyze in water to such an extent that the solubility product constant for the slightly soluble metal hydroxide is exceeded, and a precipitate forms when a salt of these metals is placed in solution. For example, when Zn(NO$_3$)$_2$ is placed in water, a precipitate of Zn(OH)$_2$ forms if the zinc ion concentration is greater than 0.002 M.

$$\text{Zn}^{++} + 2\text{H}_2\text{O} \rightleftarrows \text{Zn(OH)}_2 \!\downarrow + 2\text{H}^+$$

This hydrolysis reaction is reversed, and the precipitate dissolves with the addition of an acid. Since nitrate ions already are in solution, nitric acid is the probable choice.

This technique of adding acid to suppress hydrolysis is used frequently to prepare solutions of metal ions that form slightly soluble hydroxides. Some of the metal ions that undergo hydrolysis are Al^{3+}, Be^{++}, Bi^{3+}, Fe^{++}, Hg^{++}, Sb^{3+}, Sn^{++}, and Sn^{4+}.

DISSOLUTION OF PRECIPITATES

Precipitates dissolve when the concentration of the ions in equilibrium is substantially reduced. This is most frequently accomplished by (a) formation of a complex ion, (b) formation of a gas, and (c) formation of a slightly dissociated molecule.

The behavior of silver chloride in ammonium hydroxide is an example of the role of complex ion formation in the dissolution of precipitates.

$$\text{AgCl} + 2\text{NH}_4\text{OH} \rightleftarrows \text{Ag(NH}_3)_2{}^+ + \text{Cl}^- + 2\text{H}_2\text{O}$$

The complex ion is said to be more stable than AgCl, since fewer Ag$^+$ ions exist in equilibrium with the complex than with the solid at moderate concentrations of ammonium hydroxide. The fact that Ag$^+$ ions are in equilibrium with the complex is demonstrated by the formation of a AgI precipitate upon the addition of I$^-$ ions.

$$\text{Ag(NH}_3)_2{}^+ \rightleftarrows \text{Ag}^+ + 2\text{NH}_3$$
$$\text{Ag(NH}_3)_2{}^+ + \text{I}^- \rightarrow \text{AgI} \!\downarrow + 2\text{NH}_3$$

The value of K_{sp} for AgI is much smaller than that for AgCl (Table 11.3). Therefore, the concentration of Ag^+ ions that exists in equilibrium with solid AgI is much lower. In fact this concentration is so low that enough Ag^+ ions are removed from the complex ion equilibrium by the formation of AgI to destroy the complex. AgI may be dissolved by the formation of a more stable complex ion.

The dissolution of metal sulfides in acid illustrates the use of gas formation. Hydrogen sulfide (H_2S), a gas with limited solubility, forms a weak acid solution.

$$H_2S \rightleftarrows 2H^+ + S^=$$

Nickel sulfide dissolves in an acid solution, since its solubility is great enough to permit the formation and escape of H_2S.

$$NiS \rightleftarrows Ni^{++} + S^=$$
$$NiS + 2H^+ \rightarrow Ni^{++} + H_2S\uparrow$$

As the slightly soluble H_2S gas escapes, more NiS dissolves.

Copper sulfide is much more insoluble than NiS and does not dissolve by the formation of H_2S. Rather, CuS dissolves in an acid such as nitric acid which reacts with the sulfide ion to form free sulfur.

$$CuS \rightleftarrows Cu^{++} + S^=$$
$$S^= + 2HNO_3 \rightarrow 4H_2O + 2NO\uparrow + 3S\downarrow$$

If NiS were placed in HNO_3, H_2S and sulfur would be formed; much of the H_2S reacts with HNO_3 to form sulfur also.

The dissolution of an insoluble hydroxide in an acid illustrates the formation of a slightly dissociated molecule. The formation of H_2O molecules reduces the OH^- ion concentration in equilibrium with the solid, causing it to dissolve.

$$Zn(OH)_2 \rightleftarrows Zn^{++} + 2OH^-$$
$$Zn(OH)_2 + 2H^+ \rightarrow Zn^{++} + 2H_2O$$

SIGNIFICANT TERMS AND CONCEPTS IN CHAPTER XI:

Reaction rate, rate equation, activation energy, catalyst, effect of temperature on reaction rate; chemical equilibrium, equilibrium constant, effect of concentration changes, pressure and temperature upon the equilibrium constant and the point of equilibrium; K_p, K_a, K_b, common ion effect, buffers, K_w, pH, pOH, hydrolysis, complex ions, K_{sp}, K_{ip}, dissolution of a precipitate.

Review questions

11.1. How is a buffer prepared?

11.2. Under what conditions is hydrolysis to be expected?

11.3. What is the significance of the brackets in the equilibrium constant expressions?

11.4. Why is the invariance of the concentrations not sufficient proof that a system is at equilibrium?

11.5. Explain why the concentration of each species in a system that is at chemical equilibrium does not change?

11.6. For each of the following reactions (all species are gases) give the effect (increase, decrease, no change) on the equilibrium constant and on the concentration of the underscored species when these actions are taken on the system at equilibrium: (i) temperature is increased; (ii) pressure is increased by the addition of an inert gas; (iii) pressure is increased by a volume decrease; (iv) a catalyst is added; (v) oxygen gas is added.

(a) $2SO_2 + O_2 \rightleftarrows 2SO_3 + 47$ kcal

(b) 27 kcal $+ 2\underline{NO_2} \rightleftarrows 2NO + O_2$

(c) 43 kcal $+ 2NO \rightleftarrows \underline{N_2} + O_2$

(d) $4NH_3 + 5O_2 \rightleftarrows 4\underline{NO} + 6H_2O + 216$ kcal

11.7. Write the expression for the equilibrium constant for each reaction given in question 11.6.

11.8. The pressure on an equilibrium mixture of H_2, I_2, and HI is increased by decreasing the volume. What effect does this pressure change have upon (a) the concentration of H_2, I_2, and HI at the newly attained equilibrium, (b) the number of molecules of H_2, I_2, and HI at the newly attained equilibrium?

11.9. If sodium cyanide is added to each of the following systems, what is the effect (increase, decrease, no change) on the concentration of the underscored species?

(a) $HCN \rightleftarrows \underline{H^+} + CN^-$

(b) $CN^- + H_2O \rightleftarrows HCN + \underline{OH^-}$

(c) $Ag(CN)_2^- \rightleftarrows Ag^+ + 2CN^-$

(d) $\underline{Hg_2(CN)_2}(solid) \rightleftarrows \underline{Hg_2^{++}} + 2CN^-$

11.10. Mercurous cyanide $Hg_2(CN)_2$ is very insoluble. What is the effect on the concentration of the underscored species in question 11.9 if mercurous nitrate is added to each solution instead of NaCN.

11.11. Indicate whether aqueous solutions of each of the following are acidic, basic, or neutral.

(a) NaCN (b) NH_4NO_3 (c) NH_4OH (d) KBr (e) Na_2SO_3 (f) KClO (g) Na_3PO_4 (h) CaS

11.12. Why is BaS soluble in HCl, while $BaSO_4$ is not?

11.13. Cupric hydroxide $(Cu(OH)_2)$ dissolves in NH_4OH but not in NaOH. Give a possible explanation on the basis of the equilibria involved.

11.14. Explain why the following statement is false. "There are no sulfide ions in a solution prepared by dissolving NiS in HCl."

11.15. Write appropriate expressions for the equilibrium constants for the following reactions. Give the correct name for each constant.
  (a) $HF \rightleftarrows H^+ + F^-$
  (b) $HgCl_4^= \rightleftarrows Hg^{++} + 4Cl^-$
  (c) $CaCO_3(s) \rightleftarrows Ca^{++} + CO_3^=$
  (d) $Ag_2S(s) \rightleftarrows 2Ag^+ + S^=$

Problems

11.16. Consider the formation of phosphine from the elements at a temperature sufficiently high so that all substances are gases.

$$P_2 + 3H_2 \rightleftarrows 2PH_3$$

If 6.0 moles of phosphine are found at equilibrium after 5.0 moles of P_2 and 12 moles of H_2 are mixed in a closed 5.0 liter container,
  (a) How many moles of P_2 remain at equilibrium?
  (b) How many moles of H_2 remain at equilibrium?
  (c) What is the molar concentration of PH_3?
  (d) Evaluate the equilibrium constant.
                   answers: (a) 2.0 moles P_2 (d) 16.7

11.17. If 0.50 mole NO remains at equilibrium after 3.0 moles of NO and 4.0 moles of O_2 are mixed in an 8.0 liter container to undergo the reaction $2NO + O_2 \rightleftarrows 2NO_2$,
  (a) How many moles of NO_2 have been formed?
  (b) How many moles of O_2 remain at equilibrium?
  (c) What is the molar concentration of NO at equilibrium?
  (d) Evaluate the equilibrium constant.

11.18. The equilibrium constant is 8.00 for the reaction

$$2NOCl(g) \rightleftarrows 2NO(g) + Cl_2(g)$$

After some NOCl is allowed to come to equilibrium in a 3.0 liter container, 0.060 moles of Cl_2 was found. Calculate the concentration of NOCl at equilibrium.

11.19. Calculate the pH of the following solutions:
  (a) 0.20 M HClO (b) 0.056 M NH_4OH (c) 0.25 M HCN
                   answer: (a) 4.1

11.20. What is the pH of a solution that is 0.120 M in NaCN and 0.030 M in HCN?   answer: 10

11.21. What is the pH of a solution prepared by adding 1.645 g $NaClO \cdot 5H_2O$ to 500 ml of 0.10 M HClO?

11.22. What is the H^+ ion concentration in a solution of 4.1 g $NaC_2H_3O_2$ in 2.5 liters of 0.050 M $HC_2H_3O_2$?
                   answer: 4.6×10^{-5} M

11.23. What molar ratio of $HC_2H_3O_2$ to $NaC_2H_3O_2$ is needed to prepare a solution buffered at a $pH = 4.00$?
                   answer: 5.4 moles $HC_2H_3O_2$ per mole $NaC_2H_3O_2$

11.24. What molar ratio of HCN to KCN is needed to prepare a solution with an OH$^-$ ion concentration of 2.5×10^{-4}?

11.25. What weight of KCN is to be added to 600 ml of 0.50 M HCN to obtain a H$^+$ ion concentration of 1.0×10^{-12} M?

11.26. What is the pH, pOH, H$^+$ ion concentration, and OH$^-$ ion concentration in each of the following solutions?
(a) 0.002 N H$_2$SO$_4$ (b) 0.01 M NaOH (c) 0.01 M HCl
(d) 0.005 M Ba(OH)$_2$ (e) 10.0 ml of 0.10 M HCl + 12.5 ml of 0.08 M NaOH

11.27. A 0.1 M hypobromous acid solution is 0.0010 per cent ionized. Calculate the acid dissociation constant for HBrO $\rightleftarrows$ H$^+$ + BrO$^-$.

11.28. The hydrogen ion concentration in a 0.100 M cyanic acid (HCNO) solution is 4.5×10^{-3} moles per liter. Calculate K_a for cyanic acid.   answer: 2.1×10^{-4}

11.29. The hydrogen ion concentration in a 0.50 M chlorous acid (HClO$_2$) solution is 7×10^{-2} moles per liter. Calculate K_a for chlorous acid.

11.30. The solubility of calcium fluoride is 1.6×10^{-3} g per 100 ml. Calculate the K_{sp} for CaF$_2$.   answer: 3.4×10^{-11}

11.31. The solubility of barium oxalate, BaC$_2$O$_4$, is 1.2×10^{-4} moles per liter. Calculate K_{sp} for BaC$_2$O$_4$.

11.32. What is the lead ion concentration in a 0.20 M NaI solution when PbI$_2$ begins to precipitate?
answer: 4×10^{-7} M

11.33. What is the chromate ion concentration in a 0.30 M AgNO$_3$ solution when Ag$_2$CrO$_4$ begins to precipitate?

11.34. At what concentration of Fe^{3+} ion does Fe(OH)$_3$ precipitate from an aqueous solution?

11.35. At what concentration of Sn^{++} ion does Sn(OH)$_2$ precipitate from an aqueous solution?
answer: 3×10^{-13} M

11.36. Does AgCl precipitate if 0.10 ml of 0.0010 M AgNO$_3$ is added to 100 ml of 0.00010 M HCl?
answer: No, since $K_{ip} = 1 \times 10^{-10}$ is less than K_{sp}

11.37. Does PbSO$_4$ precipitate when 10 ml of 0.0010 M Pb(NO$_3$)$_2$ is mixed with 40 ml of 0.0010 M H$_2$SO$_4$?

11.38. Lead ions are added slowly to a solution containing 0.10 M CO$_3^=$ and 0.10 M IO$_3^-$. Does Pb(IO$_3$)$_2$ or PbCO$_3$ precipitate first? What is the lead ion concentration when this precipitation begins?
answer: PbCO$_3$ at Pb^{++} = 1.5×10^{-12} M

11.39. Lead ions are added slowly to a solution containing 0.1 M NaI and 0.10 M Na$_2$SO$_4$. Does PbI$_2$ or PbSO$_4$ precipitate first? What is the lead ion concentration when this precipitation begins?

11.40. When 0.01 mole each of Fe(OH)$_3$, Mg(OH)$_2$, Cr(OH)$_3$, and Sn(OH)$_2$ are added to a liter of an acid, the pH of the final solution is 3.00. Which of these hydroxides are completely dissolved in this acid solution?

oxidation-reduction

The reactions considered in this chapter are those in which there is a change in oxidation number. Some of the reactions take place under the influence of an electrical current. Other reactions occur when two or more substances are combined. Under appropriate conditions, an electrical current may be generated as a result of these reactions.

Redox reactions

The term *oxidation* originated to describe the reaction of a substance with oxygen. Using the present description of a chemical reaction as the transfer of electrons, it is seen that oxygen atoms take on electrons from the substance being oxidized. Thus oxidation now refers to any process where there is a loss of electrons. If some substance loses electrons, another must gain electrons. The gain of electrons by a substance is called *reduction*. (Remember: reduction implies a reduction of the oxidation number.) Chemical reactions involving the transfer of electrons are made up of two parts. One half of the reaction is oxidation; the other half is reduction. Reactions involving oxidation and reduction are called *redox* reactions.

Oxidation and reduction are not limited to ionic compounds only. When a covalent bond is formed, each element contributes one or more electrons to bond formation. The more electronegative element is assigned a negative oxidation number, while a positive oxidation number is assigned to the other element or elements. Whenever there is a change in oxidation numbers in the course of a chemical reaction, redox has taken place.

As implied in the last sentence, not all chemical reactions involve oxidation and reduction. Neutralization of an acid and base and simple precipitation are examples of reactions that are not redox reactions.

Example 12.1 Which of the following reactions are redox reactions? Indicate the element that undergoes oxidation and the element that undergoes reduction in the redox reactions.

(a) $H_2^0 + O_2^0 \rightarrow H_2O$

(b) $2HI \rightarrow H_2^0 + I_2^0$

(c) $CaCO_3 + 2H^+ \rightarrow Ca^{++} + H_2O + CO_2$

(d) $Cu^0 + 4H^+ + 2NO_3^- \rightarrow Cu^{++} + 2NO_2 + 2H_2O$

(e) $Ba^{++} + SO_4^= \rightarrow BaSO_4\downarrow$

(f) $2MnO_2 + 3BiO_3^- + 10H^+ \rightarrow 2MnO_4^- + 3Bi^{3+} + 5H_2O$

answers:

(a) hydrogen is oxidized; oxygen is reduced.

(b) iodide is oxidized; hydrogen is reduced.

(c) not a redox reaction.

(d) copper is oxidized; nitrogen is reduced.

(e) not a redox reaction.

(f) manganese is oxidized; bismuth is reduced.

Since the number of electrons lost in an oxidation reaction is equal to the number of electrons gained in the reduction reaction, electron balance as well as atomic balance must be maintained in a redox reaction. The following steps are involved in balancing a redox equation.

(a) Select the species that contain the elements which have changed oxidation number.

The species may be an atom, molecule, or ion. The magnitude of the change need not be determined as long as a change is recognized. Ionic equations are very useful when working with reactions involving ions.

(b) Write each pair of species in a partial equation form.

Each of these partial equations develops into the half reactions. There are only two equations to be considered in most redox reactions, although the possibility of more than one species being oxidized or reduced cannot be overlooked.

(c) Balance the number of atoms in each partial equation.

First, balance the atoms other than hydrogen and oxygen. Then if there is an excess of hydrogen atoms on either side of an equation, add that number of H^+ ions to the other side if the reaction is being carried out in an acid solution, or that number of H_2O molecules to the other side if the reaction is in a basic solution. If the number of oxygen atoms is in excess, add the same number of H_2O molecules to the other side for an acid solution or twice as many OH^- ions to the other side for a basic solution. The atomic balance is completed by the appropriate addition of H^+ (in acid), OH^- (in base) or H_2O molecules.

(d) Balance electrically by adding electrons to each partial equation.

Upon the completion of step (c), the net numbers of charges on each side of each equation are not equal. Negative charges, as electrons, are added to the more positive side of each equation to achieve an equal number of charges on both sides of the equations. These equations now represent the oxidation and reduction half reactions. Electrons appear as products in the oxidation half reaction and as reactants in the reduction half reaction.

(e) Each half reaction is multiplied by an appropriate factor to equalize the number of electrons in each half reaction.

This step is necessary to maintain electron balance in the overall equation.

(f) Add the two half reactions.

The sum of the half reactions represents the total redox reaction. Cancellation of H_2O, H^+, or OH^- should be made, if these species appear on both sides of the final equation. A final check should be made for atomic and electrical balance at this point to insure that no error has been made.

Example 12.2 Balance the following reaction using the method given above. Indicate the oxidation and the reduction half reactions.

$$Na + Cl_2 \rightarrow NaCl$$

Step *a*. Na and Cl_2 are the species of interest

Step *b*. partial equations

$$Na \rightarrow Na^+ \qquad\qquad Cl_2 \rightarrow Cl^-$$

Step *c*. atomic balance

$$Na \rightarrow Na^+ \qquad\qquad Cl_2 \rightarrow 2Cl^-$$

Step *d*. charge balance

$$Na \rightarrow Na^+ + 1e^- \qquad\qquad 2e^- + Cl_2 \rightarrow 2Cl^-$$
(oxidation half reaction)   (reduction half reaction)

Step *e*. electron balance

$$2(Na \rightarrow Na^+ + 1e^-) \qquad\qquad 1(2e^- + Cl_2 \rightarrow 2Cl^-)$$
$$2Na \rightarrow 2Na^+ + 2e^- \qquad\qquad 2e^- + Cl_2 \rightarrow 2Cl^-$$

Step *f*. total reaction

$$2Na + Cl_2 \rightarrow 2NaCl$$

Example 12.3 Balance the following reaction and indicate the oxidation and the reduction half reactions.

$$Fe^{++} + MnO_4^- \rightarrow Fe^{3+} + Mn^{++} \text{ (acid solution)}$$

Step *a*. the species of interest are Fe^{++} and MnO_4^-

Step *b*. partial equations

$$Fe^{++} \rightarrow Fe^{3+} \qquad\qquad MnO_4^- \rightarrow Mn^{++}$$

Step *c*. atomic balance

$$Fe^{++} \rightarrow Fe^{3+} \qquad\qquad MnO_4^- \rightarrow Mn^{++} + 4H_2O$$
$$8H^+ + MnO_4^- \rightarrow$$
$$Mn^{++} + 4H_2O$$

Step *d*. charge balance

$$Fe^{++} \rightarrow Fe^{3+} + 1e^- \qquad\qquad 5e^- + 8H^+ + MnO_4^- \rightarrow$$
(oxidation half reaction) $Mn^{++} + 4H_2O$
(reduction half reaction)

Step *e*. electron balance

$$5(Fe^{++} \rightarrow Fe^{3+} + 1e^-) \qquad\qquad 1(5e^- + 8H^+ + MnO_4^- \rightarrow$$
$$Mn^{++} + 4H_2O)$$
$$5Fe^{++} \rightarrow 5Fe^{3+} + 5e^-$$
$$5e^- + 8H^+ + MnO_4^- \rightarrow Mn^{++} + 4H_2O$$

Step *f*. add for the total reaction

$$5Fe^{++} + 8H^+ + MnO_4^- \rightarrow Mn^{++} + 5Fe^{3+} + 4H_2O$$

Example 12.4 Given the reaction

$$Bi(OH)_3 + SnO_2^= \rightarrow Bi + SnO_3^=$$

Balance the reaction and identify the species that are oxidized and reduced.

Step *a*. The species of interest are $Bi(OH)_3$ and $SnO_2^=$

Step *b*. partial equations

$$Bi(OH)_3 \rightarrow Bi \qquad\qquad SnO_2^= \rightarrow SnO_3^=$$

Step *c*. atomic balance

$$Bi(OH)_3 \rightarrow Bi + 3OH^- \qquad\qquad 2OH^- + SnO_2^= \rightarrow SnO_3^=$$
$$2OH^- + SnO_2^= \rightarrow$$
$$SnO_3^= + H_2O$$

(OH⁻ is added since $Bi(OH)_3$ exists only in a basic solution)

Step *d.* charge balance

$$3e^- + Bi(OH)_3 \rightarrow \qquad\qquad 2OH^- + SnO_2^= \rightarrow$$
$$Bi + 3OH^- \qquad\qquad SnO_3^= + H_2O + 2e^-$$
(reduction half reaction) \qquad (oxidation half reaction)
$Bi(OH)_3$ is reduced \qquad\qquad $SnO_2^=$ is oxidized

Step *e.* electron balance

$$2(3e^- + Bi(OH)_3 \rightarrow \qquad\qquad 3(2OH^- + SnO_2^= \rightarrow$$
$$Bi + 3OH^-) \qquad\qquad SnO_3^= + H_2O + 2e^-)$$
$$6e^- + 2Bi(OH)_3 \rightarrow 2Bi + 6OH^-$$
$$6OH^- + 3SnO_2^= \rightarrow 3SnO_3^= + 3H_2O + 6e^-$$

Step *f.* add

$$2Bi(OH)_3 + 6OH^- + 3SnO_2^= \rightarrow$$
$$2Bi + 6OH^- + 3SnO_3^= + 3H_2O$$

Subtracting $6OH^-$ from both sides of the equation yields the final answer.

$$2Bi(OH)_3 + 3SnO_2^= \rightarrow 2Bi + 3SnO_3^= + 3H_2O$$

Normality of redox solutions

In Chapter V, the normality of a solution is defined as the number of equivalents of solute per liter of solution. The weight of one equivalent of an acid or base is the weight of the substance that contains one mole of replaceable H^+ ions or OH^- ions. The weight of one equivalent of a redox agent is the weight of the substance that loses or gains one mole of electrons during the reaction. This definition of the equivalent weight broadens the one given in Chapter II. From the half reaction

$$4e^- + O_2 \rightarrow 2O^=$$

it is seen that 1/4 mole of oxygen gas takes on one mole of electrons. Therefore, the equivalent weight of O_2 is 8 g. Thus, the weight of any element that reacts with 8 g of O_2 yields one mole of electrons to the reaction.

The equivalent weight of a substance undergoing a redox reaction is based on the balanced half reaction. Some redox reagents form different products when conditions are varied. Thus the normality of a redox solution depends on the redox reaction it undergoes as well as on the weight of solute per liter. For example, the equivalent weight of iron(III) is 55.8 g if the reduction product is iron(II), or 18.6 g if the product is iron metal.

$$3e^- + Fe^{3+} \rightarrow Fe \quad \text{eq wt} = 55.8\,g/3$$

$$1e^- + Fe^{3+} \rightarrow Fe^{++} \quad \text{eq wt} = 55.8\,g/1$$

Thus, a solution containing 16.23 g $FeCl_3$ per liter is 0.30 *N* in Fe^{3+} ions if the first reaction takes place, and 0.10 *N* if the second reaction occurs.

Example 12.5 What weight of $K_2Cr_2O_7$ is required to prepare 600 ml of 0.500 N solution for use in the reaction

$$3Sn^{++} + Cr_2O_7^- + 14H^+ \rightarrow 3Sn^{4+} + 2Cr^{3+} + 7H_2O$$

Answer: The half reaction involving $Cr_2O_7^-$ is

$$6e^- + 14H^+ + Cr_2O_7^- \rightarrow 2Cr^{3+} + 7H_2O$$

The equivalent weight of $K_2Cr_2O_7$ is $\dfrac{294 \text{ g/mole}}{6 \text{ eq/mole}} = 49.0$ g/eq

Wt of $K_2Cr_2O_7$ required $= (0.500 \text{ eq/l})(0.600 \text{ l})(49.0 \text{ g/eq}) = 14.7$ g

Example 12.6 What weight of $SnCl_2$ is contained in 250 ml of solution if 10.0 ml of it reacts with 12.2 ml of the above $K_2Cr_2O_7$ solution?

Answer: Normality of Sn^{++} solution $= \dfrac{(0.500 \text{ eq/l})(0.0122 \text{ l})}{0.0100 \text{ l}} = 0.610 N$

Equivalent weight of $SnCl_2 = \dfrac{(190 \text{ g/mole})}{(2 \text{ eq/mole})} = 95$ g/eq

Wt of $SnCl_2 = (0.610 \text{ eq/l})(0.250 \text{ l})(95 \text{ g/eq}) = 14.5$ g

Electrochemical reactions

There are two types of electrochemical reactions. In an electrolytic cell, a redox reaction is brought about by the passage of an electrical current. In a voltaic cell, the redox reactions generate an electrical current. Redox principles are applicable to both types of cells.

An electrical current is the movement of charged particles. Electrons carry current through a metal; there is no movement of atoms. Ions carry the electrical current through a molten salt or liquid solution. Solutions of strong electrolytes are good electrical conductors, since there are many ions. Solutions of non-electrolytes, which contain dissolved molecules rather than ions, are non-conductors. Solutions of weak electrolytes are poor electrical conductors, since there are few ions.

Electrolytic cells

In an electrolytic cell, two electrically conducting solids called electrodes are placed in a container of liquid and connected to a battery or generator which causes the electrons to move from one electrode to the other. The ions in the liquid solution or molten salt between the electrodes carry the current from one electrode to the other. One electrode becomes positively charged due to a slight deficiency of electrons, while the other electrode becomes negatively charged due to a slight excess of electrons. Positively charged ions (cations) are attracted to the negative cathode where they undergo a reduction reaction by the taking on of electrons. Negatively charged ions (anions) are attracted to the positive anode where they give up electrons and undergo an oxidation reaction.

ELECTROLYSIS OF A FUSED SALT

The behavior of NaCl in an electrolytic cell is typical of an ionic solid. The Na^+ and Cl^- ions are rather rigidly held together in the solid. Since all of the electrons are tightly bound to the ions, there is no electrical conduction in the solid. When the salt melts, the ions are free to move with respect to one another (see Fig. 12.1). The Na^+ ions move to the cathode where metallic sodium is formed when electrons are taken on. The Cl^- ions move toward the anode where Cl_2 gas is formed as the ions give up electrons. The reactions may be written as two separate equations.

$$Na^+ + e^- \rightarrow Na \quad \text{(cathode)}$$
$$2Cl^- \rightarrow Cl_2 + 2e^- \quad \text{(anode)}$$

The number of electrons taken up must be equal to the number of electrons produced. Therefore, two moles of Na^+ ions react for every two moles of reacting Cl^- ions. Multiplying the cathode reaction by two and adding the electrode reactions gives the overall cell reaction.

$$2Na^+ + 2e^- \rightarrow 2Na \quad \text{(cathode)}$$
$$2Cl^- \rightarrow Cl_2 + 2e^- \quad \text{(anode)}$$
$$\overline{2Na^+ + 2Cl^- \rightarrow 2Na + Cl_2} \quad \text{(overall)}$$

ELECTROLYSIS OF AQUEOUS SOLUTIONS

The presence of water in an aqueous solution of an electrolyte permits the formation of hydrogen and oxygen, instead of the

Fig. 12.1

Diagram of a Cell Used for the Electrolysis of Fused NaCl to Produce Sodium Metal and Chlorine.

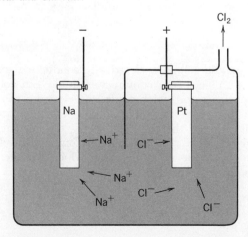

neutralization of the electrolyte ions. Hydrogen is produced at the cathode, if the hydrogen ion is reduced more easily than the other cations. Hydrogen ions are present as a part of the water equilibrium. Combining this with the reduction reaction gives the overall cathode reaction.

$$2H_2O + 2e^- \rightarrow H_2 + 2OH^-$$

If Na^+ ions are present in a solution, two cathode reactions are possible.

$$Na^+ + e^- \rightarrow Na$$

$$2H_2O + 2e^- \rightarrow H_2 + 2OH^-$$

Since electrons are more strongly attracted to hydrogen than to sodium, the second reaction takes place. Furthermore, one would not predict the formation of metallic sodium in this case because of the extreme reactivity of the metal in water. In general, metals above hydrogen in the activity series are not liberated from aqueous solution by electrolysis.

At the anode, oxidation of the OH^- ion to form oxygen is possible.

$$4OH^- \rightarrow O_2 + 2H_2O + 4e^-$$

Thus the anode oxidation of water is

$$2H_2O \rightarrow 4H^+ + O_2 + 4e^-$$

Only a few of the simple anions, such as Cl^-, Br^-, and I^-, are oxidized before water is oxidized. Therefore, oxygen is the usual product during electrolysis of solutions containing ions such as SO_4^- and NO_3^-.

The following reactions take place during the electrolysis of a NaCl solution.

$$2H_2O + 2e^- \rightarrow H_2 + 2OH^- \quad \text{(cathode)}$$

$$2Cl^- \rightarrow Cl_2 + 2e^- \quad \text{(anode)}$$

Combining these gives the overall reaction

$$2H_2O + 2Cl^- \rightarrow H_2 + Cl_2 + 2OH^-$$

Note that a sodium hydroxide solution develops as electrolysis continues.

When K_2SO_4 is added to water, the electrolysis products are hydrogen and oxygen since the reactions are

$$\begin{aligned} 4H_2O + 4e^- &\rightarrow 2H_2 + 4OH^- \quad &\text{(cathode)} \\ 2H_2O &\rightarrow 4H^+ + O_2 + 4e^- \quad &\text{(anode)} \\ \hline 6H_2O &\rightarrow 2H_2 + O_2 + 4H^+ + 4OH^- \end{aligned}$$

Subtracting $4H_2O$ from both sides yields the overall reaction.

$$2H_2O \rightarrow 2H_2 + O_2$$

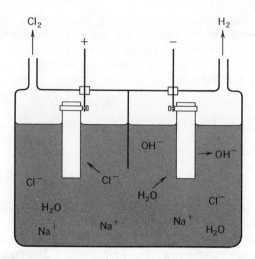

Fig. 12.2

Electrolysis of NaCl Solution. Cl⁻ ions are attracted to the anode (+) where they are oxidized. Since water is more easily reduced than Na⁺ ions, H₂ gas and OH⁻ ions are formed at the cathode (−).

A $CuCl_2$ solution illustrates the case where the metal is less active than hydrogen. The reactions are

$$Cu^{++} + 2e^- \rightarrow Cu \qquad \text{(cathode)}$$
$$2Cl^- \rightarrow Cl_2 + 2e^- \qquad \text{(anode)}$$
$$\overline{Cu^{++} + 2Cl^- \rightarrow Cu + Cl_2} \quad \text{(overall)}$$

In the above reactions, it is assumed that inert electrodes such as platinum or graphite are used. Other electrode materials may enter into the chemical reaction under the influence of the electrolysis conditions. For example, copper electrodes often are active because electrons may be removed easily from the atoms in the anode.

$$Cu \rightarrow Cu^{++} + 2e^-$$

This oxidation reaction occurs if the other possible reactions require more energy. Since copper is more easily oxidized than H_2O, the reaction takes place in preference to the oxidation of H_2O. If copper electrodes are used in the electrolysis of a $CuSO_4$ solution, there is a transfer of copper from the anode, where Cu^{++} ions are formed, to the cathode, where the ions are plated out as the metal. There is no change in the concentration of ions in the solution.

$$Cu \rightarrow Cu^{++} + 2e^- \quad \text{(anode)}$$

$$Cu^{++} + 2e^- \rightarrow Cu \quad \text{(cathode)}$$

POTENTIALS FOR ELECTROLYTIC REACTIONS

Electrolysis reactions are driven by the applied voltage or potential. At very low voltages there is insufficient driving force to cause any reaction to take place or any current to flow. There is a minimum potential at which the most easily reduced cation and the most easily oxidized anion begin to react at the electrodes. Above this minimum potential, redox reactions take place readily. The voltage at which a reaction just begins is the *decomposition potential* for that reaction. Each oxidation and reduction half reaction has a characteristic decomposition potential which increases with decreasing concentration of the reactant.

If several ionic species are in a solution, their separation is possible by control of the applied potential. For example, silver ions may be removed from an aqueous solution that also contains copper ions, if the applied voltage is kept below that required to reduce Cu^{++} ions. If the voltage is above the decomposition potential for copper, both copper and silver are plated out. If the applied voltage is increased above that required to reduce the H_2O molecule, silver, copper, and hydrogen are produced.

The decomposition potential is affected by concentration. Most of the above discussion is based on 1 molar concentrations. The electrode reactions may change in very dilute or very concentrated solutions, when the applied voltage is increased sufficiently to cause a reaction. At very low Cl^- ion concentrations, some O_2 may be produced as well as Cl_2. Some H_2 may form at the cathode during the electrolysis of a very dilute Cu^{++} solution. Similarly, H_2 may be produced in the electrolysis of a 1 M Cu^{++} solution, if the current is very large due to a high voltage. In this case, the solution near the cathode becomes depleted of metal ions, providing a very dilute Cu^{++} solution for the electrode. Some of the metals just above hydrogen in the activity series may be deposited in small amounts along with the H_2 evolution, if the concentration of these ions is very high.

The concentration of an ion sometimes is lowered purposely by the addition of a complexing agent. It is possible then to remove another ion preferentially from the solution. For example, copper ions may be separated electrolytically from silver ions in a solution by the addition of cyanide ions. The cyano- complex of silver is much more stable than that of copper. The concentration of free silver ions is lowered sufficiently so that copper plates out of solution while the silver ions remain, although the decomposition potential of silver is lower than that of copper.

THE LAWS OF ELECTROLYSIS

The definition of the equivalent weight of a substance undergoing oxidation or reduction implies that the passage of one mole of electrons through an electrolysis cell liberates one equivalent weight of an element. Thus, if an electrical current is passed through electrolysis cells for the production of silver, copper, and chlorine, the same number of equivalents of the elements is produced.

$$Ag^+ + e^- \rightarrow Ag$$

$$\text{1 equivalent weight Ag} = \frac{107.87 \text{ g Ag}}{1 \text{ mole electrons}} = 107.87 \text{ g}$$

$$Cu^{++} + 2e^- \rightarrow Cu$$

$$\text{1 equivalent weight Cu} = \frac{63.55 \text{ g Cu}}{2 \text{ moles electrons}} = 31.77 \text{ g}$$

$$2Cl^- \rightarrow Cl_2 + 2e^-$$

$$\text{1 equivalent weight Cl}_2 = \frac{71.0 \text{ g Cl}_2}{2 \text{ moles electrons}} = 35.5 \text{ g}$$

One mole of electrons is called a *Faraday* of electricity. Since electrical current is the flow of electrons, the Faraday is related to the electrical measurement of current flow, the basic unit of which is the ampere (amp). One *coulomb* is the amount of current that passes a point when a current of one amp flows for one second. One Faraday is equal to 96,500 coulombs. Putting all this in equation form,

1 coulomb = 1 amp-sec
1 Faraday = 96,500 coulombs = 6.023×10^{23} electrons

During electrolysis, 96,500 coulombs (one Faraday) of electricity reduces or oxidizes one equivalent weight of a substance.

Example 12.7 Calculate the weight of copper produced by passing a current of 1.60 amps through a $CuSO_4$ solution for 1.00 hour.

Coulombs = (1.60 amps)(1 hr)(60 min/hr)(60 sec/min)
= 5760 coulombs

Fig. 12.3

Relationship Between the Faraday and Some Equivalent Weights. When one Faraday (96,500 coulombs) of electricity is passed through these cells, one equivalent weight of each substance undergoes chemical reaction. If silver electrodes are used in $AgNO_3$ solution, 107.9 g silver deposits on the cathode. 107.9 g of the silver anode dissolves. In the $Cu(NO_3)_2$ cell the copper anode loses 31.77 g, and the cathode gains 31.77 g. If inert electrodes are used, the cathode reactions are the same; however, 8.00 g oxygen is produced at the anode. Inert electrodes are used in HCl solution.

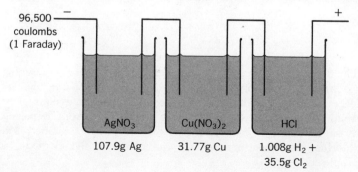

96,500 ──── −   + ────
coulombs
(1 Faraday)

AgNO₃   Cu(NO₃)₂   HCl

107.9g Ag   31.77g Cu   1.008g H₂ +
                                   35.5g Cl₂

$$\frac{5760 \text{ coulombs}}{96,500 \text{ coulombs/eq}} = 0.0597 \text{ eq Cu}$$

$$(0.0597 \text{ eq Cu})(31.77 \text{ g/eq}) = 1.90 \text{ g Cu}$$

Voltaic cells

Current is produced in voltaic or galvanic cells as the result of a chemical reaction or of the difference in concentration of the same ion. All voltaic cells involve a spontaneous chemical reaction in which the energy of the products is less than the energy of the reactants. An external battery is needed to supply energy to reverse the reaction.

Theoretically, a voltaic cell is made by separating the oxidation and reduction reactions into two chambers and connecting the electrodes with a wire and the chambers by a salt bridge. The salt bridge provides a pathway for the current to be carried through the cell. Frequently it is a U-shaped tube filled with a salt such as KCl. As electrons are produced by the oxidation half reaction, they flow through the wire to the reduction half cell. Since the final state of the system is of lower energy, this is energetically feasible. The driving force, or the potential of the cell, is a function of the magnitude of the energy difference. The electrons can be made to do work, such as running a motor or lighting a bulb, in going from one half cell to the other.

One simple voltaic cell makes use of the reaction of zinc metal in a solution of copper ions

$$Zn + Cu^{++} \rightarrow Zn^{++} + Cu + \text{energy (as heat)}$$

This is composed of two half reactions.

$$Zn \rightarrow Zn^{++} + 2e^-$$
$$Cu^{++} + 2e^- \rightarrow Cu$$

These reactions are separated into two chambers to make the Daniell cell, which is schematically illustrated in Fig. 12.4. The potential difference as measured on the meter (M) is 1.10 volts when the ionic concentrations are 1 M.

Voltaic cells are often represented by an abbreviated cell notation which shows the electrodes and ions involved in the reaction. Certain conventions are used in the notation. The oxidation half cell is always written on the left side. The solid electrode is listed first, followed by a semicolon to denote a phase change. If a gas is present as a part of the half cell, it is noted next, usually followed by the pressure enclosed in parentheses. The ions involved in the oxidation reaction and their concentration are listed. Each ion is separated by a comma. A set of double vertical lines indicates a bridge between the two half cells. The same data are repeated in reverse order for the reduction half cell; thus, the electrode appears at the right end of the notation. The Daniell cell is represented as

$$Zn; Zn^{++} \ (1 \ M) \ \| \ Cu^{++} \ (1 \ M); Cu$$

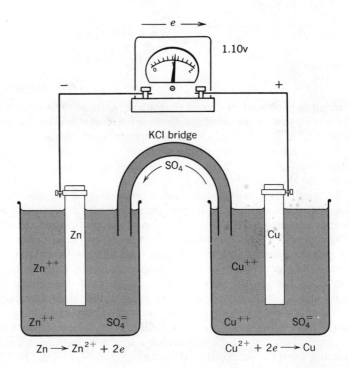

Fig. 12.4

*Daniell Cell. Rather than increasing the solution temperature, energy
released in the reaction of Zn with Cu^{++} provides an electrical current in a
Daniell cell.*

The use of inert electrodes in a voltaic cell is illustrated using
the redox reaction.

$$MnO_4^- + 5Fe^{++} + 8H^+ \rightarrow 5Fe^{3+} + Mn^{++} + 4H_2O$$

Iron is not used as the oxidation electrode, since the electrode
reaction is $Fe \rightarrow Fe^{++} + 2e^-$ instead of $Fe^{++} \rightarrow Fe^{3+} + 1e^-$.
Thus, an inert platinum electrode is used as a surface where
the latter reaction occurs. Also there is no means of making a
(Mn^{++}, MnO_4^-) electrode other than using a platinum electrode
as a reaction site. In the abbreviated notation, the cell is written

Pt; $Fe^{++}(1\ M)$, $Fe^{3+}(1\ M)$ ||

H$^+(1\ M)$, $MnO_4^-(1\ M)$, $Mn^{++}(1\ M)$; Pt

The potential for this cell is 0.73 volt.

Half-cell potentials

The driving force in a voltaic cell is the difference in the tenden-
cies for oxidation to occur in each of the half cells. The potential
for oxidation in a single half cell cannot be measured. It is possible

to measure the voltage produced when two half cells are connected. A scale of relative oxidation potentials may be developed by arbitrarily assigning a value to one half cell and measuring all other half-cell potentials with respect to it. A value of 0.00 volts has been chosen for the standard reference, the hydrogen half cell.

$$H_2 \text{ (1 atm)} \rightarrow 2H^+ \text{ (1 } M\text{)} + 2e^- \qquad E^\circ = 0.00 \text{ v}$$

This half cell is connected to another. The potential of the cell is measured and is assigned to the second half cell. If oxidation occurs in the half cell when it is connected to the hydrogen half cell, the potential is given a positive value. If reduction takes place, the potential is given a negative value.

When the zinc half cell is attached to the hydrogen electrode, a potential of 0.76 volts is observed.

$$Zn; Zn^{++}\text{(1 } M\text{)} \parallel H^+ \text{ (1 } M\text{)}, H_2\text{(1 atm)}; Pt \qquad E^\circ = 0.76 \text{ v}$$

Since zinc undergoes oxidation, the zinc half cell is assigned a potential of $+0.76$ volts.

Fig. 12.5

Diagram of an Electrochemical Cell Which Uses Inert Electrodes. For convenience, a porous plate which permits the flow of ions between half cells is used as the bridge in place of a U-tube.

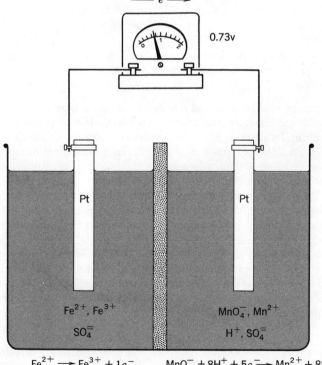

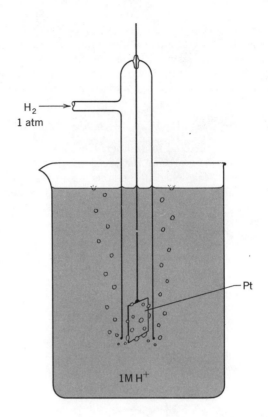

H_2
1 atm

Pt

1M H$^+$

Fig. 12.6

Hydrogen Half Cell. Consists of a platinum electrode in a 1 M acid solution. H_2 gas (pressure 1 atm) passes over the electrode as it bubbles through the solution. The half cell has an assigned potential of 0.00 volts.

Extensive tabulations of standard oxidation potentials ($E°$) are available. Some of the more common half-cell potentials are given in Table 12.1. The correlation between the ordering in this table and the activity series (Table 2.2) should be noted. The value of $E°$ represents a measure of the tendency for the oxidation reaction to take place.

The cell potential for any combination of half cells may be calculated from the table of oxidation potentials. The half cell with the more positive value of $E°$ represents the oxidation reaction. The reaction with the lower value of $E°$ undergoes reduction, the reverse of the reaction as written in the table. The potential of a cell representing a chemical reaction is equal to the difference between the oxidation potential for the half cell undergoing oxidation and the oxidation potential for the half cell undergoing reduction.

Example 12.8 Calculate the cell potential for the following and write the chemical reaction.

(a) Zn; Zn^{++}(1 M) ‖ Cu^{++}(1 M); Cu
(b) Pt; Fe^{++}(1 M), Fe^{3+} (1 M) ‖ Br$^-$(1 M), Br$_2$; Pt
(c) Pt; Sn^{++}(1 M), Sn^{4+}(1 M) ‖ Ag$^+$(1 M), Ag

answers:

(a)

$$\text{Zn} \rightarrow \text{Zn}^{++} + 2e^- \qquad E° = +0.76 \text{ v}$$
$$-(\text{Cu} \rightarrow \text{Cu}^{++} + 2e^-) \qquad -(E° = -0.34)$$

or:

$$\underline{\text{Cu}^{++} + 2e^- \rightarrow \text{Cu}} \qquad \underline{-(E° = -0.34)}$$
$$\text{Zn} + \text{Cu}^{++} \rightarrow \text{Zn}^{++} + \text{Cu} \qquad E°_{cell} = +1.10 \text{ v}$$

(b)

$$\text{Fe}^{++} \rightarrow \text{Fe}^{3+} + 1e^- \qquad E° = -0.77 \text{ v}$$
$$\underline{2e^- + \text{Br}_2 \rightarrow 2\text{Br}^-} \qquad \underline{-(E° = -1.07)}$$
$$2\text{Fe}^{++} + \text{Br}_2 \rightarrow 2\text{Fe}^{3+} + 2\text{Br}^- \qquad E°_{cell} = +0.30 \text{ v}$$

(c)

$$\text{Sn}^{++} \rightarrow \text{Sn}^{4+} + 2e^- \qquad E° = -0.15 \text{ v}$$
$$\underline{\text{Ag}^+ + 1e^- \rightarrow \text{Ag}} \qquad \underline{-(E° = -0.80)}$$
$$\text{Sn}^{++} + 2\text{Ag}^+ \rightarrow \text{Sn}^{4+} + 2\text{Ag} \qquad E°_{cell} = +0.65 \text{ v}$$

PREDICTIONS OF CHEMICAL REACTIONS

A reaction takes place spontaneously, if the energy of the products is less than the energy of the reactants. Since the half-cell potentials represent the tendency for oxidation to occur, the cell poten-

Table 12.1

Standard Oxidation Potentials for Selected Half-Cell Reactions

Reaction	$E°$ (volts)
K $\rightarrow$ K$^+$ + e$^-$	+2.92
Na $\rightarrow$ Na$^+$ + e$^-$	+2.71
Mg $\rightarrow$ Mg^{++} + 2e$^-$	+2.38
Zn $\rightarrow$ Zn^{++} + 2e$^-$	+0.76
S$^=$ $\rightarrow$ S + 2e$^-$	+0.51
Fe $\rightarrow$ Fe^{++} + 2e$^-$	+0.44
Ni $\rightarrow$ Ni^{++} + 2e$^-$	+0.23
Sn $\rightarrow$ Sn^{++} + 2e$^-$	+0.14
Pb $\rightarrow$ Pb^{++} + 2e$^-$	+0.13
H$_2$ $\rightarrow$ 2H$^+$ + 2e$^-$	0.00
Sn^{++} $\rightarrow$ Sn^{4+} + 2e$^-$	−0.14
Cu $\rightarrow$ Cu^{++} + 2e$^-$	−0.34
Cu $\rightarrow$ Cu$^+$ + e$^-$	−0.52
2I$^-$ $\rightarrow$ I$_2$ + 2e$^-$	−0.54
Fe^{++} $\rightarrow$ Fe^{3+} + e$^-$	−0.77
Ag $\rightarrow$ Ag$^+$ + e$^-$	−0.80
2Br$^-$ $\rightarrow$ Br$_2$ + 2e$^-$	−1.09
2H$_2$O $\rightarrow$ O$_2$ + 4H$^+$ + 4e$^-$	−1.23
2Cl$^-$ $\rightarrow$ Cl$_2$ + 2e$^-$	−1.36
Au $\rightarrow$ Au^{3+} + 3e$^-$	−1.42
Mn^{++} + 4H$_2$O $\rightarrow$ MnO$_4^-$ + 8H$^+$ + 5e$^-$	−1.49
2F$^-$ $\rightarrow$ F$_2$ + 2e$^-$	−2.87

tial is a measure of the tendency for a redox reaction to take place spontaneously. To determine the spontaneity of a reaction, it is first expressed as the sum of two half reactions. The cell potential is determined by subtracting the oxidation potential E° for the reduction half reaction from the E° value for the oxidation half reaction. If the cell potential is positive, the reaction is spontaneous. If the cell potential is negative, the reaction proceeds in the opposite direction.

Example 12.9 Do the following reactions take place as written?

(a) $Zn^{++}(1\ M) + Cu \rightarrow Zn + Cu^{++}(1\ M)$
(b) $Pb + 2Fe^{3+}(1\ M) \rightarrow 2Fe^{++}(1\ M) + Pb^{++}(1\ M)$
(c) $5Au + 3MnO_4^- + 24H^+ \rightarrow 5Au^{3+} + 3Mn^{++} + 12H_2O$

answers:

(a) The half reactions corresponding to the reaction are

$$
\begin{array}{lr}
Cu \rightarrow Cu^{++} + 2e^- & E° = -0.34\ v \\
2e^- + Zn^{++} \rightarrow Zn & -(E° = +0.76) \\
\hline
 & E°_{cell} = -1.10\ v
\end{array}
$$

Not a spontaneous reaction. From the previous discussion, it is known that zinc reduces copper ions.

(b)

$$
\begin{array}{lr}
Pb \rightarrow Pb^{++} + 2e^- & E° = +0.13\ v \\
1e^- + Fe^{3+} \rightarrow Fe^{++} & -(E° = -0.77) \\
\hline
 & E°_{cell} = +0.90\ v
\end{array}
$$

Reaction is spontaneous and proceeds as written. Lead does reduce ferric ions.

(c)

$$
\begin{array}{lr}
Au \rightarrow Au^{3+} + 3e^- & E° = -1.42\ v \\
MnO_4^- + 8H^+ + 5e^- \rightarrow Mn^{++} + 4H_2O & -(E° = -1.50) \\
\hline
 & E°_{cell} = +0.08\ v
\end{array}
$$

Reaction is spontaneous when the concentrations of all ions are 1 *M*.

EFFECT OF CONCENTRATION

The concentration of ions has an effect on the half-cell potential. The oxidation potential of a half cell increases (becomes more positive) as the concentration decreases.

If two half cells involving the same ions at different concentrations are connected, a small cell potential develops. The potential for the cell

$$Cu;\ Cu^{++}(0.1\ M) \parallel Cu^{++}(0.5\ M);\ Cu$$

is +0.019 volt. This reflects the tendency for the system to equalize concentrations in the two half cells. In order to do this, electrons from the electrode in the dilute solution moving to the more concentrated solution (a) cause more copper ions to form in the dilute solution and (b) deposit copper ions from the other solution. This proceeds until the concentrations are equal, and the cell potential equals zero.

Standard oxidation potentials are the potentials for half cells when the ionic concentrations are 1 M. Equations are available to correct these values for concentration differences.

Reference Electrodes. The hydrogen half cell is used as the reference electrode for the oxidation potential scale. Unfortunately it is not a very convenient electrode for ordinary use. The voltage reflects any variation in the H^+ ion concentration as well as the H_2 pressure which is difficult to maintain at one atmosphere. The platinum surface must be kept very clean. It is more convenient to use a secondary standard that can be prepared easily and maintain its potential under normal conditions of usage. The calomel cell is one of the secondary standards for which the voltage is easily reproduced and accurately measured with respect to the hydrogen half cell.

The voltage of the calomel cell depends upon the concentration of KCl. Three standard calomel cells are used. Each has its particular application. The half-cell potentials at 25°C are as follows.

$$0.1 \ M \text{ calomel } (0.1 \ M \text{ KCl}) \ E° = -0.3338 \text{ v}$$
$$1 \ M \text{ calomel } (1 \ M \text{ KCl}) \ E° = -0.2800$$
$$\text{Saturated calomel (saturated solution of KCl) } E° = -0.2415$$

Fig. 12.7

Sketch of a Calomel Cell. A pool of mercury is in contact with a paste of mercury and calomel (Hg_2Cl_2), and covered with a KCl electrolyte solution saturated with slightly soluble Hg_2Cl_2. Several techniques are used to bridge the solution to another cell. A very small capillary tip is used in this example.

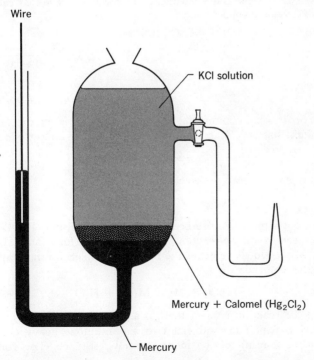

Wire

KCl solution

Mercury + Calomel (Hg_2Cl_2)

Mercury

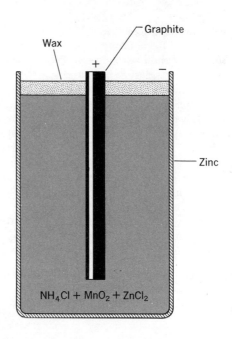

Fig. 12.8

Dry Cell. A zinc shell, the negative electrode, is filled with a paste of NH₄Cl, MnO₂, and ZnCl₂ moistened with water. The central graphite rod is the positive electrode. Voltage is 1.5 v.

Example 12.10 What is the potential of the cell made of a 1 M calomel half cell and a copper half cell?

$$2\text{Hg(l)} + 2\text{Cl}^-(1\ M) \rightarrow \text{Hg}_2\text{Cl}_2(\text{s}) + 2e^- \qquad \text{E}^\circ = \quad -0.28\ \text{v}$$
$$\text{Cu}^{++} + 2e^- \rightarrow \text{Cu} \qquad \underline{-\text{E}^\circ = -(-0.34)}$$
$$\text{E}^\circ_{\text{cell}} = +0.06\ \text{v}$$

Commercial batteries

Dry cells. One commercial type of voltaic cell is the dry cell or flashlight battery. Zinc is oxidized at the negative electrode.

$$\text{Zn} \rightarrow \text{Zn}^{++} + 2e^-$$

At the positive graphite electrode the reaction is

$$2\text{NH}_4^+ + 2e^- \rightarrow 2\text{NH}_3 + \text{H}_2$$

These gases must be absorbed; otherwise the cell may burst. The NH₃ is removed by a reaction with Zn^{++} ions to form $\text{Zn(NH}_3)_4^{++}$ ions. MnO₂ slowly removes the H₂ which collects on the graphite forming an insulating layer.

$$\text{MnO}_2 + \text{H}_2 \rightarrow \text{MnO} + \text{H}_2\text{O}$$

Since the reaction is slow, there is a reduction in the voltage of batteries, which are subjected to a continuous heavy current drain, as a result of the increased cell resistance. The voltage returns to normal when the battery is allowed to stand while no current is used.

Storage batteries. A storage battery is a cell that may be recharged by passage of a direct current from an outside source (a battery charger). In theory, it should be possible to recharge any voltaic cell. In practice, there are very few cells that are reversible. The most common storage battery used in the U.S. is the lead battery.

Ordinary car batteries consist of six two-volt cells combined to produce twelve volts. Since the cell voltage is temperature dependent, the battery voltage is substantially lower at low temperatures. The negative electrodes are pure lead plates or grids while the positive electrodes are lead grids coated with PbO_2. The electrolyte is a sulfuric acid solution.

The following reactions occur upon discharge:

Negative electrode: Lead ions are produced which combine with sulfate ions to produce a coating of $PbSO_4$ on the electrode.

$$Pb \rightarrow Pb^{++} + 2e^-$$
$$Pb^{++} + SO_4^= \rightarrow PbSO_4\downarrow$$

Positive electrode: the PbO_2 is reduced to lead ions which combine with sulfate ions to form a $PbSO_4$ coating.

$$2e^- + PbO_2 + 4H^+ \rightarrow Pb^{++} + 2H_2O$$
$$\underline{Pb^{++} + SO_4^= \rightarrow PbSO_4\downarrow \qquad\qquad}$$
$$2e^- + PbO_2 + 4H^+ + SO_4^= \rightarrow PbSO_4\downarrow + 2H_2O$$

Addition of electrode reactions yields the following cell reaction during discharge.

$$Pb + PbO_2 + 2H_2SO_4 \rightarrow 2PbSO_4\downarrow + 2H_2O$$

Since H_2SO_4 is consumed during discharge, the electrolyte becomes more dilute and less dense. The reactions are reversed during the charge cycle. This produces H_2SO_4 and an increase in electrolyte density. The density of the electrolyte is a measure of the state of charge of a battery.

High Energy-Density Batteries. With serious consideration being given to the use of batteries to power automobiles, attention is focused on developing a battery that is capable of delivering high currents over a long period of time, a high energy-density battery. The energy delivered per unit weight of the battery is important, since a heavy battery requires much energy for its own transportation. Thus very serious attention is being given to the light-weight metals in the upper left-hand corner of the periodic table as battery materials. The use of most of these elements precludes aqueous electrolytes.

Lithium and sodium are used most frequently in the experimental models of the batteries. During the discharge cycle of a sodium-sulfur battery, sodium ions form at the anode. The ions migrate through the electrolyte plug to the liquid sulfur reservoir where they combine with polysulfide ions, $(S^=)_x$, which are formed at the cathode.

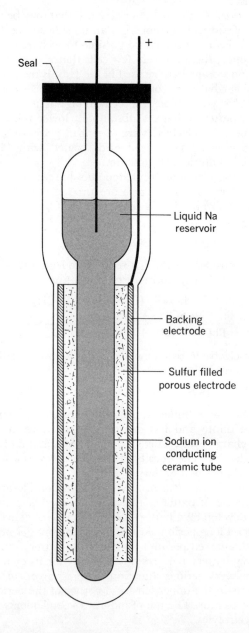

Fig. 12.9

Sketch of Sodium-Sulfur Battery. Liquid sodium and sulfur are the elec-
trodes. A solid aluminum oxide plug is the electrolyte. The plug is porous
to Na⁺ ions but not to sulfur or sodium polysulfide. The battery must be
heated to start the reactions; however, the energy released is enough to main-
tain operating temperature.

$$Na \rightarrow Na^+ + 1e^- \qquad \text{(anode)}$$
$$2xe^- + xS \rightarrow (S^=)_x \qquad \text{(cathode)}$$
$$2Na^+ + (S^=)_x \rightarrow Na_2S_x \qquad \text{(electrode chamber interface)}$$

The reactions are reversed during the charge cycle.

Another version of a high energy-density battery uses a liquid lithium anode, chlorine gas in a porous graphite cathode, and liquid LiCl as the electrolyte. This battery operates at 650°C.

Fuel cells. Fuel cells are devices for the separation of the oxidation and reduction reactions to produce electrical energy directly. The cells are designed to produce large amounts of energy relative to the weight of the cell. Most of the cells use reactants that can be fed into the cell continuously to give products that are easily removed. There is no need to recharge the cell. Electrons are produced in the oxidation reaction as long as fuel is supplied.

Most of the cells use fuels with low equivalent weights. Many of the fuel cells operating at low temperatures (below 300°C) use

Fig. 12.10

Diagram of a Hydrogen-Oxygen Fuel Cell. Porous electrodes permit the gases to diffuse to electrolyte interfaces where redox reactions occur. Electrodes are usually graphite or nickel sheets coated with appropriate catalysts. Concentrated KOH or phosphoric acid solutions are used as the electrolyte. Operating temperatures range from 25° to 250° C; pressures are 1 to 2 atm.

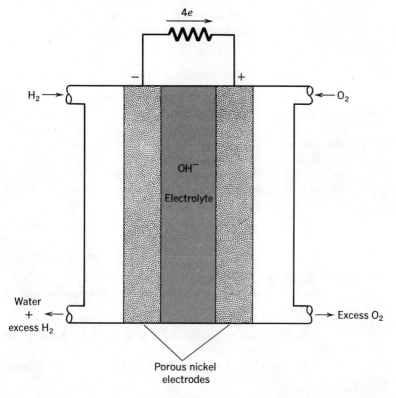

the reaction of oxygen or air with hydrogen or natural gas. Aqueous solutions, such as KOH, serve as electrolytes. High temperature (above 300°C) cells preclude the use of aqueous electrolytes. These cells use fused salts, such as the alkali metal carbonates, or ceramics, such as zirconium óxide.

In a typical H_2–O_2 fuel cell hydrogen is fed into the anode chamber where it diffuses into the anode until the electrolyte interface is reached. The oxidation reaction occurs at this point.

$$H_2 \rightarrow 2H^+ + 2e^-$$

The electrons are conducted away by the electrode to the external circuit. Since the electrolyte is strongly alkaline, the H^+ ions are converted to water to give a total anode reaction.

$$H_2 + 2OH^- \rightarrow 2H_2O + 2e^-$$

Oxygen or air is fed into the cathode chamber where the O_2 diffuses through the electrode until the electrolyte interface is reached. Reduction takes place at this point.

$$4e^- + O_2 + 2H_2O \rightarrow 4OH^-$$

Combining this reaction with the anode reaction, the overall cell reaction is

$$2H_2 + O_2 \rightarrow 2H_2O$$

Since the system is operating at high temperatures, the water is vaporized into the anode chamber where provision is made to condense and remove it.

SIGNIFICANT TERMS AND CONCEPTS IN CHAPTER XII:

Oxidation, reduction, redox, balancing of redox equations, equivalent weight of a redox agent, normality of redox solutions; electrolytic cells, electrolysis of molten salts, electrolysis of aqueous solutions, decomposition potential, laws of electrolysis, the Faraday; voltaic cells, abbreviated cell notation, standard oxidation half-cell potentials, spontaneous chemical reactions and cell potential, calomel cell, dry cell, storage battery, high energy-density battery, fuel cells.

Review questions

12.1. Balance the following oxidation-reduction reactions. Indicate the species that is oxidized and the species that is reduced.

    (a) $MnO_2 + I^- + H^+ \rightarrow Mn^{++} + I_2 + H_2O$

    (b) $FeCl_2 + K_2Cr_2O_7 \rightarrow FeCl_3 + CrCl_3 + KCl$ (acid solution)

    (c) $Ag_2CrO_4 + Br^- \rightarrow Ag + CrO_4^= + BrO_3^-$ (basic solution)

(d) $Br^- + H^+ + SO_4^= \rightarrow Br_2 + S + H_2O$
(e) $V^{3+} + NO_3^- \rightarrow VO_4^{4-} + N_2$ (acid solution)
(f) $Cu + NO_3^- \rightarrow Cu^{++} + NO_2 + H_2O$ (acid solution)

12.2. Distinguish between a voltaic cell and an electrolytic cell.
12.3. What would be the products when electrolysis is carried out in each of the following cells?

(a) Platinum electrodes in 1.0 M KNO_3
(b) Platinum electrodes in 1.0 M $CuSO_4$
(c) Silver electrodes in 1.0 M Na_2SO_4
(d) Silver electrodes in 1.0 M $AgNO_3$
(e) Platinum electrodes in 1.0 M $RbCl$
(f) Graphite electrodes in molten $CaCl_2$

12.4. A dry cell consists of zinc, graphite, NH_4Cl, MnO_2, and $ZnCl_2$. What is the purpose of each?

12.5. Give the overall reaction for the discharge of (a) the dry cell, (b) the sodium-sulfur cell.

Problems

12.6. In an acid solution, MnO_4^- is reduced to Mn^{++}; in a neutral or basic solution it is reduced to MnO_2. If a solution is marked 0.600 M $KMnO_4$, what is the normality of the solution when used with an acid? when used with a base?

12.7. Ceric sulfate ($Ce(SO_4)_2$) is used in the determination of iron in a solution.

$$Ce^{4+} + Fe^{++} \rightarrow Fe^{3+} + Ce^{3+}$$

What is the normality of a solution prepared by adding 4.00 g $Ce(SO_4)_2$ to 100 ml solution?

answer: 0.120 N

12.8. What is the normality of a $CuSO_4$ solution that is used in the following reaction

$$2CuSO_4 + 4KI \rightarrow 2CuI + 2K_2SO_4 + I_2$$

if 16.0 g $CuSO_4 \cdot 5H_2O$ is used to make 250 ml of solution?

12.9. When 9.80 g of $K_2Cr_2O_7$ is dissolved in 1.00 liter of solution, 35.10 ml of the solution reacts with 28.08 ml of a KI solution.

$$Cr_2O_7^= + 6I^- + 14H^+ \rightarrow 2Cr^{3+} + 3I_2 + 7H_2O$$

(a) What is the normality of the $K_2Cr_2O_7$ solution?
(b) What is the normality of the KI solution?
(c) How many grams KI would be in 800 ml of the KI solution?   answer: (c) 33.2 g

12.10. What weight of aluminum metal is produced by the electrolysis of Al_2O_3 in one hour at a current of 50.0 amps?

answer: 16.8 g

12.11. Electrolysis of 3 liters of 2.00 M $CuSO_4$ solution is carried out for 30.0 minutes with a current of 0.810 amps and platinum electrodes. Calculate the weight of the products produced in this reaction.

12.12. An electrical current is passed through a cell containing silver electrodes in a silver nitrate solution and then is passed into a sulfuric acid solution with platinum electrodes. If 3.24 grams of silver are plated out, what is the weight and volume (at STP) of each of the gases produced in the H_2SO_4 solution?

12.13. Given the cell:

$$Fe; Fe^{++}(1.0\ M) \| Sn^{++}(1.0\ M), Sn^{4+}(1.0\ M); Pt$$

    (a) Sketch the arrangement of the cell.
    (b) Show the reactions in each half cell.
    (c) Indicate the direction of electron flow.
    (d) Write the chemical equation represented by the cell.

12.14. For each of the following cells: (a) Write the corresponding chemical equation; (b) what is the voltage of the cell if the concentration of all ions is 1 M; (c) does the reaction take place as written?
    (a) Pt; Sn^{++}, Sn^{4+} $\|$ Cl^-, Cl_2(1 atm); Pt
    (b) Pb; Pb^{++} $\|$ H^+, H_2(1 atm); Pt
    (c) Pt; Mn^{++}, MnO_4^-, H^+ $\|$ Br^-, Br_2; Pt
    (d) Fe; Fe^{++} $\|$ Zn^{++}; Zn

12.15. Write the abbreviated notation for the cell representing each of the following reactions. Calculate the cell potential for each assuming the concentration of all ions to be 1 M. Does the reaction proceed as written?
    (a) $Au + 3Fe^{3+} \rightarrow Au^{3+} + 3Fe^{++}$
    (b) $F_2 + 2H_2O \rightarrow 2F^- + O_2 + 4H^+$
    (c) $Zn + Br_2 \rightarrow Zn^{++} + 2Br^-$
    (d) $Pb + Ni^{++} \rightarrow Pb^{++} + Ni$

12.16. Does permanganate ion oxidize stannous ion to stannic ion in acid solution? Justify your answer.

12.17. Does sulfur oxidize silver metal? Justify your answer.

12.18. What voltage is produced when a saturated calomel cell is connected to a chlorine-chloride half cell?

the halogens

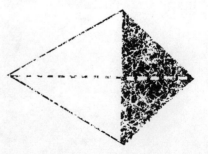

Compounds containing the halogens have been known for many centuries. Common salt (NaCl) and salt-like substances are found to be sources of the halogens. Thus, the name *halogen*, or *salt former*, is applied to this family of elements.

The halogens are a group of reactive nonmetals whose chemical and physical properties follow predictable trends. The four naturally occurring halogens (fluorine, chlorine, bromine, iodine) have been studied extensively. The fifth halogen, astatine, does not occur naturally; its properties are not considered in this chapter.

Discovery and occurrence

Fluorine was first recognized as a component of the mineral fluorspar (CaF_2) from which its name is derived. Hydrofluoric acid and hydrogen fluoride were prepared in the eighteenth century, as were other fluorine compounds. Due to its extreme reactivity, the element was not isolated until 1886, when Henri Moissan electrolyzed a solution of HF in molten KHF_2. The same basic method is used today for fluorine manufacture.

Muriatic acid (HCl) was prepared during the seventeenth century. Chlorine was prepared from this acid by the addition of an oxidizing agent. Carl Scheele is credited with preparing elemental chlorine in 1774. Since an oxidizing agent was involved in the preparation, Scheele thought he had an oxide. It was not until 1810, when Sir Humphry Davy found he could not decompose the gas any further, that chlorine was recognized as an element.

Bromine was first prepared by Antoine Balard in 1825. He found that a dark, reddish-brown liquid was released when chlorine was passed through the liquid remaining from the preparation of NaCl by evaporation of sea water.

In the early nineteenth century, sodium and potassium salts were recovered from the leachings of seaweed ashes. Bernard Courtois, a French chemical manufacturer, noted that violet-colored vapors were given off when the residual solution was treated with sulfuric acid. The vapors were easily condensed to black, metal-like platlets. In 1814 Gay-Lussac showed this material to be an element; he called it iodine.

Astatine was not discovered until 1940, when it appeared among the products of nuclear fission.

The halogens are too reactive to occur as elements in nature. The chlorides are the most commonly occurring of the halides, although all are reasonably abundant. Some of the more common halogen-containing materials are listed in Table 13.1.

Preparation

Generally, the halogens are prepared by oxidizing a halide ion.

$$2X^- \rightarrow X_2 + 2e^- \quad (X = \text{any halogen})$$

Table 13.1

Halogen-Containing Materials

fluorine	fluorspar, fluorite	CaF_2
	cryolite	Na_3AlF_6
	bones	
	teeth	
chlorine	rock salt, sea water, salt lakes	NaCl
	carnallite	$KCl \cdot MgCl_2 \cdot 6H_2O$
bromine	sea water	Br^-
	Dead Sea, other salt lakes	Br^-
	impurity in rock salt	NaBr
iodine	sea water	
	sea weeds	
	impurity in Chile saltpeter	$NaIO_3$
	thyroid gland	

The ease of oxidation increases regularly from fluoride ions to iodide ions.

Since fluorine is the strongest oxidizing agent known, it is not possible to oxidize a fluoride chemically. In addition, fluorine reacts violently with water and vigorously with most metals. Thus, it is necessary to use electrolytic oxidation in a non-aqueous solvent. A laboratory-size generator is made from a piece of bent copper tubing, graphite electrodes, and a KF–HF electrolyte. Hydrogen, produced at the cathode, is kept out of contact with fluorine by the electrolyte. Fluorine, produced at the anode, reacts with copper to form a thin layer of CuF_2 which protects the copper from further attack. Very little fluorine is prepared in the laboratory, since gas is readily available from commercial sources.

Fig. 13.1

Laboratory-size Fluorine Generator. The copper tubing contains a low melting (72°C) electrolyte solution of two moles HF per mole KF and the graphite electrodes. A steam jacket keeps the electrolyte molten.

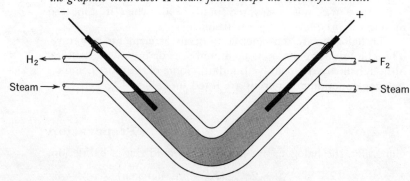

Chlorine, bromine, and iodine are prepared by the chemical oxidation of the halide ion in an acid solution. Manganese dioxide (MnO_2) is commonly used as the oxidizing agent.

$$MnO_2 + 4H^+ + 2X^- \rightarrow Mn^{++} + X_2 + 2H_2O$$

Other oxidizing agents include $KMnO_4$, $K_2Cr_2O_7$, and KNO_3. Sulfuric acid is the usual choice for the acid. The free halogen is collected over water which dissolves any gaseous hydrogen halide that may be carried over in the gas stream.

Bromine and iodine may be prepared by the passage of chlorine gas through an aqueous bromide or iodide solution. Since Cl_2 is a stronger oxidizing agent, the less active halogens are liberated. Bromine oxidizes the iodide ion; but the process seldom is used for iodine preparation, because Cl_2 is more readily available and at a lower cost. Fluorine cannot be used for the oxidation of the other halide ions, because it reacts violently with water.

Commercial preparation of fluorine is a large-scale adaptation of the laboratory method. A typical cell is shown in Fig. 13.2.

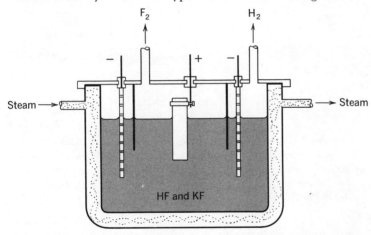

Fig. 13.2

Cell for Commercial Preparation of Fluorine. A large steel vessel fitted with a steam jacket contains the HF–KF electrolyte. Fluorine is produced at the central graphite anode; hydrogen forms at the steel cathode. Steel gas barriers prevent mixing of the two gases.

A major portion of commercial chlorine is produced by the electrolysis of aqueous sodium chloride (brine) solutions with hydrogen and NaOH as the by-products.

$$2Cl^- \rightarrow Cl_2\uparrow + 2e^-$$
$$2H_2O + 2e^- \rightarrow 2OH^- + H_2\uparrow$$
$$2Cl^- + 2H_2O \rightarrow Cl_2\uparrow + 2OH^- + H_2\uparrow$$

Precautions must be taken to keep the hydrogen and chlorine separated since the gases form an explosive mixture. Figure 13.3 shows one of the cells which have been designed for electrolysis.

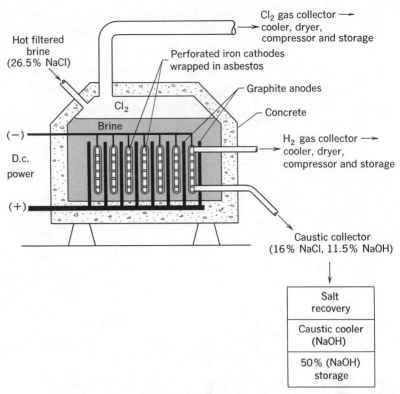

Fig. 13.3

Diaphragm Cell for Production of Cl₂, H₂, and NaOH. Chlorine is pro-duced on the graphite electrodes. Hydrogen and hydroxide ions are generated at the perforated iron cathodes. Asbestos wrapping around the cathodes keeps chlorine away from hydrogen and from the NaOH solution which settles to the bottom of the cell.

Some chlorine is produced as a by-product in the preparation of active metals such as sodium, potassium, magnesium, and calcium. The molten metal chloride is electrolyzed in a cell which keeps the chlorine separated from the metal.

Bromine is prepared by the treatment of sea water with chlorine, although there is only about 0.007% bromide in the water. After the chlorine treatment, the bromine is removed by air bubbled through the water. Bromine is removed from the air stream by mixing it with sulfur dioxide and dissolving it in water. Sulfur dioxide reduces the bromine in the presence of water.

$$SO_2 + Br_2 + 2H_2O \rightarrow 2Br^- + 4H^+ + SO_4^=$$

Treatment of the concentrated solution with chlorine liberates bromine, which is only slightly soluble in water.

Iodine is prepared by a similar process. However, the iodide concentration in sea water (about $5 \times 10^{-6}\%$) is too low for effective removal. A seaweed known as kelp concentrates iodide from sea water. Kelp is burned, and the ashes are leached to remove the iodide. Other soluble salts are precipitated before the chlorine treatment begins.

Much commercial iodine comes from sodium iodate which is a by-product of Chile saltpeter ($NaNO_3$) purification. The iodate is reduced by bubbling sulfur dioxide gas through a solution of the iodate.

$$IO_3^- + 3SO_2 + 3H_2O \rightarrow I^- + 3SO_4^= + 6H^+$$

Then sulfuric acid and more iodate are added. In an acid solution the iodide and iodate react to form iodine.

$$IO_3^- + 5I^- + 6H^+ \rightarrow 3I_2 + 3H_2O$$

Physical properties

All of the elemental halogens have an irritating, suffocating odor. All exist as diatomic molecules. The fluorine atom and molecule are the smallest of the group. Size increases as the number of electrons increase. The ionic radii increase similarly and are always larger than the corresponding atom. (See Table 13.2.)

Fluorine and chlorine are gases at room temperatures. Bromine is a liquid, and iodine is a solid; but both have appreciable vapor pressures at room temperatures. Chlorine is liquified easily by the application of pressure. The melting and boiling points of the halogens reflect the increasing molecular weights. (See Table 13.2.)

Table 13.2

Physical Properties of the Halogens

	F	Cl	Br	I
Color	Yellowish green	Greenish yellow	Reddish brown	Violet
Physical state at 25°C	Gas	Gas	Liquid	Solid
Melting point (°C)	−220	−101	−7	113
Boiling point (°C)	−188	−34	60	185
Density at 20°C	1.70 g/l	3.21 g/l	3.12 g/ml	4.94 g/cc
Atomic radius (Å)	0.72	0.99	1.14	1.33
Ionic (X^-) radius (Å)	1.36	1.81	1.95	2.16
Electron affinity (eV)	3.45	3.61	3.37	3.06
(kcal/mole)	79.5	83.3	77.6	70.6
Dissociation energy (eV)	1.64	2.51	2.33	2.21
(kcal/mole)	37.8	57.8	53.6	51.0
First ionization potential (eV)	17.4	13.0	11.8	10.6
(kcal/mole)	402.	300.	273.	244.

Ionization potentials and electronegativities decrease from fluorine to iodine. Electron affinities and dissociation energies decrease as one goes from chlorine to iodine. The electron affinity and dissociation energy of fluorine are lower than those of chlorine. There is no simple explanation for this anomaly. It may be partly due to the small size of the fluorine atom.

The halogens (except fluorine) are only slightly soluble in water but are very soluble in carbon tetrachloride, alcohol, acetone ether, and other non-polar solvents. The solubility of iodine in water is increased by the addition of potassium iodide, since the complex ion I_3^- is formed. The tri-iodide ion acts as a source of free iodine, since the equilibrium shifts rapidly.

$$I_3^- \rightleftarrows I_2 + I^-$$

The presence of free iodine can be detected by the addition of starch. Starch and iodine form a complex molecule that is an intense blue color.

Chemical properties

All of the halogens are nonmetals; fluorine is the most nonmetallic of all the elements. Iodine is the least nonmetallic of the group. Thus, fluorine is reduced most easily to the fluoride ion, while the iodide ion is oxidized readily to free iodine.

The chemical properties of the halogens reflect the presence of five p electrons in the outer energy level. Thus, all of the halogens exhibit a -1 oxidation state in covalent and ionic compounds; this results from the filling of the outermost p energy level. (See Table 6.2, page 122.) Fluorine is unique in that it does not exist in the $+1$, $+3$, $+5$, and $+7$ oxidation states which are observed for the other halogens. This results from the absence of any unfilled energy levels to which an electron may be promoted so that positive oxidation states would be possible. For the other halogens d orbitals are involved in the bonding in positive oxidation states.

Some of the more important reactions of the halogens include the following:
(1) Reactions with hydrogen

$$H_2 + X_2 \rightarrow 2HX$$

This reaction occurs with explosive violence in the case of fluorine; it is rather slow and incomplete with iodine. Hydrogen and chlorine do not react in the dark but react explosively if exposed to light. The light supplies the activation energy for the reaction. The bromine reaction is less vigorous than that of chlorine, but it is more rapid and more complete than that of iodine.
(2) Reactions with metals

$$2M + nX_2 \rightarrow 2MX_n$$

Fluorine reacts with every metal; the fluoride of the highest oxidation state of the metal is formed. This causes a severe problem in handling and storing fluorine gas. Fortunately some metals, such as copper and nickel, form a layer of protective fluoride. Once this layer is formed, no further reaction occurs. When fluorine is used for the first time in a system, it is necessary to fill the system with fluorine to form a metallic fluoride coating.

Chlorine reacts with almost all metals, although it may be necessary to heat the metal before the reaction takes place. In the presence of excess chlorine, the metal usually is oxidized to its highest oxidation state.

Bromine and iodine react with substantially fewer metals. The active metals (Groups IA, IIA) readily form stable bromides and iodides. Platinum, palladium, iridium, and osmium are among the non-reactive metals. Many of the other transition metals that are good oxidizing agents do not reach the highest oxidation state. For example, iron and iodine produce a mixture of FeI_3, FeI_2, and I_2, indicative of the reducing character of the iodide ion. Thus, when an iodide is combined with a good oxidizing agent, a redox reaction takes place. Many of the transition metal bromides and iodides are decomposed to lower halides or to the elements with relative ease because of the reducing power of iodide and bromide ions. For example, when Cu^{++} and I^- ions are combined, CuI and I_2 are formed.

$$2Cu^{++} + 4I^- \rightarrow 2CuI\downarrow + I_2$$

(3) Reactions with nonmetals

$$2Z + nX_2 \rightarrow 2ZX_n$$

The halogens do not directly combine with the nonmetals of the first period (C, N, O). However, a reaction does take place between the elemental halogens and the other elements of Group IVA, VA, and VIA.

Silicon, germanium, and tin form tetrahalides. Lead forms PbF_4, $PbCl_4$, $PbBr_2$, and PbI_2, again reflecting the reducing power of Br^- and I^-. Phosphorus, arsenic, antimony, and bismuth form pentafluoride, pentachloride, and pentabromide in excess halogen. With iodine and an excess of the Group VA element, the trihalide is formed.

$$2P + 3X_2 \rightarrow 2PX_3 \quad \text{(excess P)}$$
$$PX_3 + X_2 \rightarrow PX_5 \quad (X \neq I)$$

Sulfur, selenium, and tellurium do not react with elemental bromine and iodine. The dimer (a combination of two simple molecules) of the monochloride is formed with chlorine.

$$2S + Cl_2 \rightarrow S_2Cl_2 \text{ or } (SCl)_2 \quad \text{(also with Se and Te)}$$

(4) Formation of interhalogen compounds

$$X_2 + nX_2' \rightarrow 2XX_n'$$

The interhalogen compounds are prepared by direct combination of the elements under appropriate conditions of temperature, pressure, and relative concentrations. The following interhalogen compounds are known; all are rather reactive oxidizing agents.

IF_3	IF_5	IF_7	ICl	ICl_3	IBr
BrF	BrF_3	BrF_5	$BrCl$	ClF	ClF_3

(5) Reactions with water

$$H_2O + X_2 \xrightarrow{cold} H^+ + X^- + HOX \ (X \neq F)$$
$$3H_2O + 3X_2 \xrightarrow{hot} 6H^+ + 5X^- + XO_3^- \ (X \neq F)$$

All of the halogens are only slightly soluble in water; therefore, it is possible to obtain only very dilute solutions of hypohalous acid (HOX) or halic acid (HXO_3). If a halogen is added to a basic solution, the acid is neutralized and a more concentrated solution of the hypohalite or halate results.

$$2OH^- + X_2 \xrightarrow{cold} X^- + H_2O + OH^- \ (X \neq F)$$
$$6OH^- + 3X_2 \xrightarrow{hot} 5X^- + 3H_2O + XO_3^- \ (X \neq F)$$

If a hypohalite solution or hypohalous acid is heated or permitted to stand exposed to oxygen, oxidation to the halate ion or halic acid takes place.

Fluorine reacts explosively with water to liberate oxygen reflecting the extreme electronegativity of fluorine.

$$2F_2 + 2H_2O \rightarrow 4HF + O_2$$

Uses

Because of its extreme reactivity, elemental fluorine has very little use. Some work has been carried out in developing rocket engines which use liquid fluorine as an oxidizing agent. The techniques of handling liquid fluorine in this work may lead to other commercial applications.

Elemental chlorine is used to chlorinate organic compounds which then serve as the basis of many plastics. Some use is made of chlorine in the sterilization of water and in the bleaching of wood pulp and textiles.

Bromine is used in the preparation of dibromoethane $BrCH_3$-CH_3Br, which is added to gasolines containing tetraethyl lead to prevent deposits of lead as the gasoline is burned. Tincture of iodine, a common form of iodine, is a solution of iodine in alcohol to which some potassium iodide solution may have been added. It is used as an antiseptic.

Halogen compounds

The major uses of the halogens involve their compounds. Space permits the discussion of only a few.

Fluorocarbons

A very important group of fluorine compounds are sold under the trade names of Freon and Genetron. These compounds are relatively simple molecules containing one to four carbon atoms and fluorine. Chlorine, bromine, and hydrogen atoms also may be in the molecule. The molecules are similar in structure to, and derive their names from, the organic hydrocarbon molecules. Some fluorocarbons and their properties are listed in Table 13.3. The fluorocarbons are used extensively as refrigerants, propellants of aerosol products, lubricants, solvents, and plastics.

Another important fluorine compound is Teflon, the trade name for polymerized tetrafluoroethylene, $(C_2F_4)_n$. This substance is very inert chemically and withstands temperatures up to 300°C.

Table 13.3

Some Commercially Important Fluorocarbons

Formula	Chemical name	Boiling point (°C)	Melting point (°C)	Density at 25°C (g/cc)*	Genetron or Freon** number
CCl_3F	Trichloromono-fluoromethane	23.8	−111	1.476	11
CCl_2F_2	Dichlorodi-fluoromethane	−29.8	−158	1.311	12
$CClF_3$	Monochlorotri-fluoromethane	−81.4	−181	—	13
$CBrF_3$	Monobromotri-fluoromethane	−57.8	−168	1.538	13B1
CF_4	Tetrafluoro-methane	−128	−184	—	14
$CHCl_2F$	Dichloromono-fluoromethane	8.9	−135	1.366	21
$CHClF_2$	Monochlorodi-fluoromethane	−40.8	−160	1.194	22
CHF_3	Trifluoromethane (Fluoroform)	−82.0	−155	0.670	23
$C_2Cl_3F_3$	Trichlorotri-fluoroethane	47.6	−35	1.565	113
$C_2Cl_2F_4$	Dichlorotetra-fluoroethane	3.8	−94	1.456	114
$C_2Br_2F_4$	Dibromotetra-fluoroethane	47.3	−110	2.163	114B2
C_2ClF_5	Monochloropenta-fluoroethane	−38.7	−106	1.291	115
C_2F_6	Hexafluoroethane	−78.2	−101	—	116
C_4F_8	Octafluorocyclo-butane	−5.8	−41.4	1.480	C318

* The density values are for the liquified gas at 25°C for those fluorocarbons which boil below this temperature.
** Freon is the registered trade name of E. I. DuPont de Nemours and Co.; Genetron, of the Allied Chemical Corporation.

Silver halides, in particular AgBr and AgI, are used in photography. The hydrogen halides are of very great importance. The usual laboratory preparation of HF and HCl is to add concentrated sulfuric acid to a fluoride or chloride salt.

$$CaF_2 + H_2SO_4 \rightarrow CaSO_4 + 2HF\uparrow$$

When a chloride salt is used, the hydrogen sulfate ion is formed unless excess acid and heat are used.

$$NaCl + H_2SO_4 \rightarrow NaHSO_4 + HCl\uparrow$$

$$2NaCl + H_2SO_4 \overset{\Delta}{\rightarrow} Na_2SO_4 + 2HCl\uparrow$$

HF is obtained also by heating the purified double salt KHF_2.

$$KHF_2 \overset{\Delta}{\rightarrow} KF + HF\uparrow$$

It is not possible to prepare pure HBr and HI in the presence of concentrated H_2SO_4, since the bromide and iodide are reduced by H_2SO_4. The product is a mixture of the element and the hydrogen halide. The relative reducing power of the iodide and bromide is illustrated by the observed products of the H_2SO_4 reaction with HI and HBr.

$$2HBr + H_2SO_4 \rightarrow Br_2 + SO_2 + 2H_2O$$

$$8HI + H_2SO_4 \rightarrow 4I_2 + H_2S + 4H_2O$$

Some free sulfur is formed in both reactions. The primary product in the HBr reaction is sulfur in the $+4$ oxidation state. HI is a much stronger reducing agent, and sulfur in a -2 oxidation state is the major product.

HBr and HI usually are produced by the hydrolysis of a covalent bromide or iodide such as PBr_3, PBr_5, or PI_3.

$$PBr_3 + 3H_2O \rightarrow H_3PO_3 + 3HBr\uparrow$$

A mixture of I_2 and red phosphorus may be substituted for PI_3.

$$2P + 3I_2 + 6H_2O \rightarrow 2H_3PO_3 + 6HI\uparrow$$

It should be noted that with the exception of the last reaction, the preparation of hydrogen halides does not involve oxidation-reduction; rather, a volatile compound is formed.

Commercially, HF is prepared from the large-scale reaction of CaF_2 with H_2SO_4. HCl is a by-product of the chlorination of organic compounds. Additional HCl is produced from NaCl and H_2SO_4. Sufficient HBr is available as a by-product of the bromination of organic compounds. HI is prepared by the large-scale hydrolysis of iodine and phosphorus.

All of the hydrogen halides are colorless, corrosive, irritating gases, readily soluble in water. Hydrofluoric acid is a weak acid; the other gases form strong acid solutions. Much heat is evolved when HF is placed in water because of the formation of hydrogen

Table 13.4

267
Halogen compounds

Physical Properties of the Hydrogen Halides

	HF	HCl	HBr	HI
Melting point (°C)	−83	−114	−87	−51
Boiling point (°C)	20*	−85	−67	−35
Density (at STP)	(1.00 g/cc) (liquid)	1.64 g/l	3.50 g/l	5.66 g/l
Solubility in H_2O at 20°C, 1 atm				
(g/100 g H_2O)	35.3	42	49	57
moles/l H_2O	17.6	11.5	6.0	4.4

* High boiling point attributed to hydrogen bonding in the liquid.

bonds with water molecules. Little heat is released when the other gases are placed in water.

A unique reaction of hydrofluoric acid occurs with SiO_2 and silicates ($SiO_3^=$); volatile SiF_4 is formed. This results in the etching of glass (Na_2SiO_3) and quartz (SiO_2).

$$SiO_2 + 4HF \rightarrow SiF_4\uparrow + 2H_2O$$
$$Na_2SiO_3 + 6HF \rightarrow SiF_4\uparrow + 2NaF + 3H_2O$$

These reactions preclude the use of glass containers for hydrofluoric acid. Plastic bottles are used instead. Hydrofluoric acid skin burns are painful and slow to heal.

Hydrochloric, hydrobromic, and hydriodic acids are typical strong acids. Dry HCl, HBr, and HI are unreactive due to the covalent character of the molecule. The molecule readily ionizes in the presence of water. Commercially, hydrochloric acid is the most important of the hydrohalic acids.

Halogen oxides

It is not possible to produce halogen oxides by direct combination of the elements. Oxygen difluoride (OF_2) is prepared by passing fluorine through a dilute sodium hydroxide solution.

$$2F_2 + 2OH^- \rightarrow 2F^- + OF_2 + H_2O$$

OF_2 is a gas boiling at −145°C. It is a strong oxidizing agent.

Chlorine monoxide (Cl_2O) and chlorine dioxide (ClO_2) are gases that readily dissolve in water to form strongly oxidizing solutions. The gases are rather unstable and may decompose explosively.

Chlorine heptoxide (Cl_2O_7) is distilled from a mixture of P_2O_5 and perchloric acid ($HClO_4$) at −10°C under vacuum. It is a colorless, oily liquid boiling at 80°C. All of the known bromine oxides (Br_2O, Br_3O_8, and BrO_2) are unstable except at low temperatures. Very little is known about them. Iodine pentoxide (I_2O_5) is a white solid which is prepared by heating iodic acid.

$$2HIO_3 \xrightarrow{\Delta} H_2O + I_2O_5$$

No other oxides of iodine are known.

Oxyacids and oxysalts of the halogens

Since fluorine exists only in the -1 oxidation state, oxyacids and oxysalts of fluorine do not occur. All of the predicted oxyacids and oxysalts of chlorine are known.

Hypochlorous acid (HOCl) is found only as a dilute solution. It is a weak acid but a strong oxidizing agent and is formed by passing Cl_2 into cold water. It is possible to crystallize hypochlorites of the active metals from solution. Household bleach is a 5.25% solution of sodium hypochlorite.

Chlorous acid ($HClO_2$) is prepared by the reaction of ClO_2 in a basic solution or by acidifying a chlorite salt solution. $HClO_2$ occurs only as the weak acid solution, but it is a good oxidizing agent. Thus, $NaClO_2$ is a mild bleaching agent.

Chloric acid ($HClO_3$) is a strong acid prepared by the addition of H_2SO_4 to a chlorate. The chlorates are prepared by passing chlorine into a warm basic solution. Chlorates (except for $KClO_3$) are very soluble in water. Chloric acid and chlorates are strong oxidizing agents, since they decompose to oxygen upon heating. Organic materials such as paper or cloth may ignite spontaneously in the presence of the chlorates or concentrated $HClO_3$.

Perchloric acid ($HClO_4$) is a strong acid that is isolated as a pure acid by carefully distilling $KClO_4$ and H_2SO_4 under vacuum. $HClO_4$ is a liquid which boils at 90°C. It explodes if not carefully heated. Perchlorates and perchloric acid spontaneously ignite combustible materials. Dilute solutions of perchloric acid are very stable and behave as typical strong acids. The perchlorates (except for $KClO_4$) are very soluble in water. Silver perchlorate is unique in that it is very soluble in water and alcohols, as well as in non-polar solvents.

Only HOBr and $HBrO_3$ are known in the bromine group. HOBr is very similar to HOCl. The hypobromites are less stable than the hypochlorites but otherwise are similar chemically. $HBrO_3$ and the bromates are similar to $HClO_3$ and the chlorates; the bromine compounds are stronger oxidizing agents.

Hypoiodous acid is similar to HClO, but it is a much weaker oxidizing agent. The hypoiodite ion readily decomposes.

$$3IO^- \rightarrow IO_3^- + 2I^-$$

Iodic acid (HIO_3) is a strongly oxidizing acid quite similar to $HClO_3$. It is prepared by the action of concentrated nitric acid on iodine.

$$3I_2 + 10HNO_3 \rightarrow 6HIO_3 + 10NO\uparrow + 2H_2O$$

There appears to be a family of periodic acids with the general formula $I_2O_7 \cdot xH_2O$ which are weak acids with powerful oxidizing properties.

SIGNIFICANT TERMS AND CONCEPTS IN CHAPTER XIII:

Methods of preparation, physical properties, chemical properties; unique properties of fluorine; preparation and properties of the hydrogen halides, reducing character of the iodides; preparation and properties of the halogen oxyacids and oxysalts.

Review questions

13.1. Complete the following reactions.
    (a) $NaCl + H_2SO_4$ (conc.) $\rightarrow$
    (b) $NaI + H_2SO_4$ (conc.) $\rightarrow$
    (c) $I^- + Cl_2 \xrightarrow{H_2O}$
    (d) $SO_2 + I_2 \xrightarrow{H_2O}$
    (e) $BrO_3^- + I^- + H^+ \rightarrow$
    (f) $H_2 + Br_2 \rightarrow$
    (g) $Ni + F_2 \rightarrow$
    (h) $Fe^{3+} + I^- \rightarrow$
    (i) $P + I_2 \rightarrow$
    (j) $PBr_3 + H_2O \rightarrow$
    (k) Passage of Cl_2 into hot NaOH solution
    (l) Br_2 in cold water

13.2. Compare the electronegativities of the halogens with the electron affinities. Why is electronegativity a better guide to the chemical reactivity of an element?

13.3. Would the astatide ion be a good reducing agent or a good oxidizing agent? Explain.

13.4. Labels are removed from bottles of hydrofluoric, hydrochloric, hydrobromic, and hydriodic acids. Give a series of tests that could be made to identify each acid.

13.5. Give the formulas for the following.
    (a) perchloric acid,
    (b) calcium chlorite,
    (c) sodium hypochlorite,
    (d) hypoiodous acid,
    (e) potassium iodate,
    (f) lithium bromate,
    (g) muriatic acid,
    (h) Chile saltpeter,
    (i) potassium triiodide,
    (j) arsenic pentabromide,
    (k) the anhydride of hypobromous acid,
    (l) the anhydride of perchloric acid.

sulfur and its congeners

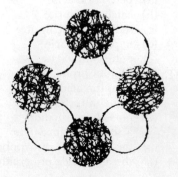

Oxygen and sulfur are the most abundant and most important of the Group VIA elements. Because of its unique relationship to the chemistry of the other elements, oxygen is discussed throughout this text, especially in Chapter II. Sulfur is of primary concern to us in this chapter, although brief references are made to selenium and tellurium to illustrate the trends within the group. Polonium, the fifth member of the group, is a radioactive metal and is omitted.

Occurrence and preparation

Free sulfur is an incidental by-product of the oxidation of sulfides with nitric acid. Otherwise sulfur, selenium, and tellurium are seldom prepared in the laboratory.

Sulfur occurs widely in nature as the element, the sulfides, and the sulfates. The principal sulfide ores are pyrite (FeS_2), cinnabar (HgS), sphalerite (ZnS), and galena (PbS). The common sulfates are gypsum ($CaSO_4 \cdot 2H_2O$) and kieserite ($MgSO_4 \cdot H_2O$). Living organisms, coal, and petroleum contain chemically combined sulfur. However, very little sulfur is obtained from these compounds.

Most of the world's supply of elemental sulfur occurs in the form of crystals in limestone, gypsum, or sedimentary rocks as a result of the reduction of the sulfate or the action of hydrogen sulfide on calcium carbonate (limestone). Extensive deposits of this type are found in Texas, Louisiana, the Gulf of Mexico, and Sicily. Sulfur deposits in Japan and Chile are found near volcanic vents where hydrogen sulfide gas has been oxidized. The Frasch Process is used to mine the U.S. deposits which occur at depths of 500 to 2000 feet.

Selenium and tellurium occur as trace impurities in sulfide ores and are recovered from the flues of sulfide roasters. During the roasting process, the sulfides, selenides, and tellurides react with oxygen in the air to form dioxides. Since SO_2 is a good reducing agent and SeO_2 and TeO_2 are readily reduced, elemental selenium and tellurium are deposited in the flues.

$$2SO_2 + SeO_2 \rightarrow 2SO_3 + Se\downarrow$$

Physical properties

Some of the physical properties of the Group VIA elements are given in Table 14.1. The trend of the increasing melting points, boiling points, and density with increasing atomic weight is as anticipated. Oxygen forms diatomic molecules which are weakly attracted to each other as reflected in the low boiling point of oxygen.

As is typical of many of the nonmetals, the elements of Group VIA exhibit allotropic behavior. The term *allotrope* is used to designate the existence of a substance in two or more forms in the

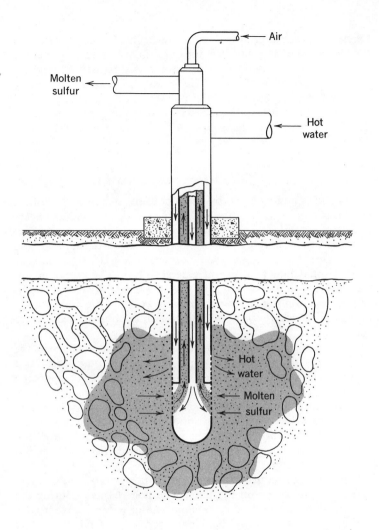

Fig. 14.1

Frasch Process. Three concentric pipes are sunk into the sulfur deposit. Hot water is forced under pressure down the outer pipe which is perforated at the bottom to allow the hot water to escape and the molten sulfur to collect at the bottom. Compressed air in the inner pipe forces the molten sulfur up through the middle pipe.

same physical state. One form is stable at à given temperature and pressure. Sometimes other allotropic forms are found under the same conditions, because conversion to the more stable form takes place slowly. These forms are said to be *metastable*. There is a temperature, the *transition temperature*, at which two allotropes are equally stable and exist together.

Ozone (O_3) is an allotrope of oxygen. It is prepared by an electrical discharge in O_2 gas or by ultraviolet irradiation of O_2. Ozone has a characteristic odor which is evident after a severe

Table 14.1
Some Physical Properties of the Group VIA Elements

Element	Color	Physical state at 25°C	Melting point (°C)	Boiling point (°C)	Density (25°C)
O	colorless	gas	−219	−183	1.31 g/l
S	yellow	solid	115	444.6	2.06 g/cc
Se	gray	solid	217	685	4.81 g/cc
Te	silver-white	solid	450	1087	6.23 g/cc

thunderstorm and near high voltage transformers. Pure ozone is a toxic, corrosive gas that is unstable toward the formation of ordinary oxygen and is a much more reactive material than O_2. Ozone is used for the purification of water and of air.

Sulfur exists in several allotropic forms. Rhombic sulfur is the stable form at room temperature. When it is heated above 95.4°C, it converts to the monoclinic form. When monoclinic sulfur is cooled slowly, it returns to the rhombic form at this temperature. If the cooling is rapid, monoclinic sulfur exists at room temperature for several days before the slow transformation to rhombic sulfur is complete. If liquid sulfur is cooled rapidly, the amorphous (non-crystalline) plastic form is obtained. In a few days a transformation to rhombic sulfur is completed. Rhombic and monoclinic sulfur consist of molecules of eight atoms arranged in a puckered ring as sketched in Fig. 14.3.

Upon melting at 115°C, sulfur becomes a light yellow, transparent liquid composed of S_8 molecules. As the liquid is heated from 120° to 160°C, the liquid flows more readily (i.e., its viscosity is lowered). At 160°C, the liquid has turned to a dark brown, and

Fig. 14.2
Rhombic and Monoclinic Forms of Sulfur

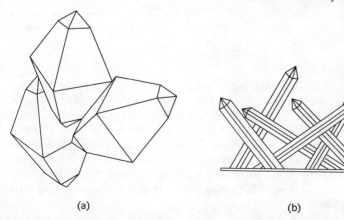

(a)   (b)

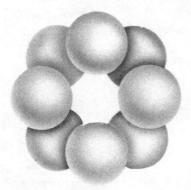

Fig. 14.3

Puckered Ring Structure of S_8. The eight-atom ring molecule is puckered rather than planar because of the orientation of the bonding orbitals.

there is an abrupt change in properties, the most obvious of which is an increase in viscosity. From temperatures of 160°C to 230°C, liquid sulfur has an increasing resistance to flow due to the formation of long chains of sulfur atoms. These chains become tangled preventing the easy flow of the liquid. Above 230°C, the viscosity of the brownish-black liquid decreases until the boiling point is reached.

Up to about 500°C, the vapor is thought to consist primarily of S_8 molecules. As the vapor is heated, it appears that the S_8 molecules break up into smaller units such as S_6, S_4, and S_2. At 900°C, the vapor is essentially S_2. The monomer predominates at 1800°C and atmospheric pressure as well as at lower pressures and temperatures.

The behavior of sulfur can be summarized as follows:

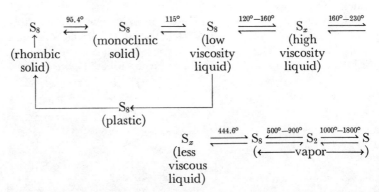

Selenium and tellurium also exist in eight-atom molecules. Two very similar red monoclinic allotropes and a gray rhombic form are recognized for selenium. A black, amorphous, plastic state also exists. Rhombic selenium is the stable form at room temperature. An amorphous and a silver-white, somewhat metallic, rhombic form of tellurium are the only forms that are known. The vapors of selenium and tellurium consist primarily of diatomic molecules which break down into the monatomic species upon heating.

Chemical properties

Sulfur behaves as a typical nonmetal, showing oxidation states of -2, $+2$, $+4$, and $+6$. Selenium and tellurium are more metallic, although both exhibit oxidation states of -2, $+4$, and $+6$.

(1) Reactions with metals

These elements react with all metals except gold and platinum to form sulfides, selenides, and tellurides. The reaction is spontaneous and vigorous with Group IA and IIA metals (except beryllium and magnesium); the reaction with copper, silver, and mercury is more sedate. Sulfur reacts vigorously with powdered zinc, aluminum, tin, or iron once the reaction is initiated by heating. Larger masses of these metals are rather resistant to attack. The other metal sulfides are formed at high temperatures.

(2) Reactions with oxygen

When the Group VIA elements burn in air or oxygen, the dioxides are formed. SO_3 is prepared only in the presence of a catalyst; the trioxides of selenium and tellurium are not known. SO_3 is a solid with an appreciable vapor pressure at room temperature. It readily forms white fumes in moist air. SO_2 is a colorless, choking gas that is moderately soluble in water. It is liquified easily under pressure or by cooling, since its normal boiling point is $-10°C$. SeO_2 and TeO_2 are solids at room temperature with a moderate solubility in water resulting in dilute weak acid solutions. The reducing power of the dioxides decreases in the order SO_2, SeO_2, TeO_2.

(3) Reactions with hydrogen

The colorless gases H_2S, H_2Se, and H_2Te are prepared by heating the elements or by the action of an acid upon a metal sulfide, selenide, or telluride. H_2S is characterized by a rotten-egg odor, while H_2Se and H_2Te have a very strong garlic-like odor. All are poisonous with the toxicity increasing with molecular weight. These gases tend to cause nerve paralysis so that one fails to detect them after being exposed to them for a short time.

H_2S is not very soluble in water, but it does form a weak acid. Either as a gas or in solution, H_2S is readily oxidized by such reagents as dilute nitric acid, iodine, sulfuric acid, and sulfur dioxide. This reflects the reducing power of H_2S.

$$3H_2S + 2HNO_3 \text{ (dilute)} \rightarrow 3S + 2NO + 4H_2O$$

$$H_2S + I_2 \rightarrow S + 2HI$$

$$H_2S + H_2SO_4 \rightarrow S + SO_2 + 2H_2O$$

The hydrogen bonding in H_2S is much less than in H_2O due to the much lower electronegativity of sulfur. As a result, H_2S is only slightly polar with very little hydrogen bonding between molecules.

Uses

Sulfur is used in the vulcanization of rubber and in the manufacture of dyes, detergents, and sulfuric acid. A small amount of selenium is used in the fabrication of rectifiers for electrical current. This is an application of the low electrical conductivity of selenium. Sulfur is very much an insulator by comparison. No major use of tellurium has been developed, although some of the tellurides are being investigated for their application to the area of thermoelectricity.

Sulfuric acid

Sulfuric acid (H_2SO_4), the most widely used industrial chemical, was first prepared as "oil of vitriol" by the alchemists from blue vitriol ($CuSO_4 \cdot 5H_2O$) and acetic acid. Two methods of sulfuric acid manufacture are used commercially today. The lead chamber process was developed from 1749 to 1859; the contact process did not become usable until 1901, although the first patent was issued in 1831.

Preparation

The lead chamber process makes use of the sulfur dioxide that is formed when sulfide ores are roasted in air. SO_2 from the burning of sulfur is used also. The gas is mixed with nitrogen oxides, water vapor, and air and fed into lead-lined reaction chambers, where 62 per cent H_2SO_4 forms as a result of several complex and poorly understood reactions. This product is concentrated to 78 per cent H_2SO_4 by further absorption of gas.

In the contact process (Fig. 14.4) SO_2 from a sulfur burner is converted to SO_3 using a V_2O_5 catalyst. Since the catalyst is easily "poisoned" (made useless as a catalyst) by arsenic and halogens, the use of by-product SO_2 is not feasible. Although SO_3 dissolves readily in water to form H_2SO_4, it is dissolved in 98% sulfuric acid to form oleum, or fuming sulfuric acid. The technique prevents the formation of a dilute sulfuric acid fog in the absorption tower. The oleum is diluted with water to obtain the desired concentration of sulfuric acid. The chemically pure, concentrated acid used in most laboratories contains 95 to 98% (by weight) H_2SO_4; common commercial grades contain 78 and 93% H_2SO_4.

Properties

Anhydrous hydrogen sulfate is a colorless, odorless, somewhat viscous liquid with a density of 1.84 g/ml and a freezing point of 10°C. Before the boiling point is reached, SO_3 gas is formed until a solution containing 98.3% (by weight) H_2SO_4 is formed. This solution boils without a change in composition at 338°C under one atmosphere of pressure. Anhydrous hydrogen sulfate is essentially a nonelectrolyte. As water is added, weak dissociation into H^+ and HSO_4^- ions occurs. The degree of dissociation increases rapidly with dilution. For example, it is reported that 18.5 M (99.2% by weight) H_2SO_4 is 4% dissociated into H^+ and

Fig. 14.4
Contact Process for Sulfuric Acid Manufacture

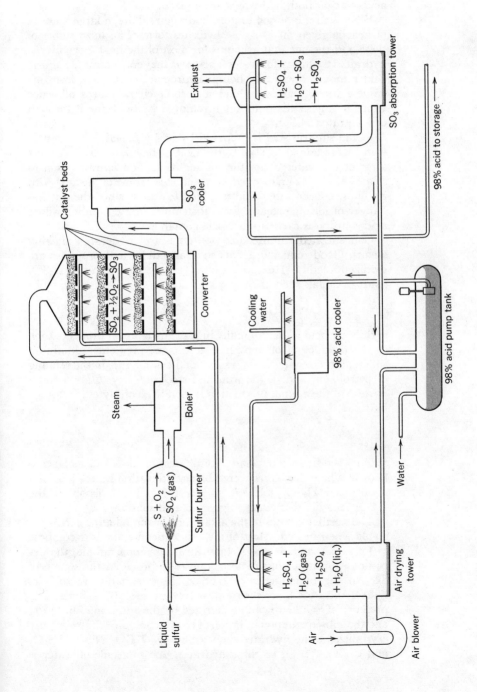

HSO_4^-; there is a 66% dissociation in 15.6 M (83.8% by weight) acid. As dilution continues, the HSO_4^- ion undergoes dissociation into H^+ and $SO_4^=$ ions. Virtually all of the H_2SO_4 molecules and more than 12% of the HSO_4^- ions are dissociated in a 10 M solution. Dilute sulfuric acid solutions behave as typical strong acids in that both hydrogens are ionized.

When water is added to pure hydrogen sulfate, a large amount of heat is given off as stable hydrates form. The most stable of these and the one that accounts for most of the heat is the mono-hydrate. Its affinity for water is so great that concentrated sulfuric acid removes chemically bound hydrogen and oxygen from organic matter, leaving behind a carbon char. Traces of water vapor in a gas stream are often removed by bubbling it through concentrated H_2SO_4.

Dilute sulfuric acid is prepared by adding H_2SO_4 to water. If water were added to H_2SO_4, the heat of reaction would convert some of the water under the surface of the concentrated acid to steam. As the steam escaped, it would carry some of the acid with it. Thus, concentrated acid is added to water, since there is less danger of forming steam. Even if steam is formed, only a dilute acid solution is carried out of the container.

Concentrated sulfuric acid solutions are moderate oxidizing agents. Good reducing agents such as iodides and bromides are oxidized readily. Heat is required before concentrated H_2SO_4 oxidizes metals such as copper and silver.

$$Cu + 2H_2SO_4 \rightarrow Cu^{++} + 2H_2O + SO_2\uparrow$$

Sulfuric acid is used in many industrial chemical processes such as the production of phosphate fertilizers, pigments, aluminum sulfate, ammonium sulfate, rayon, and cellophane, in the refining of petroleum, and in the iron and steel industry. Only a small portion of the annual production is used in electrolytes for storage batteries.

Salts

Only the hydrogen sulfates (bisulfates) of the alkali metals are known. These can be recovered by crystallization from a partially neutralized H_2SO_4 solution. When the solid is dissolved, the HSO_4^- readily dissociates to give an acid solution.

The normal sulfates of the alkali metals and alkaline earths are stable when heated. Most of the other metal sulfates decompose to form SO_3 and the oxide upon heating. For example, the decomposition of ferric sulfate at one time provided the source of SO_3 in the manufacture of H_2SO_4. Most sulfates are soluble. $BaSO_4$ and $PbSO_4$ are the most important insoluble sulfates. The presence of $SO_4^=$ ions can be detected by the addition of Ba^{++} ion and the subsequent precipitation of $BaSO_4$. Soluble salts frequently crystallize as the hydrates such as $FeSO_4 \cdot 7H_2O$, $NiSO_4 \cdot 7H_2O$, and $CuSO_4 \cdot 5H_2O$. In these hydrates, one molecule of water is hydrogen bonded to the $SO_4^=$ ion; the rest are associated with the cation. The structure of the $SO_4^=$ species is thought to be

$$\begin{bmatrix} \text{O} & \text{O}...\text{H} \\ & \diagdown \diagup & & \diagdown \\ & \text{S} & & \text{O} \\ & \diagup \diagdown & & \diagup \\ \text{O} & \text{O}...\text{H} \end{bmatrix}^=$$

SIGNIFICANT TERMS AND CONCEPTS IN CHAPTER XIV:

Frasch process; allotropes, ozone, metastable, allotropic forms of sulfur; chemical reactions of sulfur, selenium, and tellurium; properties of the oxides and hydrides, lead chamber process, contact process, chemical and physical properties of H_2SO_4, dilution of H_2SO_4; properties of the hydrogen sulfates.

Review questions

14.1. Give the products of the following reactions.
   (a) Sulfur is heated in oxygen.
   (b) Tellurium is heated in oxygen.
   (c) Selenium is heated in hydrogen.
   (d) Hydrochloric acid is added to sodium telluride.
   (e) H_2S is oxidized in air.
   (f) Sulfur is heated with silver.
   (g) Copper(II) sulfate is heated to 500°C.
   (h) Barium hydroxide is neutralized with sulfuric acid.
   (i) Concentrated sulfuric acid is added to sugar ($C_{12}H_{12}O_{11}$).
   (j) Zinc telluride is roasted.

14.2. Why is it necessary to keep the hot water under high pressure in the Frasch Process?

14.3. Which of the hydrides of sulfur, selenium, and tellurium are soluble in water? What is the name of the solution in each case? Which are strong electrolytes and which are weak electrolytes?

14.4. List the allotropes of the Group VIA elements. Give two physical characteristics of each allotrope that distinguish it from the other allotropes of the element.

14.5. Give the equations for preparing sulfuric acid from sulfur using the contact process.

14.6. Give equations for the following:
   (a) Dissolution of silver in hot concentrated sulfuric acid
   (b) $H_2S + SO_2 \rightarrow$
   (c) Preparation of sodium hydrogen sulfate
   (d) Addition of sodium sulfide solution to a solution of lead(II) nitrate
   (e) $SeO_2 + TeO_2 \rightarrow$

the nitrogen family

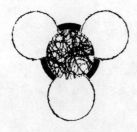

Bathed as we are in an atmosphere which contains about 78 per cent nitrogen, we tend to forget the vital role played by this gas in sustaining life. Nitrogen also forms a number of important inorganic compounds. In this chapter we will discuss the inorganic chemistry of nitrogen; its organic and biological applications are considered later. The other elements of the nitrogen group receive less attention. The others—phosphorus, antimony, arsenic, and bismuth—show a wide variety of properties; often, however, no regular trends are observed.

Occurrence and preparation

About 78 per cent of the air we breathe is nitrogen. Very few deposits of inorganic nitrogen compounds are found due to their solubility in water. The most extensive deposits are those of $NaNO_3$ (Chile saltpeter) and KNO_3 (saltpeter). Nitrogen is an important constituent of all living matter, since it is a part of the compounds known as proteins.

Phosphorus occurs primarily in the form of mineral phosphates and in bones. Small deposits of elemental arsenic are known. However, most arsenic is found with the sulfides of such metals as iron and copper.

Nitrogen is the only element in this group that is commonly prepared in the laboratory. High purity nitrogen is prepared in the following ways.

(a) Heating a concentrated solution of ammonium nitrite

$$NH_4NO_2 \xrightarrow{\Delta} N_2 + 2H_2O$$

Due to the explosive character of anhydrous NH_4NO_2 the solution is prepared from sodium nitrite and ammonium chloride. The gas is usually collected over water.

(b) Heating solid ammonium dichromate

$$(NH_4)_2Cr_2O_7 \xrightarrow{\Delta} Cr_2O_3 + 4H_2O + N_2$$

(c) Thermal decomposition of ammonia
If ammonia is passed over hot copper oxide, the hydrogen is removed as water.

$$3CuO + 2NH_3 \xrightarrow{\Delta} 3Cu + 3H_2O + N_2$$

(d) Heating solid sodium azide in a vacuum

$$2NaN_3 \xrightarrow{\Delta} 2Na + 3N_2$$

(e) Removal of oxygen from air
This method is useful when large quantities of N_2 are needed in the laboratory, although the ready availability of the compressed gas in cylinders reduces this need. The oxygen in an air sample is removed by reacting the oxygen with a sufficient amount of white phosphorus to form the pentoxide. If this is done over water, the P_4O_{10} is absorbed by the water

Table 15.1
Composition of the Atmosphere

Element or compound	Per cent by volume at sea level	Element or compound	Per cent by volume at sea level
nitrogen	77.08	hydrogen	0.01
oxygen	20.75	neon	trace
water vapor	1.20 (variable)	helium	trace
		krypton	trace
argon	0.93	xenon	trace
carbon dioxide	0.03 (variable)		

to form a dilute solution of H_3PO_4. Alternatively, it is possible to remove the oxygen using hot copper and forming copper oxide.

$$2Cu + O_2 \xrightarrow{\Delta} 2CuO$$

Neither of these methods of oxygen removal produces a pure product. The product contains a total of about 1% argon,

Fig. 15.1
Furnace for Production of Phosphorus

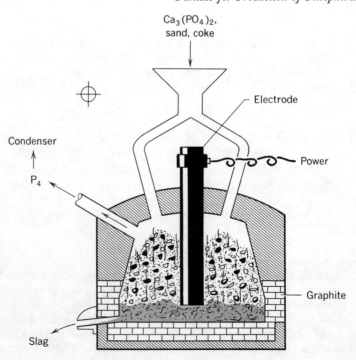

water vapor, carbon dioxide, and other atmospheric gases. However, this mixture is usually sufficiently inert to demonstrate the common properties of nitrogen.

The major commercial source of nitrogen is the liquefaction of air. Traces of oxygen and argon are present but usually cause no problem in most commercial applications.

Some nitrogen is prepared commercially by removing the oxygen from the atmosphere with red-hot carbon to form CO_2. If it is necessary to remove the CO_2, the gas mixture is passed through a potassium hydroxide solution where the carbonate is formed.

White phosphorus is the usual commercially prepared form. Phosphate rock, sand, and coke are heated to 1400°C in an electric furnace consisting of a graphite lining and a central graphite electrode. At these temperatures the sand and phosphate react to form phosphorus pentoxide which is then reduced by the coke.

$$2Ca_3(PO_4)_2 + 6SiO_2 \xrightarrow{\Delta} 6CaSiO_3 + P_4O_{10}$$
$$P_4O_{10} + 10C \rightarrow 10CO + P_4\uparrow$$

The phosphorus vapor is purified, condensed, and cast into sticks. Since white phosphorus ignites spontaneously in air, the sticks must be kept under water.

Arsenic sulfide ores are converted to arsenic trioxide (As_4O_6) which then is reduced with carbon in a manner not unlike phosphorus. High purity arsenic is prepared by the thermal decomposition of $AsCl_3$ which has been purified by distillation through several stages. Antimony and bismuth occur as the sulfide ores. These are roasted to oxides and then reduced with carbon.

Physical properties

Some of the physical properties of these elements are given in Table 15.2. As is found in Group VIA, the first member of the group, nitrogen, is a diatomic gas at room temperature. The

Table 15.2

Physical Properties of the Group VA Elements

Element	Color	Physical state at 25°C	Melting point (°C)	Boiling point (°C)	Density (25°C)
N	colorless	gas	−210	−196	1.15 g/l
P	white	solid	44	277	1.83 g/cc
	violet	solid	sublimes	431	2.31 g/cc
As	black	solid	sublimes	613	5.78 g/cc
Sb	silver-white	solid	630	1440	6.70 g/cc
Bi	reddish-white	solid	271	1559	9.81 g/cc

nitrogen–nitrogen bond in N_2 is one of the most stable chemical bonds known, requiring 225 kcal to break a mole of molecules into atoms. The very low melting and boiling points indicate that the forces of attraction between N_2 molecules in the solid and the liquid are very weak.

The nonmetallic solids of Group VA exhibit typical allotropic behavior. Three allotropic forms of phosphorus are known. Black phosphorus is stable only at high pressures. White and violet modifications exist at room temperatures and ordinary pressures. The stable form is violet phosphorus, sometimes called red phosphorus. Most commercial red phosphorus is amorphous. It vaporizes as P_4 molecules when heated. The vapor consists primarily of P_2 molecules above 800°C. When the vapor is cooled, P_4 molecules condense as white phosphorus. If the white form is heated at 250–300°C in a sealed tube, crystalline red phosphorus forms. The properties of the two allotropes are very different. For example, white phosphorus ignites spontaneously in air and must be stored under water. Red phosphorus is stable in air. A comparison of properties is made in Table 15.3.

Gray and yellow arsenic allotropes are known. The yellow form is prepared by condensing arsenic vapor in cold carbon disulfide. Its properties are very similar to those of white phosphorus. It is readily transformed to the more stable gray arsenic.

Fig. 15.2

Structure of White and Red Phosphorus. When white phosphorus is heated under pressure, one bond in the tetrahedral unit breaks. It re-forms with an adjacent molecule. This structure is polymeric red phosphorus.

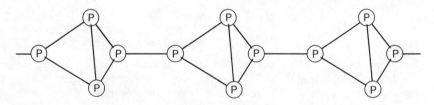

Red phosphorous

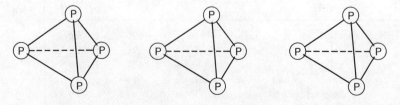

White phosphorous

Table 15.3

285

Chemical properties

Comparison of the Properties of White and Red Phosphorus

	White	Red
Physical State:	soft, white, wax-like solid	dark red powder
Density	1.8 g/cc	2.3 g/cc
Melting Point	44°C volatile in steam soluble in CS_2, benzene, other solvents fumes poisonous ignites in moist air at 30°C	416°C (sublimes) not volatile in steam insoluble in these solvents non-poisonous ignites in air at 300°C

The properties of the gray form are similar to those of red phosphorus; however, it has the luster and heat conductivity associated with a metal. Antimony forms a stable black allotrope and an unstable yellow one; bismuth exists only in the metallic black form.

Chemical properties

With the exception of white phosphorus, the Group VA elements are unreactive at room temperatures. The trend from nonmetallic nitrogen to metallic bismuth is quite distinct. For example, the positive oxidation states of nitrogen and phosphorus occur only in covalent compounds, while the ionic $+3$ state is the most stable state for bismuth. Nitrogen exhibits several oxidation states ranging from -3 to $+5$. However, the $+5$ state is a formal value and is found only in oxygen-containing compounds. Phosphorus, arsenic, and antimony are found in the $+5$, $+3$, and -3 oxidation states; the $+5$ state becomes less stable as the atomic weight increases. Compounds with bismuth in the $+5$ state are known but are not very stable.

At elevated temperatures, nitrogen reacts with oxygen to form nitric oxide,

$$N_2 + O_2 \xrightarrow{\Delta} 2NO$$

with hydrogen to form ammonia,

$$N_2 + 3H_2 \xrightarrow{\Delta} 2NH_3$$

and with various metals to form nitrides.

$$3Mg + N_2 \xrightarrow{\Delta} Mg_3N_2$$

The Group IA and IIA nitrides are ionic solids wherein the nitride ion, N^{-3}, exists. These metal nitrides produce ammonia upon hydrolysis.

$$Mg_3N_2 + 6H_2O \rightarrow 3Mg(OH)_2 + 2NH_3\uparrow$$

The nitrides of aluminum, gallium, and boron are bonded covalently throughout the crystal; thus, they are macromolecules. AlN and GaN hydrolyze to produce ammonia; BN does not undergo hydrolysis. In general, the transition metal nitrides are hard and high melting, existing over a range of nitrogen ratios rather than as fixed compounds. Many of the transition metals can be coated with a nitride layer by heating the metal in air in a process called "case hardening" or "nitriding."

Phosphorus reacts with oxygen to form pentoxide and trioxide. Only arsenic trioxide is formed when arsenic is heated in oxygen. The pentoxide can be prepared indirectly. The molecular weights of these oxides indicate that the correct molecular formulas for these species are P_4O_{10}, As_4O_{10}, P_4O_6, and As_4O_6, although the older nomenclature persists. The oxides react with water to form H_3PO_4, H_3PO_3, H_3AsO_4, or H_3AsO_3. Water is taken on so readily by P_4O_{10} that it is a useful desiccant. This oxide is a white powder; when exposed to water vapor a syrupy liquid forms.

Phosphides and arsenides are prepared from the same metals as the nitrides. The reactions of the phosphides and arsenides are analogous to the nitride reactions; however, decomposition takes place at somewhat lower temperatures.

Antimony and bismuth are somewhat inert. When heated in air, antimony and bismuth trioxides are formed. Sb_4O_{10} is prepared by reacting the metal with concentrated nitric acid; Bi_2O_5 is not easily prepared. When a concentrated base is added to Sb_4O_{10}, the antimonate ion $[Sb(OH)_6]^-$ is formed. Sb_4O_6 dissolves in strong acid to form Sb^{3+} ions and in strong base to form the antimonite ion $[Sb(OH)_4]^-$. Bi_2O_3 dissolves only in an acid. Antimony and bismuth trichlorides readily hydrolyze in water to form insoluble oxychlorides (or basic chlorides): SbOCl or $Sb(OH)_2Cl$, and BiOCl or $Bi(OH)_2Cl$.

Uses

Elemental nitrogen is used as a cryogenic (low temperature) liquid, since it is non-reactive at low temperatures and leaves no residue when warmed. Much nitrogen gas is converted to ammonia, the starting material for almost all of the important nitrogen compounds.

Important phosphorus chemicals are the phosphates which are used as fertilizers, and phosphoric acid. The use of white phosphorus in matches has been discontinued because of its poisonous character. Safer phosphorus compounds are now used.

Elemental arsenic is used in the preparation of certain arsenides that have applications in the field of electronics. Other compounds of arsenic are used as insecticides.

Antimony and bismuth are used as low-melting metals or as alloys in such devices as fire alarms and sprinkler systems.

Some nitrogen compounds

While there is an ample supply of nitrogen in the atmosphere, it is of little chemical usefulness until it is converted into its compounds. These conversion processes have been given the general name of *nitrogen fixation*, since the fixed nitrogen readily undergoes reaction in the laboratory and in biological processes. The most important non-biological nitrogen fixation processes are the preparation of ammonia and the formation of nitric oxide. Industrially, more nitrogen is fixed by ammonia preparation than by any other means. Because of this, ammonia serves as the starting material for the preparation of nearly all industrial nitrogen compounds.

Ammonia (NH_3)

Preparation. Ammonia is prepared in the laboratory by the following methods.

(1) Heating a mixture of any ammonium salt and a strong base either as a solid or in solution.

$$NH_4^+ + OH^- \xrightarrow{\Delta} NH_3\uparrow + H_2O$$

(2) Heating a mixture of solid ammonium chloride and calcium oxide.

$$2NH_4Cl + CaO \xrightarrow{\Delta} CaCl_2 + 2NH_3\uparrow + H_2O$$

Water is removed with additional CaO. Ammonia is collected by the upward displacement of air which is more dense. This is a better method than (1).

(3) Heating magnesium metal in nitrogen to form the nitride. The nitride is decomposed with a small amount of H_2O to form solid $Mg(OH)_2$ and ammonia.

Most commercial ammonia is produced by the Haber process (Fig. 15.3). Nitrogen and hydrogen react in the presence of a catalyst to form ammonia.

$$N_2 + 3H_2 \xrightarrow[\text{catalyst}]{\Delta} 2NH_3 + 24\,\text{kcal}$$

High pressures favor the formation of NH_3, while high temperatures favor decomposition. Due to the somewhat inert character of the gases at room temperature, it is necessary to increase the rate of formation by increasing the temperature. Since this temperature rise has an adverse effect on the equilibrium, ammonia is removed constantly from the system before equilibrium is attained. The best operating conditions are found to be 200 atmospheres and 500°C using a catalyst of iron mixed with Al_2O_3. When the gases emerge from the reaction vessel, they cool and the ammonia liquefies. The unreacted (about 90%) N_2 and H_2 are returned to the reaction vessel.

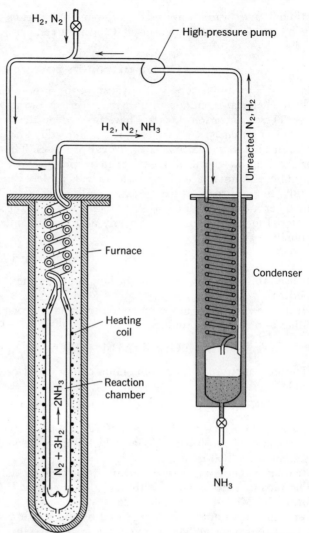

Fig. 15.3

Sketch of Haber Process. Exiting gases heat N_2 and H_2 before they enter the reaction chamber which is filled with metal oxide catalyst. NH_3 is cooled in the condenser and liquefied.

Some ammonia is produced by the older cyanamide process in which finely ground calcium carbide reacts with nitrogen gas at 1100°C to form calcium cyanamide.

$$CaC_2 + N_2 \rightarrow CaCN_2 + C + 72\,kcal$$

Once this reaction starts, it is self-sustaining. When cooled, the product is washed with water to remove unreacted CaC_2. $CaCN_2$ is decomposed with superheated steam to form ammonia.

$$CaCN_2 + 3H_2O \rightarrow 2NH_3\uparrow + CaCO_3$$

A small percentage of the annual ammonia production is recovered from coal gas, a by-product of the coking process. Since coal originates from organic material, it contains some nitrogen as well as hydrogen. When the coal is heated, ammonia forms and subsequently dissolves in the water which also forms.

Properties. At room temperatures and atmospheric pressures, ammonia is a colorless gas, somewhat less dense than air, with a pungent odor (Table 15.4). It is liquefied easily by cooling or by applying pressures of eight to nine atmospheres at room temperatures. Ammonia is very soluble in water. At 0°C, one liter of water dissolves 1200 liters of ammonia gas. The solubility decreases with temperature (700 liters of gas per liter of water at 20°C), making it possible to remove almost all ammonia from water by boiling.

Table 15.4

Physical Properties of Ammonia

Melting Point	−77.7°C
Boiling Point	−33.3°C
Density at 20°C	0.712 g/l
Critical Temperature	132.9°C
Critical Pressure	111.3 atm

Ammonia readily dissolves in water to form a species that is written as NH_4OH or as $NH_3 \cdot H_2O$. In either case, the species dissociates slightly to give NH_4^+ and OH^- ions and behaves as a typical weak base. Thus, there are many ionic ammonium salts in which the ammonium ion is chemically similar to the alkali metal ions with the exception that NH_4^+ undergoes hydrolysis in solution.

Many transition metal ions form soluble ammine complexes in an ammonium hydroxide solution. Some of the common ones are $[Cu(NH_3)_4^{++}]$, $[Ni(NH_3)_6^{++}]$, and $[Ag(NH_3)_2^+]$. Most of these metal ions first form a hydroxide precipitate upon addition of NH_4OH. The precipitates dissolve to form the complex ion when more NH_4OH is added.

$$Zn^{++} + 2NH_4OH \rightarrow Zn(OH)_2\downarrow + 2NH_4^+$$

$$Zn(OH)_2 + 4NH_4OH \rightarrow [Zn(NH_3)_4^{++}] + 4H_2O + 2OH^-$$

Ammonia burns in pure oxygen to give N_2. If a platinum catalyst is present, however, the product is NO which is converted to nitric acid.

$$4NH_3 + 3O_2 \rightarrow 2N_2\uparrow + 6H_2O$$
$$4NH_3 + 5O_2 \xrightarrow{\text{Pt catalyst}} 4NO\uparrow + 6H_2O$$

Ammonia is used extensively in commercial refrigeration, since it is condensed readily and has a high heat of vaporization (330 cal/g). Ammonia or ammonium salts are used as fertilizers. Much ammonia is used to prepare other compounds of nitrogen.

Oxides of Nitrogen

N_2O. Five oxides of nitrogen corresponding to nitrogen oxidation states of $+1$, $+2$, $+3$, $+4$, and $+5$ are known. Nitrous oxide or dinitrogen oxide (N_2O) is prepared by cautiously heating ammonium nitrate.

$$NH_4NO_3 \rightarrow N_2O\uparrow + 2H_2O$$

N_2O is a colorless, nonflammable, non-toxic gas with a slightly sweet taste and odor and moderate solubility in water. It is chemically unreactive at low temperatures. When heated, N_2O decomposes to the elements, the decomposition being aided by the presence of such metals as copper, lead, or iron. Its major uses are as an inhalation anesthetic (laughing gas) and as a propelling agent in pressurized containers.

NO. Nitric oxide is formed in nature from N_2 and O_2 during electrical storms. In the laboratory, it is formed when dilute nitric acid is used to dissolve a metal less active than hydrogen. A common example is the dissolution of copper in dilute nitric acid.

$$3Cu + 8H^+ + 2NO_3^- \rightarrow 3Cu^{++} + 4H_2O + 2NO\uparrow$$

There is also some NO_2 in the product gas. Pure NO is prepared by heating a mixture of potassium nitrate, potassium nitrite, and chromic oxide.

$$3KNO_2 + KNO_3 + Cr_2O_3 \xrightarrow{\Delta} 2K_2CrO_4 + 4NO\uparrow$$

Commercially, nitric oxide is prepared by the catalytic oxidation of ammonia at 500°C as described above. Attempts have been made to combine catalytically N_2 and O_2 in the air to form NO. The equilibrium constant for the reaction is too small for practical use below 2100°C. Decomposition of NO is very rapid above 1500°C, making it necessary to cool the gaseous reaction mixture from 2100°C to 1500°C at a rate of 40,000 degrees per second. The feasibility of such a reaction has been demonstrated in a pilot plant, but it is cheaper to use Haber process ammonia to prepare NO at present.

Nitric oxide is a colorless, toxic, nonflammable gas, slightly soluble in water. It is oxidized rapidly in air to NO_2 at room temperature. It is reduced to N_2 and the oxide by many metals. Nitric oxide is used primarily as an intermediate in the manufacture of nitric acid.

NO_2. Nitrogen dioxide is the major product when metals below hydrogen in the activity series react with concentrated nitric acid.

$$Cu + 4HNO_3 \text{ (conc)} \rightarrow Cu^{++} + 2NO_3^- + 2H_2O + 2NO_2\uparrow$$

NO_2 and O_2 are liberated when heavy metal nitrates are heated.

$$2Pb(NO_3)_2 \xrightarrow{\Delta} 2PbO + 4NO_2\uparrow + O_2\uparrow$$

NO_2 is a reddish-brown, highly toxic gas with a sharp, choking odor. When cooled to $-10°C$, crystals form. The colorless liquid boils at $22.4°C$ to form a colorless gas which becomes reddish-brown upon further heating. Density measurements show that the vapor is an equilibrium mixture of the colorless dimer, nitrogen tetroxide (N_2O_4), and the highly colored NO_2. Below the boiling point, the vapor is almost all N_2O_4. As the temperature increases, the equilibrium is shifted toward NO_2.

$$2NO_2 \rightleftarrows N_2O_4 + 15 \text{ kcal}$$
reddish-   colorless
brown

Since the equilibrium shifts so rapidly, the dimer does not affect the chemical properties.

NO_2 is a powerful oxidizing agent. Phosphorus, carbon, and sulfur burn in it, yielding the oxides and nitrogen. Nitrogen dioxide dissolves in water to form HNO_3 and HNO_2. The nitrous acid then decomposes to form HNO_3 and NO.

$$2NO_2 + H_2O \rightarrow HNO_3 + HNO_2$$
$$3HNO_2 \rightarrow HNO_3 + 2NO + H_2O$$

The overall reaction is

$$3NO_2 + H_2O \rightarrow 2HNO_3 + NO$$

In the presence of air the NO produced in the last reaction is immediately oxidized to NO_2. NO_2 reacts with water to form more HNO_3 and one-third the original number of moles of NO. This process continues until the conversion to HNO_3 is virtually complete.

N_2O_3. Nitrogen trioxide is the unstable anhydride of nitrous acid. It can be prepared using concentrated sulfuric acid and a nitrite salt.

$$2NaNO_2 + H_2SO_4 \text{ (conc)} \rightarrow Na_2SO_4 + 2HNO_2$$
$$\phantom{2NaNO_2 + H_2SO_4 \text{ (conc)} \rightarrow Na_2SO_4 +}\downarrow$$
$$\phantom{2NaNO_2 + H_2SO_4 \text{ (conc)} \rightarrow Na_2SO_4} \rightarrow N_2O_3\uparrow + H_2O$$

This decomposition of the HNO_2 is aided by the removal of the water by the concentrated sulfuric acid. The trioxide readily decomposes to NO and N_2O_4.

N_2O_5. Nitrogen pentoxide is the anhydride of nitric acid and is prepared by dehydrating nitric acid with phosphorus pentoxide.

$$4HNO_3 + P_4O_{10} \rightarrow 4HPO_3 + 2N_2O_5$$

It appears to be a crystalline material composed of (NO_2^+) and

(NO_3^-), which decomposes readily to N_2O_4 and reacts violently with water to form HNO_3.

Nitric Acid (HNO_3)

Preparation. Nitric acid is another extremely important chemical. It is prepared in the laboratory by heating a nitrate with concentrated sulfuric acid.

$$NaNO_3 + H_2SO_4 \xrightarrow{\Delta} NaHSO_4 + HNO_3\uparrow$$

Commercially, it is prepared from ammonia. HNO_3 melts at $-42°C$ to a colorless liquid with a density of 1.54 g/ml; it boils at 86°C. Concentrated nitric acid is the constant boiling mixture that contains about 67% (by weight) HNO_3 or about 16 moles per liter.

Properties. Nitric acid is a vigorous oxidizing agent. Most of the nonmetals are oxidized to the oxygen acid. NO is the reduction product.

$$S + 2HNO_3 \text{ (conc)} \rightarrow H_2SO_4 + 2NO\uparrow$$

It reacts with all of the common metals except gold and platinum, although some metals such as aluminum, iron, cobalt, and nickel become passive (do not react) in concentrated nitric acid, possibly because of an oxide coating. Active metals in dilute HNO_3 yield N_2O, N_2, and NH_4^+ as reduction products with the lower oxidation states favored in the more dilute solutions.

$$4Zn + 10H^+ + NO_3^- \rightarrow 4Zn^{++} + NH_4^+ + 3H_2O$$

The less active metals form NO in dilute HNO_3, and NO_2 in concentrated HNO_3. Cations with more than one possible oxidation state, such as Fe^{++} and Sn^{++}, are oxidized to the higher state with HNO_3. Gold and platinum dissolve in aqua regia, a mixture of three volumes concentrated hydrochloric acid and one volume concentrated nitric acid, to form NO and a metal-chloride ion complex.

$$Au + 4H^+ + NO_3^- + 4Cl^- \rightarrow [AuCl_4]^- + NO\uparrow + 2H_2O$$

Nitric acid finds widespread use in the manufacture of explosives, nitrocellulose (used in lacquers), nitrate fertilizers, and silver nitrate, the last of which is used in the preparation of photographic emulsions.

SIGNIFICANT TERMS AND CONCEPTS IN CHAPTER XV:

Preparation, physical properties and chemical properties of Group VA elements; allotropes of phosphorus, preparation and properties of ammonia, Haber process; properties of the nitrogen oxides, preparation and properties of nitric acid.

Review questions

15.1. Write the balanced equation for the reaction of each of the Group VA elements when heated with an excess of:
(a) oxygen, (b) hydrogen, (c) chlorine.

15.2. Give the formula and the name of the product when magnesium is heated with: (a) nitrogen, (b) phosphorus, (c) arsenic.

15.3. List the oxides of the Group VA elements.

15.4. List the products when each of the above oxides is placed in water.

15.5. Why is the reaction of zinc and nitric acid not a good method of preparing pure nitrous oxide?

15.6. Give the equations for the preparation of nitric acid from nitrogen using the Haber process.

15.7. Give the equation for: (a) silver reacting with concentrated nitric acid, (b) phosphorus reacting with concentrated nitric acid, (c) the preparation of phosphoric acid from phosphorus, (d) the preparation of pure bismuth metal from a Bi_2S_3 ore.

15.8. Explain, using equations, how the precipitate that forms when $BiCl_3$ is placed in water can be dissolved.

15.9. Show that ammonia is not an ideal gas. Use the data in Table 15.4.

sixteen

group IVA elements

The predicted trend from nonmetallic properties in carbon to metallic properties in lead is found in the Group IVA elements. All are characterized by a s^2p^2 ground state electron configuration.

The chemistry of carbon can be divided into two parts, the organic and the inorganic. The distinction between the two is rather arbitrary in many cases. In general, organic compounds are characterized by the presence of chains or rings of carbon atoms. Inorganic carbon chemistry, which is discussed in this chapter, deals with compounds containing a single carbon atom. Organic compounds are discussed in Chapter XIX. Silicon, germanium, tin, and lead do not exhibit the tendency to form chains and rings.

Occurrence and preparation

Carbon in the form of coal and diamonds has been known since ancient times, as have carbonates such as limestone and marble. Carbon dioxide is widespread as a small portion of the earth's atmosphere.

Coke, charcoal, and lampblack are amorphous forms of carbon which are prepared by heating coal, wood, or petroleum products in a limited air supply. These amorphous forms are converted to graphite by heating in the absence of air for several hours.

Silicon is a common constituent of clays and rocks, where it is found in the form of the silicate. Sand is almost pure SiO_2. Silicon in the form of its compounds makes up about 28 per cent by weight of the earth's crust.

Impure silicon is prepared in the laboratory by the reduction of white sand (SiO_2) with magnesium.

$$SiO_2 + 2Mg \xrightarrow{\Delta} 2MgO + Si$$

Silicon is prepared commercially by the reduction of sand (SiO_2) with coke or silicon carbide in an electric furnace at 2000°C. Very high purity silicon is obtained from the reaction of the impure silicon with chlorine to form the tetrachloride. After the tetrachloride has been purified by distillation, it is reduced either on a hot wire filament or by heating in the presence of hydrogen.

The existence and properties of germanium were predicted by Mendeleev in his periodic tables about fifteen years before the element was discovered. Germanium compounds are rather rare, occurring as impurities in the ores of silver, lead, and zinc. Germanium dioxide (GeO_2) is formed during the roasting of these ores. The oxide is recovered from the ash and converted to the tetrachloride with hydrochloric acid. Germanium tetrachloride ($GeCl_4$) is hydrolyzed to reform GeO_2 in higher purity. The oxide is then reduced with carbon or aluminum. Semiconductor grade (very high purity) germanium is prepared by carefully reducing distilled $GeCl_4$ with pure hydrogen.

Tin was known during the Bronze Age as a constituent of bronze. It is found primarily as SnO_2 (cassiterite). After the ore has been purified, SnO_2 is reduced readily with carbon. The molten metal is drawn out of the reaction furnace and cast into molds.

Lead also has been known since ancient times. The Romans made use of the metal as water pipes, some of which survive to this day. Rich deposits of the sulfide, PbS (galena), the sulfate, $PbSO_4$ (anglesite), and the carbonate, $PbCO_3$ (cerussite), are known. These sulfides and carbonates are converted to oxides by heating in air (roasting). They are reduced with more sulfide, or with carbon or carbon monoxide in the case of PbO.

$$2PbO + PbS \rightarrow 3Pb + SO_2\uparrow$$

$$PbSO_4 + PbS \rightarrow 2Pb + 2SO_2\uparrow$$

$$PbO + C \rightarrow Pb + CO\uparrow$$

It is possible to reduce PbS directly with iron.

$$PbS + Fe \rightarrow Pb + FeS$$

Physical properties

The Group IVA elements exist as liquids over a long range of temperatures. The trend of a longer liquid range with increasing molecular weight is abruptly reversed at lead. Tin, with a liquid range of 2455 degrees, has the longest liquid range of the lower melting (below 500°C) elements. Several of the transition metals have longer temperature ranges for the liquid than silicon, but most (Groups IVB through VIIIB) melt at much higher temperatures.

Probably the most outstanding example of allotropic behavior is that of carbon, which exists as stable graphite, metastable diamond, and the amorphous form at room temperatures. The

Table 16.1

Some Physical Properties of the Group IVA Elements

Element	Allotropic form	Color	Density at 25°C (g/cc)	Melting point (°C)	Boiling point (°C)	Liquid range (degrees)
C	graphite	black	2.25	—	4347	—
	diamond	colorless	3.51			
	amorphous	black	1.8-2.1			
Si	diamond	gray	2.33	1410	3167	1757
	amorphous	brown	2.00			
Ge	diamond	gray-white	5.32	937	2830	1893
Sn	alpha	gray	5.77			
	beta	silver-white	7.29	232	2687	2455
Pb	cubic	silver blue-white	11.34	327	1753	1426

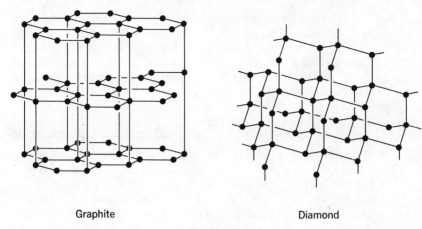

Graphite   Diamond

Fig. 16.1
Allotropic Forms of Carbon

carbon atoms in graphite are arranged in sheets of hexagons (Fig. 16.1). The distances between carbon atoms in the plane is 1.42 Å; the planes are 3.35 Å apart. This means that the bonding between planes is relatively weak. The planes slip over one another easily if a few water molecules are trapped between the layers, making graphite a good dry lubricant.

The carbon atoms in diamonds are held in tetrahedra. Each carbon is bonded to four other carbon atoms in a three-dimensional array (Fig. 16.1). As a result, diamond is a very hard, electrically insulating substance. Diamond is unstable at room temperature and pressure, but the rate of conversion to graphite is so slow that diamonds appear to be permanent. If diamond is heated, the rate of conversion is increased and it soon turns to graphite. Graphite can be converted to diamond at high temperatures and pressures. These conditions existed in the earth at the time the natural diamond was formed. Small industrial diamonds are now made by subjecting graphite and a metal catalyst to temperatures of 1200 to 2400°C and pressures of 55,000 to 100,000 atmospheres.

Silicon occurs in both an amorphous and a diamond-like crystalline form. Because of this diamond structure, crystalline silicon is a hard, brittle, unreactive solid with a high melting point.

Germanium has a diamond-like structure also. It is more brittle, since the bonds are weaker than those in diamond and silicon.

Tin exists in three allotropic forms. Gray tin, which is stable below 13°C, has the diamond structure. White tin is stable from 13° to 161°C at which point a conversion to rhombic tin takes place rapidly. The white-to-gray conversion is slow at the transition temperature but is more rapid at lower temperatures. Since gray tin has a greater volume than white tin, objects made of tin often disintegrate into powder at low temperatures. Gray tin is brittle, while white tin is very malleable and can be rolled into thin sheets or foils.

Lead is a very soft metal with little structural strength. It can be drawn into fine wire or rolled in thin sheets, but for practical use it must be hardened by the addition of antimony or one of the Group IIA metals.

Chemical properties

The trend toward metallic properties in the heavier Group IVA elements is very obvious. The increased stability of the $+2$ oxidation state at the expense of the $+4$ state is also apparent. Carbon, silicon, and germanium exhibit the $+4$ state primarily. The $+4$ state of tin is more stable than the $+2$ state, although both oxidation states are found. Few compounds of lead in the unstable $+4$ oxidation state are known.

(1) Reaction with oxygen

All of the Group IVA elements react when heated with excess oxygen to form the $+4$ oxide, although PbO_2 decomposes to PbO above 500°C. The oxidation of silicon and germanium is slowed by the formation of an oxide layer. No such protective layer forms in the case of carbon, since CO_2 and CO are gases. Lead and tin melt at relatively low temperatures; any oxide coating is of limited value.

(2) Reaction with acids

Carbon and silicon are too inert to react with acids. Germanium is sufficiently active to be dissolved in the concentrated oxidizing acids, HNO_3 and H_2SO_4.

Tin liberates hydrogen slowly from a non-oxidizing acid such as hydrochloric acid and forms the stannous ion.

$$Sn + 2HCl \rightarrow SnCl_2 + H_2\uparrow$$

In an oxidizing acid such as nitric acid the product is a hydrated stannic oxide precipitate.

$$Sn + 4HNO_3 \rightarrow SnO_2\downarrow + 4NO_2\uparrow + 2H_2O$$

Although lead is slightly above hydrogen in the activity series, it is not attacked by reducing acids, since the metal becomes protectively coated with an insoluble salt. Lead(II) nitrate is formed slowly in the reaction of lead with nitric acid. Due to the solubility of lead acetate, lead is attacked by acetic acid in the presence of oxygen.

$$2Pb + 4HC_2H_3O_2 + O_2 \rightarrow 2Pb(C_2H_3O_2)_2 + 2H_2O$$

(3) Reaction with bases

Carbon does not react with the alkali metal hydroxides. Silicon and germanium liberate hydrogen from concentrated base forming a solution of the silicate (SiO_4^{4-}) or germanate $[Ge(OH)_6]^=$. Tin and lead react slowly at room temperature and rapidly when heated to form stannate $[Sn(OH)_6]^=$ and plumbate $[Pb(OH)_6]^=$ ions.

The nomenclature for the complex hydroxy ions should be noted. The complex with the higher oxidation state has an *-ate* ending, while the *-ite* ending denotes the lower oxidation state. There are four OH^- ions closely associated with the metal atom in the lower oxidation state and six OH^- ions about the atom in the higher oxidation state. The formulas given here are for the species which probably exist in solution. If the ions are precipitated and the compound dried, the names would be applicable to the general formulas $M^{IV}O_3^=$ and $M^{II}O_2^=$.

(4) Reaction with nonmetals

Elemental carbon does not combine directly with any of the other non-metals except fluorine and oxygen, although carbon tetrahalides and carbon disulfide, which are prepared from carbon-containing compounds, are important chemicals. The product of the graphite–fluorine reaction is a white polymeric solid with a composition approximating $(CF)_n$.

Silicon, germanium, tin, and lead react directly with halogens to form tetrahalides (except for PbI_2). It is necessary to initiate the reaction by heating, except for the fluorine reactions. The formation of PbI_2 reflects the instability of the $+4$ oxidation state for lead in comparison to the $+2$ state, as well as the fact that iodine is not a strong oxidizing agent. Further evidence of the instability of the $+4$ state in the heavier members of this group is the formation of $GeCl_2$ by strongly heating $GeCl_4$.

The instability of the $+4$ state for lead is seen in the reaction of the Group IVA elements with sulfur. Lead forms PbS; while the other elements form disulfides, MS_2.

None of the Group IVA elements react directly with nitrogen, although the nitrides, SiN, GeN, and cyanogen (CN_2), are prepared indirectly.

(5) Reactions with metals

Many metals combine with carbon to form carbides which are classified into two types: (a) the salt-like carbides, which are primarily non-transition metal carbides, and (b) the refractory carbides, which include most of the transition metal carbides. The Group IA and IIA carbides (M_2C_2 and MC_2) hydrolyze to give acetylene and the hydroxide. CaC_2 is the most important carbide commercially, as it is used to prepare acetylene.

$$CaC_2 + 2H_2O \rightarrow Ca(OH)_2 + C_2H_2$$

The other salt-like carbides hydrolyze to form methane (CH_4) and the hydroxide. The refractory carbides are characterized by their high melting points and their hardness.

Silicon dissolves in many metals to form solid solutions and metal silicides. The transition metal silicides are high melting and hard. The most important of the silicides is $FeSi$ which is used in the manufacture of silicon steels.

Tin and lead do not undergo a chemical reaction with other

metals but readily form solutions known as alloys. Most of the alloys of tin and lead have low melting points.

Uses

Only a few diamonds have sufficient size and purity to be of value as gems. Large numbers of small and imperfect diamonds are used for abrasive and cutting purposes. Graphite is used in many electrical applications, in electrodes, and in high temperature service. Carbon in the form of coal and coke is used as a reducing agent in the refining of several metals. Small amounts of carbon in iron impart desirable properties of strength and hardness to steel.

Small amounts of silicon in the form of FeSi produce desirable properties in steel. Elemental silicon is used in transistors.

The major use of germanium is in transistors. A controlled amount of impurity is added to ultra-high purity (in the parts-per-million range) germanium. The electrical properties of germanium are modified by the impurity type and level.

Tin is used for plating iron and some steels. The protection lasts as long as the surface is unbroken. Once the film is broken, corrosion is accelerated. This plating has been used extensively in tin cans, but other coatings are now coming into use. Tin foil has been used for protective wrappings but is being replaced by plastics and aluminum foil. The remaining major use of tin is in the formation of alloys. Bronze consists of approximately 90 per cent copper and 10 per cent tin. Solder is a 50 per cent tin–50 per cent lead alloy. Various other tin–lead alloys such as pewter and Babbitt metal also are in use.

The major use of lead is in the manufacture of automobile storage batteries. It also is used as tetraethyl lead ($Pb(C_2H_5)_4$), an antiknock additive for gasoline. It is used in some low melting alloys and in plumbing.

Some group IVA compounds

Oxides of carbon

CO. Carbon monoxide, a colorless, odorless gas, is formed when carbon or carbon-containing compounds are burned in a limited supply of oxygen. Carbon monoxide is useful as a fuel, since it readily burns in oxygen to form carbon dioxide. It is useful as a reducing agent in many processes. For example, CO plays a vital role in the reduction of iron ore to iron.

$$Fe_3O_4 + 4CO \rightarrow 3Fe + 4CO_2$$

Carbon monoxide is dangerous physiologically since it destroys the oxygen-carrying ability of the blood.

CO₂. Carbon dioxide is a colorless, odorless, non-toxic gas. When solidified, it is used extensively as a cooling agent called

Dry Ice. Solid CO_2 does not melt before the vapor pressure reaches one atmosphere at $-78°C$. Thus, the temperature of Dry Ice or a mixture of crushed Dry Ice and a low melting liquid, such as acetone, never rises above $-78°C$. Since CO_2 vaporizes as heat is absorbed, there is no problem of disposal.

Carbon dioxide is also used in fire extinguishers, since it cannot be oxidized further. Because of its density (about 1.5 that of air), CO_2 displaces air from around the fire, cutting off the oxygen supply.

A dilute solution of carbonic acid is formed when CO_2 is passed into water. Such a solution is a weak acid containing several species which are involved in the equilibrium.

$$CO_2 + H_2O \rightleftarrows H_2CO_3 \rightleftarrows H^+ + HCO_3^- \rightleftarrows 2H^+ + CO_3^=$$

The concentration of these species is limited by the low solubility of CO_2, which decreases further with increasing temperature. It is possible to recover metal carbonates and metal hydrogen-carbonates from such a solution. Carbonates and hydrogen-carbonates hydrolyze readily, establishing the above equilibrium. The addition of an acid to a carbonate solution or to a solid carbonate shifts the equilibrium toward evolution of CO_2 gas.

Oxides of silicon

Silicon monoxide is known to exist as a gas at temperatures above 1000°C, but it is not stable at lower temperatures. Thus, the only important oxide of silicon occurs as a solid which is a large network of silicon and oxygen atoms in a ratio corresponding to the formula, SiO_2. Quartz and sand are two forms of essentially pure, naturally occurring SiO_2. The silicon atoms are held together through bonds with the oxygen atoms.

Natural quartz has a well-defined crystal structure. Upon cooling, molten SiO_2 forms a glassy solid called fused quartz or fused silica. This glassy material has no long-range order in the crystal structure, but it does have the property of being able to withstand sudden, large changes in temperature. Thus, red-hot fused silica can be plunged into cold water without cracking.

Glassy sodium silicate is formed when white sand is fused (melted) with sodium carbonate.

$$SiO_2 + Na_2CO_3 \rightarrow Na_2SiO_3 + CO_2\uparrow$$

In addition to the metasilicate ($SiO_3^=$) the product may include greater or lesser amounts of orthosilicate (SiO_4^{4-}) and pyrosilicate ($Si_2O_7^{6-}$). It is possible to obtain glasses of different properties by adding other substances to the molten mixture. Soft glass, also called lime glass or soda glass, contains sodium and calcium silicates. A higher melting Jena glass is formed when potassium is substituted for sodium. Flint glass is a mixture of sodium and lead silicates. All of these glasses suffer from being unable to undergo rapid thermal changes without cracking. If small

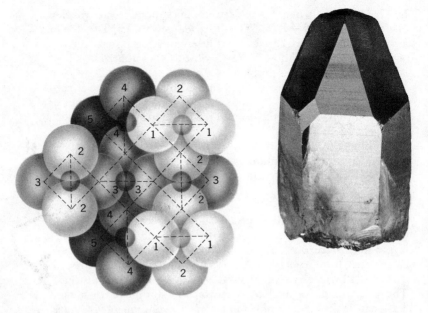

Fig. 16.2

Structure of Quartz. A silicon atom is linked to four oxygen atoms at the corner of a tetrahedron. The oxygen atoms are also part of adjacent tetrahedra. The structure extends in three dimensions to produce a large molecule. SiO_2 is the simplest formula; however, it does not represent a discrete molecule.

amounts of Al_2O_3 and B_2O_3 are added to the soft glass melt, this problem is reduced. This higher melting product is sold as Pyrex and Kimax brands of glassware.

All silicates and SiO_2 react with fluorine and hydrofluoric acid to form volatile SiF_4. This reaction makes possible the etching of glass. The object to be etched is coated with wax which then is cut away along the lines of the design. The glassware is dipped in a dilute hydrofluoric acid solution. HF reacts with the exposed glass to etch the desired pattern.

Oxides of lead

Four oxides of lead are known. Lead dioxide, formed when lead is heated in air, is a dark brown solid that dissolves in concentrated base and in concentrated acid. In the halogen acids it is reduced to the $+2$ oxidation state.

$$PbO_2 + 4HX \rightarrow 2H_2O + PbX_2 + X_2 \quad (X \neq F)$$

Lead monoxide (PbO) exists in a yellow form (massicot) and in an orange–yellow modification (litharge). Litharge is the stable form, although massicot changes to litharge only upon strong heating. PbO is amphoteric and forms Pb^{++} ions in acid and the rather unstable plumbite ion $[Pb(OH)_4]^=$ in a base.

When litharge is heated in air, the trioxide (Pb_2O_3) and red lead (Pb_3O_4) are formed. These oxides behave as lead plumbates.

$$Pb_2O_3 = Pb^{II}(Pb^{IV}O_3)$$
$$Pb_3O_4 = Pb_2^{II}(Pb^{IV}O_4)$$

Red lead is a brilliant red solid, insoluble in water. It is used as a red pigment and as a rust preventative paint on iron and steel.

Lead(IV) oxide (PbO_2) and lead(II) oxide (PbO) are amphoteric. Lead(IV) or lead(II) salts are formed when the corresponding oxide is treated with acid; although PbO_2 forms lead(II) salts with halide acids. The plumbate $[Pb(OH)_6^=]$ or the plumbite $[Pb(OH)_4^=]$ ions are formed when the oxides are treated with hot concentrated base.

Oxides of germanium and tin

Germanium dioxide is soluble only in hot concentrated hydrochloric acid. The +4 oxidation state is the only stable state for germanium in solution.

Tin(IV) oxide (SnO_2) is acid insoluble and is dissolved only by fusion with NaOH to form the soluble sodium stannate, $Na_2Sn(OH)_6$. Tin(II) oxide (SnO) is amphoteric, forming stannous solutions with non-oxidizing acids and stannite $[Sn(OH)_4^=]$ solutions with hot concentrated base.

Other compounds of lead

One characteristic of the chemistry of lead is that there are few soluble lead salts. All of the lead(IV) salts are either insoluble or hydrolyze readily. The most soluble lead(II) salt is the slightly dissociating acetate $Pb(C_2H_3O_2)_2$. Lead halides have only a limited solubility in water. $PbSO_4$ is a white insoluble salt. $PbCrO_4$ is a yellow insoluble compound.

When lead is exposed to air, it becomes coated with a thin protective layer of $Pb(OH)_2$ and $PbCO_3$. A similar basic carbonate called white lead precipitates when carbonate ion is added to a solution of lead(II) ions.

$$2Pb^{++} + 2CO_3^= + H_2O \rightarrow Pb(OH)_2 \cdot PbCO_3\downarrow + CO_2$$

It is not possible to precipitate this carbonate free of the hydroxide, since the concentration of carbonate required for the precipitation increases the pH of the solution to the point where the OH^- ion concentration is great enough to exceed the solubility product constant for $Pb(OH)_2$. Due to its protective character, white lead is used in many white exterior paints, although it does form black PbS when exposed to atmospheres containing H_2S. Therefore, many of the present white paints use titanium dioxide rather than white lead as a pigment. Although TiO_2 slowly reacts with H_2S, no discoloration occurs since titanium sulfide is white.

The brilliant colors of the lead salts have made them useful as paint pigments in the past. However there is the danger of heavy metal poisoning if any of the paint is ingested. As a result, non-toxic substitutes are now used as pigment material.

Chlorides of tin

Anhydrous stannous chloride ($SnCl_2$) is prepared by heating tin in a stream of hydrogen chloride gas; it is not possible to remove the water from the hydrate without high temperature hydrolysis taking place.

$$SnCl_2 \cdot 2H_2O \xrightarrow{\Delta} Sn(OH)Cl + HCl + H_2O$$

Stannous chloride solutions are good reducing agents readily reacting with mercuric and ferric ions.

$$2Hg^{++} + Sn^{++} + 2Cl^- \rightarrow Hg_2Cl_2 + Sn^{4+}$$

$$Hg_2Cl_2 + Sn^{++} \rightarrow 2Hg + Sn^{4+} + 2Cl^-$$

$$2Fe^{3+} + Sn^{++} \rightarrow 2Fe^{++} + Sn^{4+}$$

Stannic chloride is a colorless liquid which is composed of covalent molecules. The material fumes in moist air due to hydrolysis.

$$SnCl_4 + 2H_2O \rightarrow SnO_2 + 4HCl\uparrow$$

When placed in solution, $SnCl_4$ ionizes and undergoes hydrolysis.

SIGNIFICANT TERMS AND CONCEPTS IN CHAPTER XVI:

Preparation, physical properties, and chemical properties of the Group IVA elements; comparison of structure and properties of diamond and graphite, nomenclature of hydroxy complex ions, stability of +2 state for lead; properties of Group IVA oxides, chemical properties of the tin chlorides.

Review questions

16.1. Write the equations for the reaction of the Group IVA elements when heated to about 400°C with: (a) excess oxygen, (b) excess chlorine, (c) excess iodine, (d) excess sulfur, (e) excess nitrogen.

16.2. Write the equations for the reaction of the Group IVA elements with: (a) concentrated HCl, (b) concentrated HNO_3, (c) dilute HNO_3, (d) hot concentrated NaOH.

16.3. Is a 0.1 M Na_2CO_3 solution acidic, basic, or neutral? Justify your answer.

16.4. Write equations for the following:
  (a) $CO + O_2 \rightarrow$
  (b) $PbO_2 + HCl \rightarrow$
  (c) $PbO + HCl \rightarrow$
  (d) $SnO + OH^-$ (conc) $+ H_2O \rightarrow$
  (e) $PbO_2 + OH^-$ (conc) $+ H_2O \rightarrow$
  (f) White lead $+ H_2S$
  (g) Hydrochloric acid + sodium carbonate solution
  (h) Etching of SiO_2 with hydrofluoric acid
  (i) Sodium carbide + water
  (j) The hydrolysis of the carbonate ion
  (k) The preparation of PbI_2 from galena and iodine

16.5. Calculate the volume change when 5 g tin are transformed from the gray form to the white form.

16.6. Why should one be skeptical of a product advertised as 99.9% $PbCO_3$? Base your answer on the chemistry involved.

16.7. Give the formula for the following:
  (a) Litharge
  (b) Potassium plumbite (solid)
  (c) Potassium stannate (solution)
  (d) Sodium germanate
  (e) Sodium stannite (solution)
  (f) Carbonic acid

16.8. Various allotropes have been discussed in the last three chapters. List the various crystalline allotropes of the nonmetals along with two identifying physical characteristics.

the elements of group IIIA

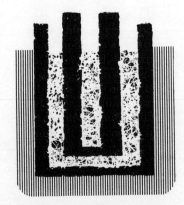

Aluminum is the only element of Group IIIA that has been commercially exploited. No other metal has the same combination of properties. In fact, each element of Group IIIA has a unique combination of properties. The differences among the elements of Group IIIA are greater than in any other group. Boron is an intermediate between a metal and a nonmetal. Aluminum is an amphoteric metal; the rest are metals with fewer amphoteric properties. The electronic configuration of s^2p^6 is the unifying property of these elements.

Occurrence and preparation

Aluminum is the most common of the Group IIIA elements. It occurs as aluminosilicates in clays, mica, and feldspar; as an oxide in corundum, emory, and bauxite; and as fluoroaluminate in cryolite. Since aluminum is an active metal, chemical reduction is not practical. The Hall process for the electrolytic production of the metal, first introduced in 1886, is still the basis for today's methods. Bauxite (a general term for ores of hydrated aluminum oxide) is dissolved in sodium hydroxide to remove impurities such as iron oxide which do not dissolve in concentrated base.

$$Al_2O_3 \cdot 3H_2O + 2OH^- \rightleftarrows 2Al(OH)_4^-$$

The reaction is reversed by the addition of water after the insoluble material has been removed. The hydrate is dried to Al_2O_3 for use in the electrolytic cell. A molten cryolite (Na_3AlF_6) bath with a small amount of CaF_2 and AlF_3 for the improvement of cell efficiency serves as an electrolyte for the electrolysis of Al_2O_3. During electrolysis, oxygen is formed on the graphite anodes and immediately reacts to form CO and CO_2, thereby consuming some of the electrode. Molten aluminum forms on the graphite-lined walls of the cell which serve as the cathode. The aluminum collects at the bottom of the cell and is drained off every day or two. The cryolite bath is maintained at 940° to 980°C by the passage of the current through the solution.

Boron is found primarily as borax ($Na_2B_4O_7 \cdot 10H_2O$). In the commercial preparation of boron, borax is converted to boric oxide (B_2O_3) with acid and heat. The oxide is reduced with magnesium to impure amorphous boron. High purity crystalline boron is prepared by forming boron bromide or iodide using the impure material. The boron halide is decomposed on a hot filament in the presence of hydrogen.

Gallium and indium are found as trace impurities in aluminum ores. The concentration of gallium and indium increases in the solution as bauxite is continually dissolved and re-precipitated. At the appropriate concentration the oxides of gallium and indium are precipitated. The metals are recovered by electrolysis of a solution of these oxides.

Thallium is recovered from iron pyrite (FeS_2) ores in which it occurs in trace amounts. During the roasting of pyrite ore, thal-

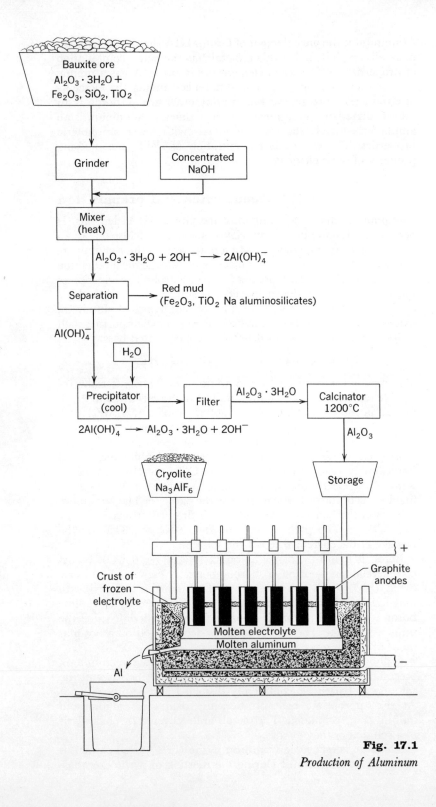

Fig. 17.1
Production of Aluminum

Table 17.1

Some Physical Properties of the Group IIIA Elements

	Melting point (°C)	Boiling point (°C)	Temperature range for liquid (°C)	Density (g/cc)
Boron	2177	3658	1481	2.46
Aluminum	659	2467	1808	2.70
Gallium	30	2403	2373	6.10 (liquid)
				5.91 (solid)
Indium	157	2300	2143	7.29
Thallium	304	1457	1153	11.85

lium is converted to the oxide and deposited in the flues. Thallium oxide is recovered from the flue ash and converted to thallium iodide which is reduced with sodium.

Physical properties

A study of the physical properties listed in Table 17.1 shows that the tendency toward long liquid ranges for the elements is similar to that found in Group IVA (Chapter XVI). The first members of both groups (boron and carbon) are high boiling elements with high melting points. The last members of the groups (thallium and lead) are low melting and relatively low boiling. It is the other three members of each group that exhibit the long temperature range for the liquid phase. Gallium and indium have the second and third longest liquid ranges of the lower melting (below 500°C) elements. Since gallium melts just above room temperature (30°C), its liquid behavior is most striking.

Amorphous boron is a black powder that is quite reactive. Crystalline boron, unique in that B_{12} clusters make up the solid, has a metallic luster and is almost inert. It is very hard, only slightly lower than diamond on the hardness scale. The electrical resistance decreases with increasing temperature, a characteristic typical of nonmetals.

Fig. 17.2

A Sample of Gallium Metal. As can be seen from the photograph, gallium has a melting point (30°C) below body temperature.

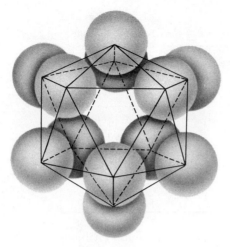

Fig. 17.3

Structure of α-Boron. Twelve boron atoms are arranged at the vertices of an icosahedron (20-sided figure). The icosahedra are closely packed to form α-boron.

Aluminum is a silver-white metal with a low density. It is malleable, ductile, and moderately hard. Gallium is a silver colored solid that melts with a decrease in volume just above room temperature. The liquid does not immediately solidify upon cooling but remains a liquid well below its melting point for long periods of time. Liquid gallium has the appearance of mercury but has a much lower density (5.9 g/cc vs 13.5 g/cc).

Indium is a relatively soft, silver-white metal. Thallium resembles lead in its appearance, density, and malleability; however, it is a poorer conductor of electricity.

General chemical properties

Oxidation states of +1 and +3 are predicted for the Group IIIA elements on the basis of their electron configuration. The +1 oxidation state becomes more stable than the +3 state as atomic weight increases. Thus, boron is found only in the +3 oxidation state, while examples of the +1 and +3 states are found for the other elements. The +3 oxidation state of thallium is very unstable. Boron compounds are covalent. Some aluminum and gallium compounds are ionic; most of the indium and thallium compounds are ionic.

(1) Reaction with oxygen

Except for thallium, which forms Tl_2O, all of the Group IIIA elements react with excess oxygen to form the M_2O_3-type oxide.

$$4M + 3O_2 \rightarrow 2M_2O_3$$

The oxidation of thallium and aluminum proceeds at room temperature, but Al_2O_3 forms a thin protective layer that permits aluminum to be melted without further oxidation. The oxidation of gallium is very slow even at high temperatures.

Except for boric oxide (B_2O_3) the oxides of Group IIIA elements dissolve readily in acid. The +3 oxidation state is stable in solution for all of the metals except thallium which exists as the $+1$ ion.

With the exception of Tl_2O_3 the Group IIA oxides dissolve in concentrated base to form a soluble hydroxy complex ion.

$$2M_2O_3 + 4OH^- + 6H_2O \rightarrow 4[M(OH)_4]^-$$

The dried solids have the general formula MO_2^- which corresponds to removal of two molecules of H_2O from the species in solution. The complex ions are named by substituting *-ate* for the last syllable of the metal name.

As a strong base is added to a solution containing ions of the Group IIIA metals, the hydroxide $(M(OH)_3)$, or the equivalent hydrated oxide $(M_2O_3 \cdot 3H_2O)$, precipitates first. The precipitate re-dissolves to form the hydroxy complex ion as more base is added.

The hydroxides precipitate when NH_4OH is added to a solution of Group IIIA ions. The precipitate does not re-dissolve since (a) the OH^- ion concentration is too low in a weak base, and (b) the Group IIIA ions do not form ammine complexes.

(2) Reaction with water and base

None of the Group IIIA metals react with water. If it were not for the protective oxide coating, aluminum would react vigorously with water, as indicated by its position in the activity series.

Thallium, indium, and crystalline boron do not react with concentrated base. It is necessary to fuse amorphous boron with an alkali metal hydroxide to get the borate $[B(OH)_4]^-$. Gallate $[Ga(OH)_4]^-$ and hydrogen are formed very slowly with concentrated base. Aluminum is readily attacked to form the aluminate $[Al(OH)_4]^-$ and hydrogen.

(3) Reaction with the nonmetals

All of the metals except thallium react with the halogens to form $+3$ halides. Thallium characteristically forms $+1$ halides.

$$2M + 3X_2 \rightarrow 2MX_3 \quad (M \neq Tl)$$
$$2Tl + X_2 \rightarrow 2TlX$$

Reactions with fluorine and chlorine are spontaneous. Boron and chlorine, however, must be heated. Reactions with bromine and iodine also must be initiated by heating.

Except for thallium and crystalline boron, the Group IIIA metals react upon heating to form $+3$ sulfides. Tl_2S is the product of the reaction with thallium.

$$2M + 3S \rightarrow M_2S_3 \quad (M \neq Tl)$$
$$2Tl + S \rightarrow Tl_2S$$

The Group IIIA metals, except for crystalline boron, form $+3$ nitrides upon heating in nitrogen. These nitrides are very hard, high melting substances.

$$2M + N_2 \rightarrow 2MN$$

Specific chemistry of group IIIA elements

Specific aspects of boron chemistry

Although boric oxide (B_2O_3) can be obtained by heating the elements, it is more feasible to prepare it by heating boric acid.

$$Na_2B_4O_7 \cdot 10H_2O \text{ (borax)} + 2H^+ \rightarrow$$
$$4H_3BO_3 + 2Na^+ + 5H_2O$$

$$2H_3BO_3 \xrightarrow{\Delta} 3H_2O + B_2O_3$$

Boric oxide tends to form a glassy solid that slowly rehydrates to form boric acid. When heated with a metal oxide, B_2O_3 forms colored borate glasses.

Boric acid is a white solid that is moderately soluble in water. It is a very weak acid with only one replaceable H^+ ion and is too weak to be titrated with a strong base without special techniques. H_3BO_3 is one of a group of boric acids and is designated as ortho-boric acid. When slowly heated, orthoboric acid forms metaboric acid and pyroboric acid.

$$H_3BO_3 \xrightarrow{\Delta} H_2O + HBO_2 \quad \text{(metaboric acid)}$$
$$4HBO_2 \xrightarrow{\Delta} H_2O + H_2B_4O_7 \quad \text{(pyroboric acid)}$$

Salts of all three acids hydrolyze considerably in solution.

A series of boron–hydrogen compounds known as the boron hydrides or boranes begin with diborane (B_2H_6). Boranes containing as many as ten boron atoms ($B_{10}H_{14}$, $B_{10}H_{16}$) have been studied. Diborane is a gas that is spontaneously flammable in air. When placed in water, it decomposes to H_3BO_3 and H_2. The higher boranes are liquids and solids but are only slightly less reactive. There has been great interest in these compounds as rocket fuels, due to their high energy of combustion. The bonding in these compounds is of interest as there are insufficient electrons for the usual electron-pair bonding. The structure of diborane is known to be

$$
\begin{array}{ccccc}
H & & H & & H \\
 \diagdown & \diagup & & \diagdown & \diagup \\
 & B & & B & \\
 \diagup & & \diagdown & \diagup & \diagdown \\
H & & H & & H \\
\end{array}
$$

It is necessary to postulate that two electrons are used in each of the B–H–B bridges.

Boron halides are covalent, reactive compounds. BF_3 and BCl_3 are gases at room temperature. The halides readily hydrolyze to H_3BO_3 and hydrogen halide.

Boron nitride can be prepared from the elements, but it is produced usually by the reaction of amorphous boron and ammonia at high temperatures. The structure of the white product

Fig. 17.4

Cubic Boron Nitride Crystals. Only small crystals of BN have been prepared. Those shown here are about 0.3 mm on a side.

is similar to that of graphite. Graphitic boron nitride is converted to a diamond form by the application of pressures of 85,000 atmospheres and temperatures of 1500°C. This product, commercially known as Borazon, is the hardest substance known. It is harder and more stable than diamond. For example, diamond burns in air at 800°C; whereas Borazon is stable to 1800°C.

Specific aspects of aluminum chemistry

Aluminum metal dissolves readily in reducing acids to liberate hydrogen. An oxidizing acid such as nitric acid renders the metal passive.

The thin oxide coating which forms immediately upon exposure to oxygen permits aluminum to be used in air, water, and very dilute acids. This film can be thickened artificially and colored by electrolytic oxidation. Sodium chloride solutions attack the oxide film; thus, aluminum is unserviceable in salt water.

Aluminum is used to reduce many metal oxides. If powdered aluminum is mixed with ferric oxide and ignited, the oxide is reduced to metal with the liberation of much heat. The heat melts the iron making it possible to do on-site welding. This *thermite* process has been used to weld iron rails on railroad beds.

AlF_3 is unreactive and relatively insoluble in water. The other halides form covalent dimers, Al_2X_6, which violently hydrolyze in water. The hydrated chloride, $[Al(H_2O)_6]Cl_3$, is crystallized from solution. Upon heating, it decomposes.

$$2[Al(H_2O)_6]Cl_3 \xrightarrow{\Delta} Al_2O_3 + 6HCl + 9H_2O$$

The alums are double salts of the formula,

$$M^IM^{III}(SO_4)_2 \cdot 12H_2O$$

where M^I is an alkali metal or ammonium ion and M^{III} is the aluminum, chromium, or ferric ion. Alums can be prepared readily by crystallization from a solution of equal molar ratios of $M_2^ISO_4$ and $M_2^{III}(SO_4)_3$. The unmodified term *alum* refers to $KAl(SO_4)_2 \cdot 12H_2O$. Alum is used in baking powders. In water the aluminum ion hydrolyzes to form an acid solution which in turn reacts with the hydrogen–carbonate ion to liberate CO_2. Alum is used in many water treatment plants to remove suspended matter that is too small to be trapped by the filters. The fine particles are trapped by the gelatinous $Al(OH)_3$ precipitate which is removed easily. The textile industry uses alum as a source of $Al(OH)_3$ which readily attaches to fibers. Dyestuffs which are not absorbed by the fiber adhere to the hydroxide.

Pure aluminum oxide is a white, insoluble, high melting (2800°C) solid that becomes resistant to attack by acids and bases if heated strongly. Impurities in the oxide impart color to the solid, resulting in the formation of semi-precious minerals such as ruby and sapphire.

Aluminum in the $+1$ oxidation state is not stable at room temperature. However, at elevated temperatures the $+1$ state does become stable. For example, aluminum and aluminum oxide react at 1000°C to form volatile Al_2O. The reaction is reversed at lower temperatures.

Aluminum is used extensively in kitchen utensils and industrial equipment, in electrical wires, as foils, and as lightweight alloys for aircraft frames.

Specific aspects of gallium chemistry

The appearance of liquid gallium varies. If washed with acid, it forms a bright, shiny ball. If washed with dilute base, it tends to be less shiny and to stick to the walls of the container. This may reflect the formation of a surface layer of gallium oxide or hydroxide.

Gallium readily forms alloys with most of the metals. The alloy forms at room temperatures with such metals as indium, aluminum, tin, zinc, copper, cadmium, and silver. Steel, Monel, and nickel must be heated to 300°C before the alloying is complete. Tungsten, rhenium, beryllium, niobium, and tantalum must be heated even more. The alloy of sodium and gallium is relatively unreactive even in water.

Gallium and the Group VA elements (except bismuth) react directly at elevated temperatures to yield binary compounds. Gallium arsenide (GaAs) has several electrical properties which make it of interest as a transistor material. It is also used in a thermoelectric device in which an electric current flowing in one direction causes cooling, and current in the reverse direction causes heating.

Covalent gallium halides with the formula Ga_2X_4 have been prepared. These are thought to contain gallium in the $+1$ and $+3$ oxidation states, as in $Ga^I[Ga^{III}X_4]$. These dihalides are quite stable. Ga_2Cl_4 appears to be formed first when chlorine is passed into gallium. When all of the metal has reacted, the conversion to $GaCl_3$ proceeds. If the reaction vessel is kept cool, the major product is Ga_2Cl_4. $GaCl_3$ is readily reduced to the lower species with sodium metal.

Although gallium(I) compounds are found at room temperature, they are rather unstable. Gallium(I) halides appear to be stable at temperatures above 500°C.

Specific aspects of indium chemistry

Indium, being definitely metallic, dissolves only in acids. Indium(III) oxide is prepared by heating the metal in oxygen or by heating the sulfate, nitrate, or hydroxide. Indium(I) oxide is prepared by heating In_2O_3 in vacuum or in a hydrogen atmosphere at 400°C. The lower oxide does not dissolve in water. It does liberate hydrogen from an acid as In(I) goes to In(III).

$$In_2O + 6H^+ \rightarrow 2In^{3+} + 2H_2 + H_2O$$

If In_2O is heated in air, it returns to In_2O_3.

Indium and the Group VA elements react at elevated temperatures to form binary compounds. The most interesting of these is InSb which has excellent thermoelectric properties.

Indium fluoride (InF_3) is a high melting solid, insoluble in water. The other three halogens form halides of the type InX_3, In_2X_4, and InX. The dihalide, prepared from the hydrogen halide gas and the metal at 200°C, is probably $In^I[In^{III}X_4]$. The metal and InX_3 is formed when In_2X_4 is placed in water. When indium and InX_3 are heated, the monohalide InX is formed. The reaction is reversed when the monohalide is placed in water, since the In^+ ion is not stable in aqueous solution.

Specific aspects of thallium chemistry

Thallium(I) oxide is more stable than the thallium(III) oxide. Tl_2O_3 is prepared by adding NaOH to a solution of Tl^{3+} ions. When Tl_2O_3 is heated to 100°C, Tl_2O is formed.

The thallic halides, except TlI_3, can be prepared but are unstable. $TlCl_3$ loses chlorine at 40°C while $TlBr_3$ loses bromine at lower temperatures, yielding $Tl^I[Tl^{III}Br_4]$, then TlBr. Thallic fluoride (TlF_3) is stable to 500°C, reflecting the greater oxidizing power of fluorine.

The thallous ion Tl^+ resembles the ions of the alkali metals and silver. The thallous salts are rather insoluble in water; however, there is no hydrolysis in solution, since Tl_2O and TlOH are rather soluble strong bases. Thallous fluoride is very soluble; the other halides are insoluble. Thallous salts are exceedingly poisonous.

SIGNIFICANT TERMS AND CONCEPTS IN CHAPTER XVII:

Hall process for aluminum, bauxite; physical and chemical properties of Group IIIA elements; stability of +1 state of thallium; reactions of the oxides; boranes, Borazon, alums, uses of alum, halides of gallium, indium, and thallium.

17.1. Compare melting points, boiling points, and temperature ranges of the liquids of the Group IIIA elements with those of the Group IVA elements.

17.2. Which electrons are removed to form Tl^{3+} and Tl^+?

17.3. Write equations for the following:
   (a) Indium heated in excess oxygen
   (b) Dissolution of aluminum oxide in concentrated sodium hydroxide
   (c) Ammonium hydroxide added to a gallium chloride solution
   (d) Aluminum reacting with concentrated potassium hydroxide
   (e) Boron heated with chlorine
   (f) Thallium heated with iodine
   (g) Gallium heated with sulfur
   (h) Aluminum heated in nitrogen
   (i) Formation of pyroboric, metaboric, and orthoboric acid from boric oxide
   (j) Diborane in water
   (k) Aluminum in nitric acid
   (l) Thallium in hydrochloric acid
   (m) Heating aluminum and ferric oxide
   (n) Aluminum chloride added to water
   (o) Heating indium sulfate
   (p) Indium iodide in water
   (q) Heating thallium(III) oxide
   (r) Heating thallium(III) bromide

17.4. Are solutions of the following acidic, basic, or neutral?
   (a) $TlNO_3$, (b) aluminum iodide, (c) alum, (d) boric acid.

17.5. Give equations for the following reactions:
   (a) Preparation of crystalline boron from borax
   (b) Preparation of gallium from the oxide ore
   (c) Aluminum metal and chromic oxide (Cr_2O_3) after ignition
   (d) Aluminum from bauxite
   (e) Thallium metal from the sulfide impurity in FeS_2
   (f) Borazon from boron

17.6. Give formulas for the following:
   (a) litharge, (b) sodium metaborate, (c) sodium aluminate (solid), (d) potassium gallate (solution), (e) ammonium alum, (f) Borazon, (g) bauxite, (h) borax, (i) diborane, (j) indium dichloride, (k) cryolite.

the transition metals, lanthanides, and actinides

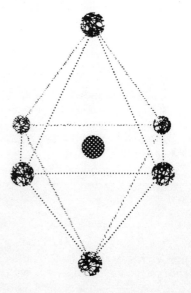

The 58 transition metals, lanthanides, and actinides constitute over half of the presently known elements. Their properties vary widely. Mercury has a melting point of $-39°C$; tungsten has a melting point of $3380°C$; platinum can be heated white hot in oxygen with no reaction, while tantalum is so reactive that it is used to remove residual oxygen in vacuum tubes. The unifying characteristic of all these elements is that d or f orbitals of an underlying energy level are being filled as electrons are added (Table 6.2). It is the general trends that result from the electronic similarities that are of greatest importance in the following discussion.

Physical properties

Generalizations about the physical properties of these elements are possible if one recognizes that abrupt changes in trends occur in the copper (IB) group and the zinc (IIB) group. These changes usually can be attributed to the filled d orbitals in these two groups. The characteristic electron configuration is $d^{10}s^1$ for the copper group and $d^{10}s^2$ for the zinc group.

The uniformity of the properties of the lanthanides is attributed to the filling of the underlying $4f$ orbitals. Electrons in f orbitals apparently modify the properties only to a small extent.

A similarity of properties is predicted for the actinides, due to the filling of the $5f$ orbitals. However, the short half lives and the radioactivity of the man-made elements limit the quantities available for study and their usefulness.

Melting and boiling points

In general, the metals under consideration have relatively high melting and boiling points (see Fig. 4.3, page 66) which indicate the strong bonding forces between the atoms. Electrons in the d orbitals are available for bonding in all of the metals except the copper and zinc groups, where the melting and boiling points are substantially lower than those of the preceding members of the series. With the exception of these two groups, there are three or more electrons available in every atom for bonding within the metal. The bond strength per electron need not be very large for the total strength of the bonds per atom to be substantial.

The increase in melting and boiling points is also effected by the increase in atomic weight. In general, the heaviest element in each group has the highest melting and boiling point. The most conspicuous exception is the zinc group in which the opposite trend is noted.

Radii

The atomic, metallic, and ionic radii of the transition metals generally decrease within each period. However, an increase in

320
Chapter 18
The transition
metals,
lanthanides,
and actinides

Legend:
- Symbol
- Atomic radius (Å)
- Metallic radius (Å)
- Ionic radius (Å)

III B	IV B	V B	VI B	VII B	VIII B			I B	II B
Sc 1.44 1.63 (3+)0.81	Ti 1.32 1.45 (4+)0.64	V 1.22 1.31 (5+)0.50	Cr 1.17 1.25 (3+)0.55	Mn 1.17 1.12 (2+)0.80 (4+)0.54	Fe 1.16 1.24 (3+)0.53 (2+)0.75	Co 1.16 1.25 (2+)0.78 (3+)0.63	Ni 1.15 1.24 (2+)0.68	Cu 1.17 1.27 (2+)0.69 (1+)0.95	Zn 1.25 1.32 (2+)0.70
Y 1.62 1.79 (3+)0.93	Zr 1.45 1.60 (4+)0.80	Nb 1.34 1.42 (5+)0.70	Mo 1.29 1.36 (4+)0.68	Tc — 1.37 —	Ru 1.24 1.33 —	Rh 1.25 1.34 —	Pd 1.28 1.37 (2+)0.86	Ag 1.34 1.44 (1+)1.13	Cd 1.41 1.48 (2+)0.92
La 1.69 1.86 (3+)1.15	Hf 1.44 1.66 (4+)0.81	Ta 1.34 1.43 (5+)0.73	W 1.30 1.36 —	Re 1.28 1.37 —	Os 1.26 1.35 —	Ir 1.26 1.35 —	Pt 1.29 1.38 —	Au 1.34 1.44 (1+)1.37	Hg 1.44 1.50 (2+)1.05

Ce	Pr	Nd	Pm	Sm	Eu	Gd	Tb	Dy	Ho	Er	Tm	Yb	Lu
1.65	1.65	1.64	—	1.66	1.85	1.61	1.59	1.59	1.58	1.57	1.56	1.70	1.56
1.82	1.82	1.82	—	1.79	1.98	1.79	1.77	1.77	1.75	1.75	1.74	1.93	—
(3+)1.18 (4+)1.02	(3+)1.09	(3+)1.08	(3+)1.06	(3+)1.04	(3+)1.03 (2+)1.12	(3+)1.02	(3+)1.00	(3+)0.99	(3+)0.97	(3+)0.96	(3+)0.95	(3+)0.94 (2+)1.13	(3+)0.93

Fig. 18.1

Atomic, Metallic, and Ionic Radii. Atomic radius is the assigned contribution of an element to internuclear separation in covalent compounds. Metallic radius is one-half the internuclear separation of the nearest neighbor atoms in the metal. Ionic radius is the average contribution of the ion to internuclear separation in several ionic compounds.

radii is noted in the copper and zinc groups. Again, this tendency may be related to the filling of d orbitals. As electrons are added to d orbitals within a period, there is an increase in the positive charge on the nucleus. Thus, all of the electrons are attracted more closely to the nucleus. Once the d orbitals are filled, the remaining transition metals in each period increase in size as the outer s orbitals are filled.

A similar reduction in size is observed in the lanthanide series, where fourteen electrons are added to the $4f$ level. As a result of this lanthanide contraction, the radii of hafnium and the subsequent transition metals are only slightly larger than those of their congeners in period five.

Density

The transition metals and the lanthanides have relatively high densities. (See Fig. 4.4, page 67, for specific values.) The trends in density parallel those in atomic radii. The elements within each period are more dense than those in the preceding period and reflect the large increase in nuclear mass and the small change in atomic radius. The transition metals of period six (Hf—Hg) are some of the densest elements. This is to be expected, since the atomic size has been reduced in the lanthanide contraction along with an increase of about 40 atomic mass units in the nucleus. Osmium and iridium are the densest elements known. While the densities of only a few actinides are known, the values are probably near 19 g/cc which is reported for uranium.

Additional physical characteristics

In general these metals are hard. The notable exceptions are in the copper and zinc groups, again reflecting the absence of d electrons in the bonding.

Since the electron configurations and the atomic sizes are so similar, the transition metals readily form alloys. The alloying property of iron is used extensively in the preparation of steels. The properties of steel can be varied by changing the concentrations of vanadium, chromium, manganese, cobalt, nickel, and molybdenum in the final product. Silver used in silver coinage, sterling silver, and so on, is hardened by the addition of copper. Mercury, a liquid at room temperatures, readily dissolves many of the metals throughout the periodic table to form solutions called *amalgams*. The chemical behavior of many metals in an amalgam is different from that of the bulk materials in that protective coatings no longer develop in the amalgam.

The transition metals form many *interstitial compounds* with small nonmetal atoms such as hydrogen, nitrogen, carbon, and oxygen. If spheres are used to represent the atoms, one can see that when large atoms are closely packed, the open spaces between atoms are large enough to accomodate a smaller atom. These are known

322
Chapter 18
The transition
metals,
lanthanides,
and actinides

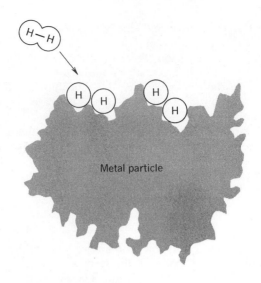

Fig. 18.2

Catalytic Action of a Transition Metal Surface. Transition metals in the form of fine powder serve as catalysts in many gaseous reactions. The mechanism of catalytic action is not well understood. One possible mechanism is shown. The metal may provide a reaction site by dissociating hydrogen molecules into atoms on its surface. Another molecular species may then interact with hydrogen atoms.

Fig. 18.3

Interstitial Voids. Unfilled space remains when spheres are closely packed together. If large spheres are used, the void is large. If four spheres (a) surround the void, a small sphere with a radius 22 per cent that of the large spheres may be placed in the space. If six spheres (b) surround the void, the radius of the small sphere is 41.4 per cent that of the large spheres.

as *interstitial atoms*. The composition of a compound formed in this way varies according to the number of spaces, or voids, that are filled. Such compounds, existing over a range of composition, are *non-stoichiometric*. The transition metal hydrides, nitrides, oxides, and carbides are typical non-stoichiometric, interstitial compounds. Their formation is not difficult. Hot titanium, for example, absorbs nitrogen into the interstitial spaces so readily that the metal must be processed in an argon atmosphere where the gas atoms are too large for interstitial voids. When iron takes up carbon interstitially, its structure is said to be *locked*, and the resultant steel is harder and stronger than pure iron.

Many of the transition metals readily absorb gases onto their surfaces with a bond that increases the reactivity of the gas. As a result, many of them are used extensively in the hydrogenation of organic materials and in re-forming petroleum products. It is thought that hydrogen gas dissociates into atoms on the metal surface, and therefore the addition of hydrogen to organic molecules occurs more readily.

The color of the metals in these groups ranges from silver-white to silver-grey; copper is reddish, and gold has the characteristic yellow color. It is possible to polish all the metals to a lustrous sheen.

Chemical properties

The chemical properties of the actinide metals are not well established, although more is known about a few of the long-lived elements such as thorium, uranium, plutonium, and neptunium. These metals readily form oxide coatings when exposed to air and become somewhat more reactive at elevated temperatures. They are sufficiently active to liberate hydrogen from boiling water, hydrochloric acid, or sulfuric acid. Nitric acid oxidizes these four metals, although thorium does not react with concentrated acid. The study of the other actinides is hampered by problems of radiation and the difficulty of producing substantial amounts of the metals.

Scandium, yttrium, and the lanthanides are moderately active. Like the actinides, the metals tarnish in air, liberate hydrogen from boiling water and acids, and are oxidized readily by nitric acid. The reactivity of the rest of the transition metals decreases with increasing atomic number within both a period and a group. In the copper and zinc groups, however, the last two elements are more reactive than the preceding element in each period. Thus, the most inert metals are iridium, platinum, and gold. With the exception of the Group IIIB metals, zinc, and cadmium, it is necessary to heat the transition metals before the common reactions occur.

Reactions with acids

The behavior of the transition metals in three different types of acid solutions is summarized in Table 18.1. Relatively few of the

Table 18.1

Reactions of the Transition Metals with Acids

IIIB	IVB	VB	VIB	VIIB	VIIIB			IB	IIB
Sc Sc^{3+}(HCl) Sc^{3+}(HNO₃) Sc^{3+}(H₂O)	Ti Ti^{3+}(HCl)* $TiO_2 \cdot xH_2O$(HNO₃)	V −(HCl) VO^{++}(HNO₃)	Cr Cr^{3+}(HCl) p. (HNO₃)	Mn Mn^{++}(HCl) MnO_2(HNO₃)	Fe Fe^{++}(HCl) p. (HNO₃)	Co Co^{++}(HCl) p. (HNO₃)	Ni Ni^{++}(HCl) p. (HNO₃)	Cu −(HCl) Cu^{++}(HNO₃)	Zn Zn^{++}(HCl) Zn^{++}(HNO₃)
Y Y^{3+}(HCl) Y^{3+}(HNO₃) Y^{3+}(H₂O)	Zr −(HCl) −(HNO₃) −(aqua regia)	Nb −(HCl) −(HNO₃) −(aqua regia)	Mo −(HCl) p. (HNO₃) −(aqua regia)	Tc −(HCl) TcO_4^-(HNO₃)	Ru −(HCl) −(HNO₃) −(aqua regia)	Rh −(HCl) −(HNO₃) (aqua regia)**	Pd −(HCl) Pd^{++}(HNO₃) $PdCl_6^-$(aqua regia)	Ag −(HCl) Ag^+(HNO₃)	Cd Cd^{++}(HCl) Cd^{++}(HNO₃)
La(3)† La^{3+}(HCl) La^{3+}(HNO₃) La^{3+}(H₂O)	Hf −(HCl) −(HNO₃) −(aqua regia)	Ta −(HCl) −(HNO₃) −(aqua regia)	W −(HCl) −(HNO₃) −(aqua regia)	Re −(HCl) ReO_4^-(HNO₃)	Os −(HCl) −(HNO₃) −(aqua regia)	Ir −(HCl) −(HNO₃) (aqua regia)**	Pt −(HCl) −(HNO₃) $PtCl_6^-$(aqua regia)	Au −(HCl) −(HNO₃) $AuCl_4^-$(aqua regia)	Hg −(HCl) Hg^{++}(HNO₃)

* Proceeds slowly when heated, undetectable at room temperature.
** Proceeds very slowly with finely divided metal; forms $RhCl_6^{3-}$ and $IrCl_6^-$.
† Behavior of lanthanides similar to lanthanum.

M^{n+}(HCl) indicates the reaction of the metal with hydrochloric acid to form the ion indicated and hydrogen.

M^{n+}(HNO₃) indicates the reaction of the metal with nitric acid to form the species indicated and various nitrogen oxides as reduction products.

p. (HNO₃) indicates that the metal becomes passive, i.e., does not liberate hydrogen or otherwise react with nitric acid, although the general activity of the metal would predict a reaction.

M^{n+}(aqua regia) indicates the product of the reaction with aqua regia for those metals not otherwise attacked by HCl or HNO₃.

M^{3+}(H₂O) indicates those metals that liberate hydrogen slowly from cold water and readily from hot water.

−(HCl), −(HNO₃), −(aqua regia) indicate no reaction with the reagent.

transition metals liberate hydrogen from a non-oxidizing acid solution such as hydrochloric acid. Many of these active metals become passive in a concentrated oxidizing acid such as nitric acid. The primary reaction of an active metal with nitric acid is the formation of N₂O rather than hydrogen. Some of the metals that do not liberate hydrogen are oxidized by nitric acid with NO or NO₂ as the reduction product (cf. Chapter XV). Several of the more inert metals, such as platinum, gold, iridium, rhodium, and palladium, do not dissolve in nitric acid but do so in a vigorously oxidizing solution called *aqua regia*. The usual preparation of aqua regia is the addition of three volumes of concentrated hydrochloric acid to one volume of concentrated nitric acid. This solution apparently is a source of atomic chlorine.

Reactions with oxygen

As seen in Table 18.2, most of the transition metals form an oxide when heated in oxygen. The oxides of platinum, gold, and silver are stable at room temperature but decompose at temperatures

Table 18.2

Oxides Formed by the Transition Metals When Heated in Oxygen

Type Formula	IIIB	IVB	VB	VIB	VIIB	VIIIB			IB	IIB
	M_2O_3	MO_2	M_2O_5	MO_3	M_2O_7	MO_4			M_2O	MO
	Sc_2O_3	TiO_2	V_2O_5	[Cr_2O_3]	[Mn_3O_4]	[Fe_3O_4]	[Co_3O_4] (oxidation difficult)	[NiO] (oxidation difficult)	[CuO] Cu_2O (stable above 1000°C)	ZnO
	Y_2O_3	ZrO_2	Nb_2O_5	MoO_3	Tc_2O_7 (volatile)	RuO_4 (volatile)	[Rh_2O_3] (unstable above 1100°C)	[PdO] (unstable above 875°C)	Ag (no oxide formed)	CdO
	La_2O_3	HfO_2	Ta_2O_5	WO_3	Re_2O_7 (volatile)	OsO_4 (volatile)	[IrO_2] (unstable above 1100°C)	Pt (no oxide formed)	Au (no oxide formed)	HgO (unstable above 400°C)

[ ] denotes an oxide that is not representative of the type formula.

326

Chapter 18
The transition
metals,
lanthanides,
and actinides

below those required to form the oxide. Thus, no oxide of these elements is observed when the metal is heated in oxygen. Similar behavior is observed with mercury, since mercuric oxide forms at an appreciable rate at temperatures above 350°C and decomposes at temperatures above 400°C. Wider ranges of stability are observed for the oxides of rhodium, palladium, and iridium. Cupric oxide differs in that the lower oxidation state is stable above 1000°C.

In general, the metals form oxides in which the oxidation state corresponds to the group number. The major exceptions, other than those metals which form unstable oxides, occur in the first row of the transition metals. The behavior of chromium, manganese, iron, cobalt, and nickel is indicative of the greater stability of the lower oxidation states in this period. The M_3O_4 oxides of manganese, iron, and cobalt represent mixed oxidation states.

The volatility of Tc_2O_7, Re_2O_7, RuO_4, and OsO_4 is somewhat unexpected for oxides of this molecular weight. The vapors of RuO_4 and OsO_4 are poisonous, and Tc_2O_7 is radioactive. The physiological effects of Re_2O_7 are not known.

The lanthanides form stable oxides of the type M_2O_3. An exception is cerium which forms CeO_2 when heated in oxygen.

Oxidation states

The chemistry of the transition metals, lanthanides, and actinides is characterized by the numerous oxidation states which they exhibit. The $+3$ state is found for uranium and the transuranium elements, the $+4$ state for thorium through berkelium, $+5$ for protoactinium through americium, and $+6$ for uranium through americium. All of the lanthanides have a stable $+3$ oxidation state. In addition, $+4$ is found for cerium, and $+2$ for samarium, europium, and ytterbium.

Except for the elements in Groups IIIB and IIB, at least two oxidation states are known for each transition metal (Table 18.3). Thus, many of them are useful as redox reagents. Two general rules are observed concerning the oxidation states.

(a) The highest oxidation state for most of these elements corresponds to the positive value of the group number. Exceptions to this rule occur in Groups IB and VIIIB. The $+8$ state is found only for ruthenium and osmium in Group VIIIB. Copper(II) and gold(III) are the most stable states of these Group IB elements.

(b) The lowest oxidation state is $+2$ except for Groups IIIB and IB. The $+3$ state is the only one found for Group IIIB. A $+1$ state is found for all of the Group IB elements. The $+2$ state is not necessarily a stable state for the other transition metals.

Table 18.3

Major Oxidation States of the Transition Metals

IIIB	IVB	VB	VIB	VIIB	VIIIB			IB	IIB
Sc	Ti	V	Cr	Mn	Fe	Co	Ni	Cu	Zn
								1	
	(2)	(2)	(2)	2*	2	2	2	2*	2
3	3	(3)	3*	(3)	3*				
	4*	4*		4					
		5							
			6						
				7					
Y	Zr	Nb	Mo	Tc	Ru	Rh	Pd	Ag	Cd
								1	
					2		2*		2
3					3	3*			
	4		4	4	4	4	4		
		5	5						
			6*		6				
				7*					
					8*				
La	Hf	Ta	W	Re	Os	Ir	Pt	Au	Hg
								1	1
							2		2*
3				3		3		3*	
	4		4	4	4	4*	4*		
		5	5						
			6*		6				
				7*					
					8*				

* Most stable state
( ) State of lesser importance

In general, the lower oxidation states are more stable in the first transition metal series; the higher oxidation states are more stable in the second and third series.

The *d* electrons play an important role in the observed multiplicity of oxidation states. The *s* electrons, along with one or more *d* electrons, are almost always lost in the formation of a compound. As a result, the Group IIIB elements (scandium, yttrium, and lanthanum) show a +3 oxidation state corresponding to the loss of the two *s* electrons and the single *d* electron. Similarly, the Group IIB metals (zinc, cadmium, and mercury) exhibit a +2 oxidation state corresponding to the loss of the *s* electrons. Since the *d* energy levels are filled, the configuration is too stable for the removal of a *d* electron. The +1 oxidation state for mercury is

328

Chapter 18
*The transition
metals,
lanthanides,
and actinides*

found only as the dimer Hg_2^{++}. The two $6s$ electrons of both Hg atoms are involved in bonding. However, one pair of electrons make up the Hg–Hg bond in the dimer which leads to a formal value of $+1$ for the oxidation state.

Solutions of transition metal ions as well as hydrated salts often are colored. The color results from the presence of d electrons and unfilled d orbitals. In the presence of negative ions or polar molecules such as water, the energies of the five d orbitals are not identical. The d energy levels are said to be split or separated as sketched in Fig. 18.4. An electron in one of the lower energy levels is excited to one of the higher levels by the absorption of energy equal to the difference in the energy levels. In the case of many transition metal ions, this energy difference corresponds to some wave length of visible light. When visible light is passed through such a solution, the wave length is absorbed and the solution is colored. The energy difference does not always correspond to visible light; it may involve the infrared or ultraviolet, where the effect is not detected visually.

Fig. 18.4

Splitting of d Energy Levels. In the presence of polar molecules or ions the five d orbitals are no longer energetically identical. Should a vacancy exist in one of the upper levels, a lower level electron may absorb the wave length of light corresponding to the energy difference and move to the higher level. The energy difference often corresponds to a color of visible light, resulting in colored solutions.

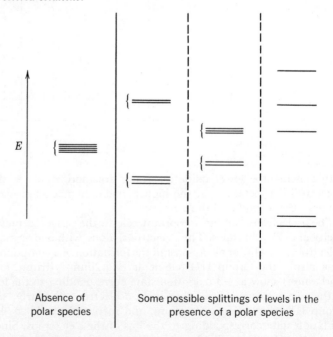

Absence of
polar species

Some possible splittings of levels in the
presence of a polar species

{ Denotes levels with identical energies

Since *d* electrons must be present for this effect, solutions of the +3 ions of Group IIIB are not colored. Solutions of the +2 ions of Group IIB are not colored, because all *d* orbitals are filled. The color varies with the ions or polar molecules that become attached to the metal ion, since each causes a different separation of the energies of the *d* orbitals. For example, solutions of cupric ion are blue due to the formation of $[Cu(H_2O)_4]^{++}$. The color persists in solid $CuSO_4 \cdot 5H_2O$ where the same species also exists. When ammonia (as NH_4OH) is added to a solution of cupric ions, the color changes to the very deep blue characteristic of $[Cu(NH_3)_4]^{++}$. In high chloride ion concentrations, the species is $[CuCl_4]^=$ which forms a greenish-yellow solution.

The color of a metal ion solution changes with oxidation state. The loss of electrons may result in a vacancy in one of the previously filled *d* orbitals. This orbital may be separated from the remaining filled orbitals by a different energy which leads to a different color. For example, Cr(II) is blue, Cr(III) is green or violet; Mn(II) is pink, the unstable Mn(III) is green, red, or violet depending on the other species present; Fe(II) is green, while Fe(III) is yellow.

Transition metal ions tend to form complex ions with many molecules and negative ions. A *complex* ion consists of a group of negative ions or polar, neutral molecules attached to a central metal ion. Central ions with a small size and high nuclear charge show the greatest tendency to form complex ions. Complexes of transition metal ions are characterized by the *d* orbitals involved in the bonding.

The number of ions or polar molecules attached to the central metal ion is called the *coordination number*. With numerous exceptions, the coordination number is twice the number of positive charges on the metal ions. Water molecules are coordinated about the metal ions in aqueous solution, unless the anions in the solution are more strongly attracted. This coordination of water molecules is seldom noted in the writing of the formulas. For example, for aqueous solutions containing cupric ion, Cu^{++} is written, rather than $[Cu(H_2O)_4]^{++}$.

Metallurgy

Metallurgy deals with the extraction of metals from ores. The principles discussed in this section are applicable to the recovery of all metals but find their greatest application with the transition metals. The common ores are metal sulfides, oxides, halides, silicates, carbonates, and sulfates. Three general steps in going from the ore to the metal are concentration, roasting, and reduction.

There is always some worthless rock, known as *gangue*, associated with the metal salt in the ore. The ore is crushed and washed to remove the low density particles. The metal salts are concentrated by leaching, flotation, or electromagnetic separation. Leaching is accomplished by washing the crushed ore with a reagent which

330

Chapter 18
The transition
metals,
lanthanides,
and actinides

selectively dissolves the metal salt. For example, dilute sulfuric acid dissolves copper sulfate from a copper ore. Flotation is the selective wetting of particles by pine oil or a detergent. The wetting agents do not adhere to the silicates. When air is passed through the mixture to cause frothing, the metal or metal salts (usually the sulfides) are taken up in the froth layer and the gangue falls to the bottom of the container. Electromagnetic separation is useful only on ores that are attracted to a magnet.

The naturally occurring metal salts are converted to the more easily used oxides in the roasting process. During roasting the salts are heated in air to drive off volatile components and decompose any organic material. Residual gangue is removed by the addition of fluxes. For example, $CaCO_3$ is used frequently for the removal of silicates. $CaCO_3$ decomposes to CaO which reacts with the gangue to form a slag.

$$SiO_2 \text{ (gangue)} + CaO \text{ (flux)} \rightarrow CaSiO_3 \text{ (slag)}$$

The slag is removed from the top of the molten material from time to time.

The methods used to reduce the transition metals are summarized in Table 18.4 and can be classified as follows:

(a) Native metals

The unreactive noble metals occur as the elements in finely divided sand and as alloyed impurities in other metals. In general, the metals are recovered by dissolving them in an appropriate low boiling metal such as mercury or zinc, after the sand has been removed by flotation. The zinc or mercury is boiled off to recover the metal. This method is particularily useful for producing silver, gold, platinum, iridium, rhodium, ruthenium, and osmium.

(b) Unstable oxides

Mercury is the only element of the transition metals that is recovered directly by the roasting process. When the common mercury ore (HgS) is heated in air, free mercury is obtained since mercuric oxide is unstable. The metal readily vaporizes from the mixture and is condensed.

$$HgS + O_2 \xrightarrow{\Delta} Hg\uparrow + SO_2\uparrow$$

(c) Reduction with carbon

Carbon is the cheapest, most readily available, and most convenient element available for the reduction of metal oxides. Since the reduction occurs at elevated temperatures, carbon provides fuel as it reacts with the oxides and with the air forced through the reduction chamber. Carbon monoxide, formed in regions of limited oxygen supply, is a gas capable of reducing more oxide. The major limitation on the use of carbon for oxide reduction is the formation of carbides. The major use of carbon reduction occurs in the iron and steel industry (Fig. 18.5).

(d) Reduction with active metals

It is necessary to use an active metal such as aluminum, magnesium, or sodium to reduce some metal salts to metals when

Table 18.4

Methods Used to Reduce Transition Metals

IIIB	IVB	VB	VIB	VIIB	VIIIB			IB	IIB
Sc Reduction of Halide with Ca	Ti Kroll process	V Kroll process	Cr reduction of oxide with Al	Mn reduction of oxide with Al	Fe reduction of oxide with C	Co reduction of oxide with C	Ni reduction of oxide with CO	Cu reduction of oxide with C	Zn reduction of oxide with C
Y Reduction of Halide with Ca	Zr Kroll process	Nb Electrolysis of complex fluoride	Mo reduction of oxide with H_2	Tc reduction of NH_4TcO_4 with H_2	Ru Native	Rh Native	Pd Native	Ag Native	Cd reduction of oxide with C
La* Reduction of Halide with Ca	Hf Kroll process	Ta Electrolysis of complex fluoride	W reduction of oxide with H_2	Re reduction of molten $ReCl_6^=$ with H_2	Os Native	Ir Native	Pt Native	Au Native	Hg roasting of HgS

*Lanthanides: Reduction of the halide with calcium after prior separation of the elemental halides.

332
Chapter 18
The transition
metals,
lanthanides,
and actinides

Fig. 18.5
Blast Furnace

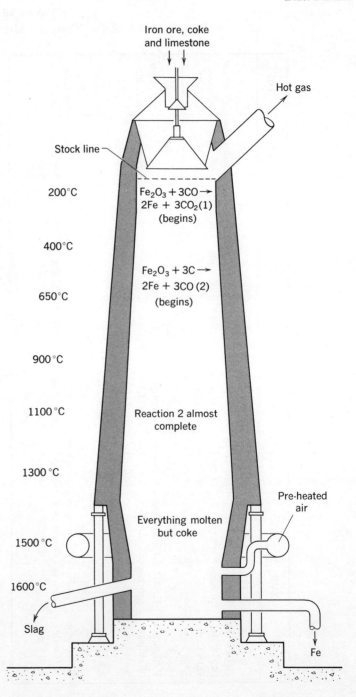

Iron ore, coke
and limestone

Hot gas

Stock line

200°C

$Fe_2O_3 + 3CO \rightarrow$
$2Fe + 3CO_2$ (1)
(begins)

400°C

$Fe_2O_3 + 3C \rightarrow$
$2Fe + 3CO$ (2)
(begins)

650°C

900°C

1100°C

Reaction 2 almost
complete

1300°C

Pre-heated
air

Everything molten
but coke

1500°C

1600°C

Slag

Fe

carbide formation is a problem. The oxides of manganese and chromium are reduced conveniently with aluminum.

The Kroll process has been developed to produce the more active Group IVB metals and vanadium. In this process the metal oxide is powdered, mixed with powdered carbon, and heated in a chlorine atmosphere. This produces the metal chloride which boils at temperatures well below those used for the reaction.

$$ZrO_2 + 2C + 2Cl_2 \xrightarrow{\Delta} ZrCl_4\uparrow + 2CO\uparrow$$

The chloride is carefully purified by repeated distillations. The pure metal chloride is reduced with magnesium or sodium under an argon atmosphere.

$$ZrCl_4 + 2Mg \xrightarrow{\Delta} 2MgCl_2 + Zr$$

The reducing agent and the chlorine are recovered by electrolysis of the $MgCl_2$ or $NaCl$ product.

Further purification of the metal is carried out on a laboratory scale using an iodine carrier. The impure metal reacts with iodine at relatively low temperatures (200°–300°C) to produce metal iodide vapor. The vapor is decomposed to the elements on a hot wire filament (1200°C). By appropriate regulation of the reaction and decomposition temperatures, a very pure product results.

$$Zr \text{ (impure)} + 2I_2 \xrightarrow[\text{heating}]{\text{moderate}} ZrI_4\uparrow$$

$$ZrI_4 \xrightarrow[\text{wire}]{\text{hot}} Zr\downarrow + 2I_2\uparrow$$

(e) Reduction with hydrogen

Hydrogen is characterized by its reducing properties, but its use in the preparation of the transition metals is limited by the formation of interstitial hydrides. Hydrogen reduction has commercial application in the preparation of molybdenum, tungsten, technetium, and rhenium. Copper oxide is reduced on a laboratory scale with hydrogen.

(f) Electrolysis

Niobium and tantalum react readily with reducing agents; therefore, it is necessary to employ electrolysis for the reduction to metal. Since K_2TaF_7 is less soluble than K_2NbOF_5, separation of the elements is brought about by the formation of these fluorides. The separated fluorides are then subjected to electrolysis.

Electrolysis is used to produce high purity copper and nickel. The product of carbon reduction is formed into a large sheet which serves as the anode of an electrolysis cell. A thin, high purity metal grid is used as the cathode. A sulfate solution is the electrolyte. The copper or nickel transfers from the anode to the cathode, resulting in a high purification. The impurity sludge that forms at the bottom of the electrolysis cell is treated to recover the metals present. In the case of copper, there is sufficient gold and silver present to make recovery worth while.

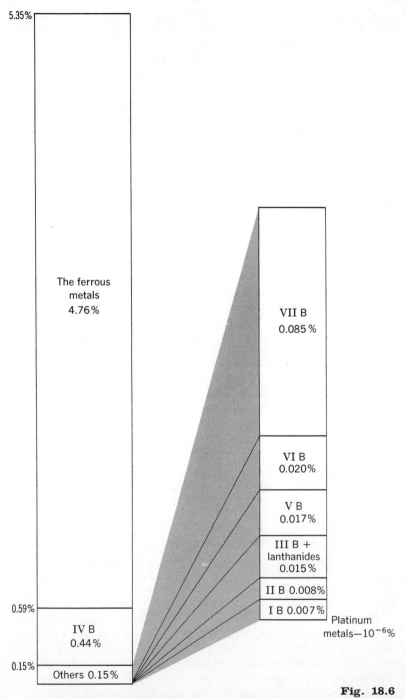

Fig. 18.6

Abundance of Transition Metals in the Earth. The transition metals and the lanthanides make up about 5.35 per cent by weight of the earth's crust. The first row elements, except Sc, are the most abundant of each group.

Other characteristics of the transition metals, lanthanides, and actinides

Lanthanides and actinides

The lanthanide series refers to the elements with atomic numbers 57 (lanthanum) through 71 (lutetium). The actinide series refers to elements with atomic numbers 89 (actinium) through 103 (lawrencium). The elements in each of these series are very similar. The actinides are characterized by their radioactivity. Each actinide is almost chemically identical to its counterpart 32 atomic numbers lower in the lanthanide series. Intense work on the lanthanides has resulted from efforts to separate the new members of the actinides and from the study of uranium and plutonium fission products.

The separation of the individual lanthanides is difficult. The classical method of repetitive dissolution and partial re-crystallization by evaporation makes use of the small differences in solubilities of the salts. The process is slow in that many re-crystallizations are needed to obtain a reasonable separation. Most lanthanide separations are now achieved with a column of ion exchange resins (Fig. 18.7).

Except in their $+3$ oxidation state, the lanthanides resemble the Group IIA (alkaline earth) elements. Like them, the lanthanides form very few complexes. Cerium in the $+4$ state is stable enough to exist in the form of solid salts and in solution. Ceric sulfate $(Ce(SO_4)_2)$ solutions with sulfuric acid are used extensively as strong oxidizing agents in quantitative studies.

Scandium and yttrium

Scandium is a very rare metal. As a result, very little is known of its properties. They appear to be almost the same as those of the lanthanides. Yttrium is almost identical to lanthanum and is frequently considered to be a part of the lanthanides.

Titanium, zirconium, and hafnium

Although titanium is the fourth most abundant element in the earth's crust, it took 150 years to isolate the pure metal after the element was recognized in 1791. The most common ore of this very active metal is rutile (TiO_2). This oxide is a white, chemically resistant compound with amphoteric behavior. The metal reacts with chlorine at room temperature to form covalent $TiCl_4$. Other titanium halides can be prepared by moderate heating. Titanium tetrahalides hydrolyze readily to produce TiO_2. Thus, a white smoke of TiO_2 forms when $TiCl_4$ is exposed to the atmosphere. This smoke is useful in the study of air movements. Because of its strength (about twice that of aluminum), low density, and high melting point, titanium is used extensively in aircraft. However,

336
*Chapter 18
The transition
metals,
lanthanides,
and actinides*

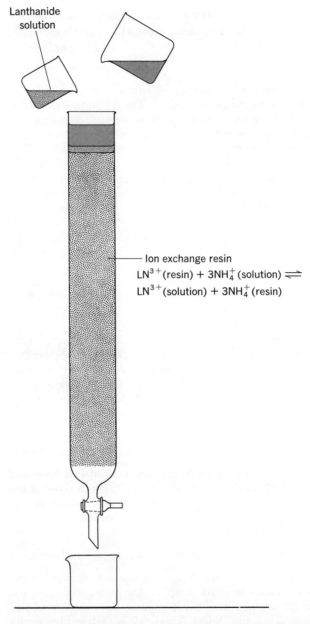

Lanthanide
solution

Ion exchange resin

LN^{3+} (resin) + $3NH_4^+$ (solution) $\rightleftharpoons$

LN^{3+} (solution) + $3NH_4^+$ (resin)

Fig. 18.7

Lanthanide Separation Using An Ion Exchange Column. Lanthanide and yttrium oxides are dissolved in HCl, and the solution is poured on the ion exchange resin bed. An ammonium citrate and citric acid buffer solution ($pH = 3.5$–4.0) is added. The buffer solution moves slowly through the column absorbing and desorbing lanthanide ions at slightly different rates. Heavy ions move down the column more rapidly than lighter ions. If the process continues long enough, a complete separation of the lanthanide ions occurs.

small amounts of impurities destroy the strength of the metal. The primary oxidation states of titanium are $+4$ and $+3$. A few compounds in the $+2$ state are known.

Zirconium and hafnium are the chemical twins of the periodic table. The outer electron configurations are the same, and the atomic and ionic radii are almost identical. As a result, both metals undergo identical chemical reactions.

Zirconium was discovered first as zirconium oxide in 1789, but it was 1824 before an impure sample of the metal was prepared. It took almost 100 years to recognize that all zirconium ores are contaminated with hafnium. So uniform is this contamination that the atomic weight of the zirconium-hafnium mixtures did not vary with the site from which the sample came. The elements are separated as zirconium and halfnium tetrachlorides using ion exchange resins.

The only known oxidation state of zirconium and hafnium is $+4$. The addition of a base to a solution of Zr^{4+} or Hf^{4+} ions produces a white gelatinous precipitate of $ZrO_2 \cdot H_2O$ or $HfO_2 \cdot H_2O$ which can be converted to insoluble dioxides by heating. The oxides with a high melting point of 2700°C have extensive commercial use. ZrO_2 (zirconia) is quite inert, but a change in crystal structure occurs at about 1200°C. When ZrO_2 passes through this transition, there is such a difference in the two crystal structures that it is reduced to a powder. This effect is overcome by adding a small amount of $CaSO_4$ resulting in a product known as stabilized zirconia. $CaSO_4$ is more volatile than zirconia, and the stabilized form cannot be used above 2400°C.

Zirconium does not absorb neutrons readily, while hafnium is a strong neutron absorber. Thus, it is necessary to remove the hafnium from the zirconium used in a nuclear reactor. The natural zirconium-hafnium mixture is used in flashbulbs where it gives an intense light, in vacuum tubes to remove residual gases, and in electrolytic condensors where the oxide coat insulates the metal foil. The mixed metal is used for surgical implants such as pins, screws, and plates. Even false teeth made of zirconium with a permanent white oxide coating have been proposed.

The vanadium group

Vanadium ores are rare and rather widespread. Compounds of the $+2$, $+3$, $+4$, and $+5$ oxidation states of vanadium are found. Each state is characterized by a unique color in aqueous solution: V(II) lavender, V(III) green, V(IV) blue, and V(V) orange.

When vanadium is burned in excess oxygen, V_2O_5 is the major product. It is only slightly soluble in water but dissolves both in acids and in bases. The only pentahalide known is VF_5 which is prepared from the elements at 300°C. Oxyhalides such as $VOCl_3$ rapidly hydrolyze in water.

The $+4$ oxidation state appears to be the most stable state. In basic solutions the vanadate ion (VO_4^{4-}) predominates, while

338

Chapter 18
The transition
metals,
lanthanides,
and actinides

the vanadyl ion (VO^{++}) is the most important species in acid solutions. Most vanadium(IV) chemistry involves the vanadyl ion. Besides vanadyl or vanadate compounds, only a few unstable V(IV) compounds are known. The $+3$ and $+2$ oxidation states of vanadium are known, but the compounds are quite unstable.

Niobium and tantalum are very similar in their chemistries, because they have the same atomic size and electron configurations. These metals differ from vanadium in that the $+5$ oxidation state is the important one. The $+4$ oxides, the trihalides, and a few dihalides are known. The elements frequently occur together in natural ores but not with the certainty or uniformity of zirconium and hafnium. Tantalum and niobium are high-melting metals with good structural strength. Tantalum is very corrosion resistant and is useful in acid-proof equipment. It also can be made into very thin walls for good heat transfer. Niobium utilization has not been developed greatly. Its greatest potential is in high-temperature nuclear reactors because of its structural strength and low absorption of neutrons. The use of both metals is limited by the need to protect them from oxidation, since they react with even the smallest trace of oxygen when hot.

Chromium, molybdenum, and tungsten

Chromium exists in the $+6$, $+3$, and $+2$ oxidation states. Chromium trioxide (CrO_3) is a bright red crystalline material which precipitates when concentrated sulfuric acid is slowly added to an aqueous chromate or dichromate solution. The solution that results, chromic acid, is used for cleaning glassware because of its strongly oxidizing property. CrO_3 is a strong oxidizing agent also. It is readily soluble in water and forms the dichromate ion ($Cr_2O_7^=$). The dichromate ion is transformed readily to the chromate ion ($CrO_4^=$) upon the addition of base since the equilibrium

$$2CrO_4^= + 2H^+ \rightleftarrows Cr_2O_7^= + H_2O$$
$$\text{(yellow)} \qquad\qquad \text{(orange)}$$

exists in the solution. Most dichromates are water soluble, while many chromates are insoluble. As indicated by the above equilibrium, chromates are soluble in acid. It is also possible to precipitate some chromates from a slightly acid solution. Acid solutions of the dichromate ion are strong oxidizing agents.

$$Cr_2O_7^= + 14H^+ + 6e^- \rightarrow 2Cr^{3+} + 7H_2O$$

The most stable and common compounds of chromium are those in the $+3$ oxidation state. Chromic oxide (Cr_2O_3) is prepared by heating the metal in air, heating chromic hydroxide, or heating ammonium dichromate.

$$(NH_4)_2Cr_2O_7 \xrightarrow{\Delta} N_2\uparrow + 4H_2O + Cr_2O_3$$

It is a green powder that is insoluble in H_2O and acid. It is not reduced by hydrogen. Chromic chloride, chromic sulfate, and chromic nitrate can be crystallized as hydrates. When a strong base is added to a solution of a chromic salt, a gelatinous precipitate of $Cr(OH)_3$ forms.

The $+2$ oxidation state compounds are rather unstable. Chromous chloride ($CrCl_2$), a white solid, forms a blue solution. It is stable only in a reducing atmosphere.

Chromium is used as a protective coating known as a chrome plate, prepared by the electrolysis of an aqueous $Cr(III)$ solution. Chromium steels are prepared by adding an iron-chromium alloy called ferrochrome. Ferrochrome is prepared by reducing the common ore of chromium, chromite ($FeCr_2O_4$), with carbon in an electric furnace.

$$FeCr_2O_4 + 4C \rightarrow Fe + 2Cr + 4CO\uparrow$$

Molybdenum is unreactive at room temperature but becomes very reactive when hot. When properly protected, the metal is used in high-temperature applications. Most molybdenum produced is used in various types of steel.

Tungsten is a hard, high-melting metal that becomes brittle upon heating. It is inert at room temperatures but very reactive when heated. About 90 per cent of the tungsten produced in the U.S. is used in iron alloys. Pure tungsten is used in electric lamp filaments and electrical contacts.

The $+6$ oxidation state is the most important for tungsten and molybdenum, although $+4$ and $+5$ states are known. Molybdates ($MoO_4^=$) and tungstates ($WO_4^=$) are common in basic solutions as well as solids. The metals form many non-stoichiometric solid phases with oxygen, nitrogen, and hydrogen.

The manganese group

Manganese is the only member of this group that is of any great importance. Technetium does not occur in nature and has been produced only recently in small amounts. Rhenium was not discovered until 1925 and is now the subject of extensive investigation. It is an unreactive metal that shows oxidation states from -1 to $+7$. As yet, no commercial uses have been developed for rhenium.

Five oxides of manganese are known; they correspond to oxidation states of $+2$, $+3$, $+4$, $+5$, and $+7$. Mn_2O_7 is a strong oxidizing agent which is not very stable. The permanganates are the most common compounds of $Mn(VII)$. The permanganate ion is characterized by its intense purple color. As little as one part per million in a solution can be detected visually. When permanganates are heated, they decompose to the manganate, manganese dioxide, and oxygen.

$$2MnO_4^- \xrightarrow{\Delta} MnO_4^= + MnO_2 + O_2\uparrow$$

The manganates ($MnO_4^=$) readily decompose to MnO_2 and MnO_4^-.

Permanganate solutions are strong oxidizing agents. In a basic

340

Chapter 18
The transition
metals,
lanthanides,
and actinides

solution the product is MnO_2. The reduction product is Mn^{++} in the presence of acid. Usually H_2SO_4 is used, since HCl is oxidized and HNO_3 is a strong oxidizing agent.

$$3e^- + MnO_4^- + 2H_2O \rightarrow MnO_2 + 4OH^-$$
$$5e^- + MnO_4^- + 8H^+ \rightarrow Mn^{++} + 4H_2O$$

Manganese dioxide (MnO_2) is the only common $+4$ oxidation state species. It is a dark brown, insoluble solid that is almost inert to the action of acids and bases. MnO_2 is a good oxidizing agent. It oxidizes chloride ions to chlorine while being reduced to Mn^{++}.

$$2e^- + MnO_2 + 2Cl^- + 4H^+ \rightarrow Mn^{++} + 2H_2O + Cl_2$$

Mn_2O_3 occurs naturally, but the Mn^{3+} ion is unstable in solution.

The most stable oxidation state is the $+2$ or manganous state. It is characterized by a pink color. Several manganous salts such as the chloride, sulfate, and nitrate are water soluble. Manganous hydroxide precipitates when a base is added to a solution of manganous ion.

The ferrous metals

The $+2$ oxidation state is found for these three metals (iron, cobalt, nickel). The $+3$ state is important only for iron. Cobalt and nickel form complexes with many ions and molecules, while iron forms very few.

Three oxides of iron are known: ferrous oxide (FeO), ferric oxide (Fe_2O_3), and magnetic iron oxide or magnetite (Fe_3O_4). Ferrous oxide decomposes to iron and Fe_3O_4 when heated to high temperatures. When dissolved in acid, FeO forms ferrous ions in solution. Ferric oxide is prepared by heating the precipitate that forms when a base is added to a solution of ferric ion. Magnetic iron oxide is the most stable of the oxides and is the product of iron reacting with oxygen as a burning or as a rusting metal. Fe_3O_4 behaves as does a mixture of FeO and Fe_2O_3.

When a base is added to a solution of ferric ion, a reddish-brown precipitate forms. This is the hydrated oxide, usually called ferric hydroxide. Since ferric hydroxide is not very soluble, ferric salts readily hydrolyze in aqueous solution. Solutions of ferric salts usually contain some acid to suppress the hydrolysis.

Cobalt and nickel are very much alike. Aqueous cobalt solutions are red, and nickel solutions are green. A precipitate called the hydroxide forms when base is added to solutions of these ions. $Ni(OH)_2$ is green; $Co(OH)_2$ is pink. The hydroxides dissolve in NH_4OH due to the formation of $Ni(NH_3)_6^{++}$ and $Co(NH_3)_6^{++}$.

Nickel metal is used as a protective plating material and in the manufacture of nickel steels. Cobalt salts are used as coloring agents in the production of blue glass.

The platinum metals

The platinum metals are ruthenium, rhodium, palladium, osmium, iridium, and platinum. A list of the precious metals usually includes these six metals as well as gold and silver. The world's annual production is in the ratio of platinum one, gold 50, silver 400.

Platinum was first reported by Europeans around 1600, when an infusible (impossible to melt) metal was found in Mexico and Panama. The South American Indians made simple ornaments of the metal. But to the Spaniards who were looking for gold, platinum was an undesirable problem. It did not take long for the "operators" of the day to coat the worthless platinum with gold and sell it to the gold-hungry Spanish.

Present-day sources are in the Soviet Union, South Africa, and Canada. The platinum metals occur in the free state as fine deposits. Platinum makes up about 70 per cent of the ore.

Few compounds of platinum are known. Hexachloroplatinic acid (H_2PtCl_6) is formed when platinum dissolves in aqua regia. Crystals of the hexahydrate form upon evaporation. $PtCl_4$ and $PtCl_2$ can be prepared from these crystals. Although platinum is inert at room temperatures, it is attacked by fused hydroxides, peroxides, nitrates, cyanides, and sulfides. The metal is used extensively as a catalyst in the form of the black sponge or powder known as platinum black.

Palladium is very similar to platinum. It is more reactive, however, and is attacked by concentrated nitric acid and concentrated sulfuric acid. Iridium is more resistant to corrosion than any other metal known. Its major use is as an alloying agent which increases the hardness of platinum. Rhodium is somewhat less resistant to corrosion but is used extensively for plating where a hard, durable surface is required.

Osmium and ruthenium are high-density, high-melting metals that find their major use as alloying agents to harden platinum. The usefulness of these metals is limited by the formation of the volatile, poisonous oxides.

The copper group

Copper, silver, and gold form a group of ductile, malleable, oxidation-resistant metals which are near the bottom of the activity series. The metals become more inert with increasing weight. Similarly, the heavier ions are more easily reduced. Because of their inertness, these metals have been used in making coins and sometimes are called the coinage metals. They form covalent as well as ionic compounds. The +1 oxidation state is found for all of these metals, since there is a single s electron that can be easily removed.

Compounds with copper in the +1 and +2 oxidation states are known. Copper(I) ions are stable in the solid and, in the form of complex ions, in aqueous solution. When Cu^+ ion is placed in water, disproportionation takes place.

$$2Cu^+ \rightarrow Cu\downarrow + Cu^{++}$$

342

Chapter 18
The transition
metals,
lanthanides,
and actinides

The cupric ion is reduced by easily oxidized anions, preventing the preparation of the cupric salts. For example, when an iodide solution is added to a solution of cupric ion, insoluble cuprous iodide and iodine are formed.

$$2Cu^{++} + 4I^- \rightarrow 2CuI\downarrow + I_2$$

In this reaction, an electron is transferred readily from the iodide to the cupric ion. Some other cupric salts undergo the same type of reaction upon heating.

$$4CuO \xrightarrow{\Delta} 2Cu_2O + O_2\uparrow$$

The cupric ion readily forms complex ions with many species. Many of these complexes have a unique color making it possible to follow changes in species about the cupric ion. The hydrated ion $[Cu(H_2O)_4]^{++}$ is blue. The chloro-complex ion $[CuCl_4]^=$ is green, and the ammine complex ion, $[Cu(NH_3)_4]^{++}$, is deep blue. The characteristic blue color of $[Cu(H_2O)_4]^{++}$ is found in solid $CuSO_4 \cdot 5H_2O$. When heated to 110°C, the four water molecules around the cupric ion are driven off; the resulting monohydrate salt is white. The fifth water molecule associated with the sulfate ion is removed at 300°C.

Silver is found primarily in the +1 oxidation state. Silver is not attacked by oxygen, but black Ag_2S forms in the presence of sulfur or H_2S. The small amount of sulfur in an egg causes silverware to tarnish. Silver metal reacts with the halogens at red heat. Silver is inert to aqua regia and dilute hydrochloric or sulfuric acid but dissolves in concentrated nitric or sulfuric acid. The silver ion readily forms the colorless diammine complex $[Ag(NH_3)_2]^+$ when NH_4OH is added. Most silver salts are insoluble in water, but several have sufficient solubility to dissolve in ammonium hydroxide by forming the complex.

Silver salts are sensitive to light, decomposing to metallic silver upon exposure. This property is utilized in photography. Finely divided silver halide is suspended in gelatin along with a trace of an activator impurity. The gelatin suspension is spread as a film on a backing paper or a glass plate. When the film is exposed to light, the halide particles are activated in proportion to the intensity of light falling upon them. The film is developed with a mild reducing agent which reduces only the silver halide particles that have been activated. The result is a finely divided suspension of metallic silver where the film was exposed to light. The film is fixed with a sodium thiosulfate ($Na_2S_2O_3$) solution which removes the unreacted silver halide. This film is a negative of the scene, since there are black silver deposits where the light was most intense and none where there was no light. In the printing process light shines through the negative onto the printing paper. Using the same procedures, the print again reverses dark and light areas to produce an image with the light and dark areas in the correct places.

Extensive use of silver is made in electrical and electronic circuits as it is the best metallic electrical conductor known. Until 1965, silver alloys were used in U.S. coinage. The increasing industrial demand for silver forced the discontinuance of silver coinage except for the half dollar, and even its silver content was greatly reduced.

Gold is found in compounds with $+1$ and $+3$ oxidation states. The $+1$ oxidation state is not stable in solution.

$$3Au(I) \rightarrow 2Au(0) + Au(III)$$

The few known gold(I) salts are insoluble covalent compounds. Most of the gold(III) compounds are covalent, AuF_3 is the only common ionic substance. The other gold(III) halides are covalent dimers with the formula Au_2X_6. When gold dissolves in aqua regia, the complex ion $[AuCl_4]^-$ is formed. The same complex ion is formed when gold chloride is added to hydrochloric acid.

The zinc group

Zinc occurs naturally as the sulfide ore which is roasted to zinc oxide and then reduced. Cadmium is an impurity in these ores and is recovered as a by-product of zinc processing. Mercury is found in cinnabar ore (HgS) which yields mercury upon heating.

All three metals have relatively low melting points and high vapor pressures. Zinc and cadmium are amphoteric, dissolving in dilute acid or concentrated base to liberate hydrogen. Mercury dissolves in neither acid nor base. All three metals form compounds in the $+2$ oxidation state. The mercury compounds are covalent. Almost all cadmium compounds are ionic. Some zinc compounds are ionic, and others are covalent. This $+2$ oxidation state is expected, since there are two s electrons in the highest energy level.

The metals are not attacked in dry air at room temperatures. In moist air, zinc and cadmium form a protective coating of "basic" carbonate, $Zn_2(OH)_2CO_3$ and Cd_2OCO_3. When heated, cadmium and zinc react with halogens, oxygen, and sulfur, but not with nitrogen. Mercury reacts with oxygen when heated; the oxide which is formed decomposes upon further heating. Mercury readily reacts with halogens or sulfur at room temperatures.

Salts of zinc, cadmium, and mercury readily hydrolyze in aqueous solution, since the hydroxides (or hydrated oxides) are insoluble. Zinc hydroxide ($Zn(OH)_2$) which forms upon the addition of base to a zinc salt solution, readily dissolves upon the addition of excess NH_4OH or excess OH^- and forms the complexes $[Zn(NH_3)_4]^{++}$ or $[Zn(OH)_4]^=$ respectively. Cadmium hydroxide ($Cd(OH)_2$) is moderately soluble in excess NH_4OH and only slightly soluble in excess OH^-; it forms the complexes $[Cd(NH_3)_4]^{++}$ and $[Cd(OH)_4]^=$. The mercuric precipitate does not dissolve upon the addition of excess NH_4OH or OH^-.

Cadmium salts and solutions are colored; zinc salts are white;

344
Chapter 18
The transition
metals,
lanthanides,
and actinides

and zinc solutions are colorless. Mercuric solutions are colorless, but the solid salts are frequently colored. Cadmium ions readily form complexes with many species; zinc ions form complexes with substantially fewer species; and mercury ions show very little tendency toward complex formation.

Mercury forms some compounds with a formal oxidation state of $+1$. Most mercurous salts are insoluble in water.

Many of the mercuric salts exist as solids with two colors. For example, red and yellow forms of mercuric oxide result from different particle sizes, but both forms undergo the same chemical reactions. Mercuric iodide (HgI_2) also occurs in a red and in a yellow form; the latter is produced, if the iodide is heated above $126°C$. Mercuric sulfide (HgS) is either brilliant red or black.

The ease with which mercury and sulfur react is useful for the elimination of the health hazard created by spilled mercury. Although the vapor pressure is not very great, continual exposure to mercury vapor can cause heavy metal poisoning in the body. When mercury falls into cracks and crevices where it is not possible to remove it, the area may be sprinkled with sulfur. Insoluble, non-volatile HgS is formed, and the hazard is eliminated. Another source of poisoning is the amalgam of mercury with gold, silver, or platinum jewelry. A ring containing a little mercury in constant contact with the skin permits the slow absorption of mercury and cumulative poisoning.

SIGNIFICANT TERMS AND CONCEPTS IN CHAPTER XVIII:

Trends in physical and chemical properties of the transition metals and lanthanides, the relationship of properties to the number of d and f electrons; lanthanide contraction; changes in properties at Group IB; amalgam, interstitial compounds, non-stoichiometric compounds, lanthanide, actinide; most stable and most important oxidation states of the metals, stable oxides, color and d electrons; metallurgical steps, methods of reduction of the transition metals, reactivities of the transition metals, ferrous metals; photographic process.

Review questions

18.1. Write the typical outer electron configuration for the following.
    (a) $+3$ ion of Group IIIB
    (b) $+4$ ion of Group IVB
    (c) $+5$ ion of Group VB
    (d) $+3$ ion of Group VIB
    (e) $+6$ ion of Group VIB
    (f) $+2$ ion of Group VIIB
    (g) $+2$ ion of the iron subgroup of Group VIIIB
    (h) $+3$ ion of the iron subgroup of Group VIIIB

(i)   +2 ion of the cobalt subgroup of Group VIIIB
(j)   +2 ion of the nickel subgroup of Group VIIIB
(k)   +1 ion of Group IB
(l)   +2 ion of Group IB
(m) +2 ion of Group IIB   answers: (a) s^0d^0 (l) s^0d^9

18.2. Indicate the predicted number of 6s, 5d, and 4f electrons in the following.
(a) La, (b) Nd, (c) Pm, (d) Ho, (e) Gd, (f) Hf, (g) Ce^{4+}, (h) Ce^{3+}, (i) Eu^{++}, (j) Tb^{4+}, (k) Tm^{3+}, (l) Lu^{3+}.
        answers: (a) $6s^25d^14f^0$, (g) $6s^05d^04f^0$, (k) $6s^05d^04f^{12}$

18.3. Plot the melting point as a function of the number of 3d electrons for the first transition metal period (i.e., Sc to Zn).

18.4. Plot the density as a function of the number of 5d electrons for the third transition metal period (i.e., La, Hf to Hg).

18.5. Write equations for the following, indicating "no reaction" by "N.R."
(a) Scandium metal in steam
(b) Chromium metal in hydrochloric acid
(c) Iron metal in concentrated nitric acid
(d) Niobium metal in nitric acid
(e) Palladium metal in aqua regia
(f) Lanthanum metal in hydrochloric acid
(g) Burning zirconium metal in air
(h) Heating tungsten in air
(i) Burning osmium in air
(j) Burning zinc in air
(k) Heating mercury to 500°C in air
(l) Ferrous oxide dissolved in hydrochloric acid
(m) Ammonium hydroxide added slowly to a NiCl$_2$ solution
(n) Sodium hydroxide added slowly to a ZnCl$_2$ solution
(o) Ferric chloride added to water
(p) Preparation of zinc metal from zinc sulfide ore
(q) Zinc chloride solid placed in water
(r) Ferrous sulfate solution added to an acid solution of potassium permanganate
(s) Heating titanium tetrachloride with sodium metal
(t) Heating cupric oxide in a hydrogen atmosphere
(u) Lanthanum chloride heated with calcium metal
(v) Sodium hydroxide added to a vanadyl sulfate solution
(w) Chromic oxide heated with aluminum metal

18.6. Give formulas for:
(a) vanadyl ion, (b) dichromate ion, (c) permanganate ion, (d) magnetic iron oxide, (e) "basic" carbonate of zinc.

18.7. On the basis of electronic structure, account for the fact that a solution of [Ag(NH$_3$)$_2$]$^+$ is colorless while a solution of [Cu(NH$_3$)$_4$]$^{++}$ is a very dark blue.

organic chemistry

nineteen

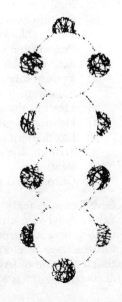

Up to this point, we have been concerned primarily with chemical theory and descriptive inorganic chemistry. Another very large and important area of interest is organic chemistry. The term *organic chemistry* came about long ago when it was thought that life processes were necessary for the production of organic compounds. This idea prevailed until 1828, when Friedrich Wöhler was able to synthesize urea, an organic compound, from strictly inorganic materials. This marked the beginning of synthetic organic chemistry; literally millions of organic compounds have been prepared from simple inorganic starting materials since that time.

Another important phase of organic chemistry is the isolation of a complex compound from a biological system and the subsequent synthesis of the compound from simpler materials. During synthesis small modifications of the compound may be made to eliminate certain undesirable properties and to enhance more desirable properties.

The focus of organic chemistry is the covalent carbon atom which is capable of binding with other carbon atoms to form chains and rings. Since there are so many possible combinations of carbon atoms, it is necessary to systematize the study. Our discussion concerns the system of nomenclature, certain important functional groups, and some important elementary reactions.

The tetrahedral carbon atom

The formation of tetrahedral hybrid orbitals about the carbon atom was discussed in Chapter VII. Each orbital is directed toward the corner of a tetrahedron, making a bond angle of 109.5°. The carbon atom is thought to contribute a single electron to each of these orbitals in bond formation. The tetrahedral arrangement of orbitals about the carbon atom describes the bonding when the atom is bound to four other atoms. Each of the four atoms shares a pair of electrons with the carbon atom in what is called a single bond.

Since the tetrahedron is a three-dimensional structure, the compounds have a three-dimensional character. As a result, the spatial arrangement of a compound as well as its formula is important in the understanding of the properties. Usually it is not possible to show the structures unambiguously in two dimensions. For a full understanding it is necessary to turn to the use of three-dimensional models.

Since carbon atoms join together, it is possible to have long chains, branched chains, or rings. A cardinal rule in writing structural formulas requires that four bonds be shown on every carbon atom. As one becomes more proficient, hydrogen atoms are left out of some of the structural representations with the understanding that there are sufficient hydrogens present to make up four bonds per carbon atom.

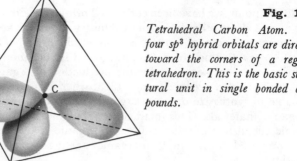

Fig. 19.1

Tetrahedral Carbon Atom. The four sp^3 hybrid orbitals are directed toward the corners of a regular tetrahedron. This is the basic structural unit in single bonded compounds.

Systematic groupings

The first step in grouping organic compounds for a study of their properties and for the nomenclature is to look at the simple *hydrocarbons*, compounds containing only hydrogen and carbon. Once this basis is established, then functional groups are considered. *Functional groups* are particular arrangements of atoms of elements other than hydrogen and carbon which are bonded to a carbon atom.

Hydrocarbons are divided into the aliphatics and the aromatics on the basis of the electron arrangement in the molecule. The aliphatics are further divided into saturated and unsaturated compounds. *Saturated hydrocarbons* are those in which all carbon-carbon bonds are single bonds. *Unsaturated* hydrocarbons have at least one carbon-carbon bond that is double (two pairs of electrons shared) or triple (three pairs of electrons shared). There are compounds that may have an aromatic structure attached to a long aliphatic structure. Such a compound shows both aromatic and aliphatic character.

Alkanes

Saturated aliphatic hydrocarbons are called *alkanes* (or the paraffins in the older literature). The alkanes are a homologous series in which each member differs by a CH_2 (methylene) group. This progression is obvious when one considers that two bonds of the added carbon atom are with atoms already in the chain. The remaining two bonds are with hydrogens. An alkane is identified by the formula C_nH_{2n+2}.

The names of all alkanes end in *-ane*. The root word denotes the number of carbon atoms in the straight chain. These roots are used for all organic nomenclature. Table 19.1 shows the first ten straight chain alkanes and their names. Particular attention should be given to the number of carbon atoms and the corresponding root word.

When naming branched chain aliphatic compounds, the longest straight chain of carbon atoms is selected as the basic alkane. The branches are treated as substitutions for the hydrogen atom

Table 19.1

The First 10 Alkanes

Number of carbon atoms	Formula	Name	Structural formula
1	CH_4	methane	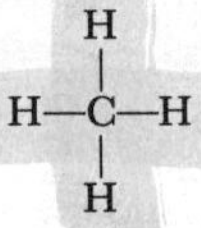 H—C—H with H above and H below
2	C_2H_6	ethane	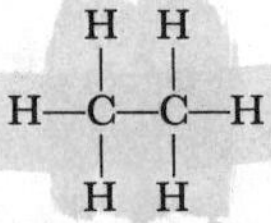 H—C—C—H with H above and below each C
3	C_3H_8	propane	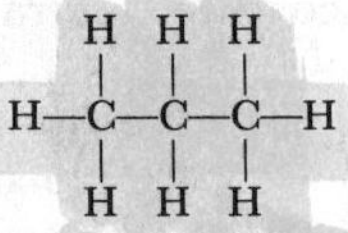 H—C—C—C—H with H above and below each C
4	C_4H_{10}	butane	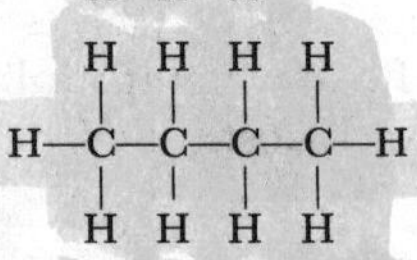 H—C—C—C—C—H with H above and below each C
5	C_5H_{12}	pentane	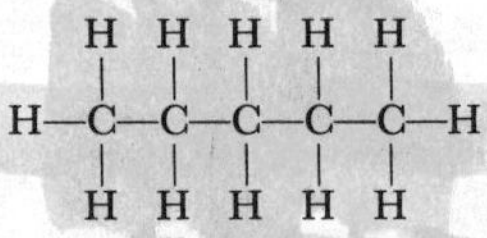 H—C—C—C—C—C—H with H above and below each C
6	C_6H_{14}	hexane	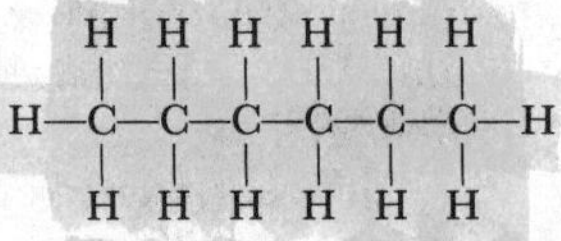 H—C—C—C—C—C—C—H with H above and below each C
7	C_7H_{16}	heptane	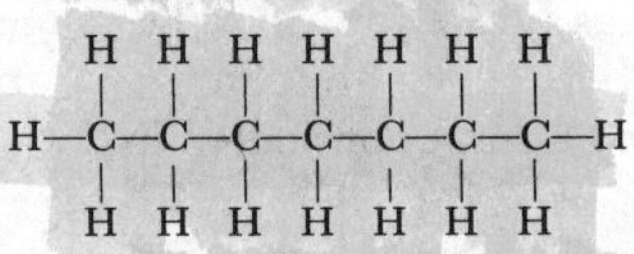 H—C—C—C—C—C—C—C—H with H above and below each C
8	C_8H_{18}	octane	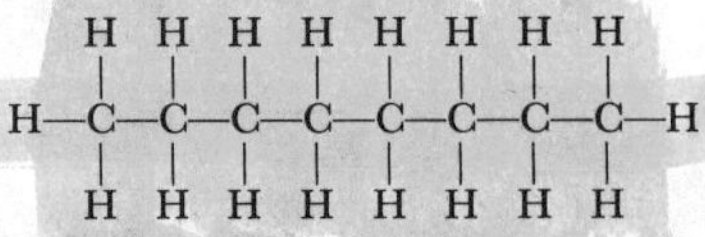 H—C—C—C—C—C—C—C—C—H with H above and below each C
9	C_9H_{20}	nonane	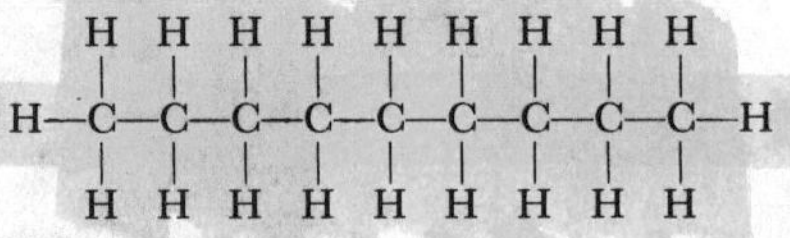 H—C—C—C—C—C—C—C—C—C—H with H above and below each C
10	$C_{10}H_{22}$	decane	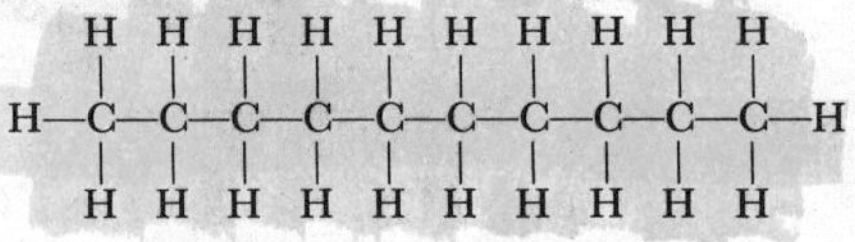 H—C—C—C—C—C—C—C—C—C—C—H with H above and below each C

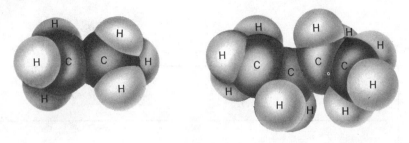

Fig. 19.2

Three-dimensional Representation of Ethane and Butane

on the carbon. Since a flat diagram represents a three-dimensional array, the obvious chain may not be the longest. For example, the longest continuous straight chain in

$$\begin{array}{ccc} & C & C\!-\!C \\ & | & | \\ & C\!-\!C\!-\!C\!-\!C \end{array}$$ is six

carbons, making this a substituted hexane. The carbon atoms are numbered to show where the substituent is located. Numbering starts from the end that gives the smallest set of digits for the substituents. In the example above, the numbering is from right to left, with the substitution on the number three carbon atom.

$$\begin{array}{ccc} 6 & 2 & 1 \\ C & C\!-\!C \\ | & | \\ C\!-\!C\!-\!C\!-\!C \\ 5 & 4 & 3 \end{array}$$

The branch is treated as a radical attached to the longest straight chain. An *organic radical* is a straight chain alkane with a hydrogen atom removed from one end. Radicals are named by adding *-yl* to the root word representing the number of carbon atoms in the radical. The names for the radicals with one to ten carbon atoms are given in Table 19.2. The name of the substituted hexane considered in the example above is 3-methyl-hexane.

Table 19.2

Organic Radicals

Name	Formula	Name	Formula
methyl	$-CH_3$	hexyl	$-C_6H_{13}$
ethyl	$-C_2H_5$	heptyl	$-C_7H_{15}$
propyl	$-C_3H_7$	octyl	$-C_8H_{17}$
butyl	$-C_4H_9$	nonyl	$-C_9H_{19}$
pentyl	$-C_5H_{11}$	decyl	$-C_{10}H_{21}$

Example 19.1 Name the following: (Note that only the carbon backbone is shown).

(a)
$$
\begin{array}{c}
\quad\quad\;\; C \\
\quad\quad\;\; | \\
\quad\quad\;\; C \\
\quad\quad\;\; | \\
C-C-C-C-C \\
\quad\; | \quad\;\; | \\
\quad\; C \quad\;\; C \\
\quad\; | \quad\;\; | \\
\quad\; C \quad\;\; C
\end{array}
$$

(a) 3,5-dimethyl-4-ethyl-heptane

(b)
$$
\begin{array}{c}
\quad\quad\quad\quad C \\
\quad\quad\quad\quad | \\
\quad\quad\quad\quad C \\
\quad\quad\quad\quad | \\
C-C-C-C-C-C-C \\
\quad\quad\; | \;\; | \;\; | \\
\quad\quad\; C \;\; C \;\; C \\
\quad\quad\quad\quad\quad\; | \\
\quad\quad\quad\quad\quad\; C
\end{array}
$$

(b) 3,3-diethyl-4,5-dimethyl-heptane

Two or more compounds may have the same formula but different structures and different properties. Such compounds are called *isomers*. A simple example of a pair of isomers is butane and 2-methyl-propane. Both have the formula C_4H_{10} but their structures are

$$
\begin{array}{ccccc}
H & H & H & H \\
| & | & | & | \\
H-C-&C-&C-&C-H \\
| & | & | & | \\
H & H & H & H
\end{array}
\quad \text{and} \quad
\begin{array}{ccc}
H & H & H \\
| & | & | \\
H-C-&C-&C-H \\
| & | & | \\
H & H & H \\
& | & \\
& H-C-H & \\
& | & \\
& H &
\end{array}
$$

The melting points are $-135°C$ and $-145°C$ respectively. The boiling points are $0.6°C$ and $-10.2°C$ respectively.

The alkanes are characterized by insolubility in water. They are soluble in non-polar solvents. All of the alkanes are colorless.

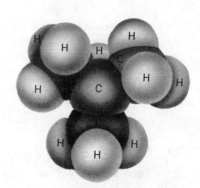

Fig. 19.3
2-Methyl-Propane.   A branched chain isomer of butane. (See Fig. 19.2.)

Table 19.3

*Melting and Boiling Points
of Selected Straight Chain Alkanes*

Alkane	Melting point	Boiling point
CH_4	$-182°C$	$-161°C$
C_2H_6	-183	-89
C_3H_8	-188	-42
C_4H_{10}	-138	0
C_5H_{12}	-130	36
$C_{10}H_{22}$	-30	174
$C_{18}H_{38}$	28	317
$C_{20}H_{42}$	36	344

In general, melting points and boiling points progressively increase with molecular weight (Table 19.3).

Alkanes occur primarily in natural gas and petroleum. Natural gas contains over 80 per cent methane. Liquified petroleum (LP) gas is a propane-butane mixture that is liquified under pressure. Alkane molecules of less than five carbon atoms are gases at room temperature. Twelve- to 15-carbon atom molecules make up the kerosenes, while fuel oil is the 15- to 19-carbon atom fraction. Lubricating oils and greases are those in the 19- to 40-carbon atom range.

Chemically the alkanes are relatively unreactive. No reactions with acids, bases, or oxidizing agents occur at room temperature. The combustion, or oxidation, products in the presence of sufficient oxygen are CO_2 and H_2O. If an alkane is heated in the absence of air, it is broken down to lower molecular weight material in a process called *pyrolysis*. If an alkane-halogen mixture is irradiated with light of the proper wavelength, a reaction occurs.

$$H-\underset{\underset{H}{|}}{\overset{\overset{H}{|}}{C}}-H + Cl_2 \xrightarrow{\text{light}} H-\underset{\underset{H}{|}}{\overset{\overset{H}{|}}{C}}-Cl + HCl$$

Other compounds such as CH_2Cl_2, $CHCl_3$, and CCl_4 are possible; the final product of the reaction above is a mixture of all four species. The ratio of products depends on the conditions under which the reaction is carried out. The reaction with Br_2 and I_2 proceeds at a slower rate than with Cl_2 while the reaction with F_2 is explosive even in the dark.

Alkenes

Alkenes are hydrocarbons with one double (two electron pairs) bond between two carbon atoms. The rest of the bonds are single electron pair bonds. The double bonding between the carbon atoms is described in terms of one bond involving a $2p$ orbital from each atom. The second bond involves an sp^2 hybrid orbital from each of the carbon atoms. A total of four bonds is necessary for every carbon atom.

Alkenes, formerly called olefins, are characterized by the general formula C_nH_{2n}. The alkene name is derived by adding the suffix *-ene* to the root word designating the appropriate number of carbon atoms. Since two carbon atoms are needed for a double

$$\underset{\underset{H}{|}\;\;\underset{H}{|}}{\overset{\overset{H}{|}\;\;\overset{H}{|}}{C=C}}$$

bond, the first member of the series is ethene, also called by the older name, ethylene. The three-carbon member, $C=C-C$ (hydrogens are omitted), is propene or, traditionally, propylene. Above propene it is necessary to designate the location of the double bond in order to distinguish the possible isomers. The carbon atoms are numbered beginning with the end nearest the double bond of the longest chain containing the double bond. The number designates the carbon atom after which the double bond is located. Thus, $C=C-C-C$ is 1-butene, and the isomer $C-C=C-C$ is 2-butene.

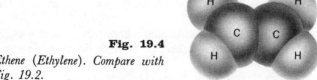

Fig. 19.4
Ethene (Ethylene). Compare with Fig. 19.2.

Geometric isomers are possible for alkenes containing four or more carbons. There are two possible geometric arrangements of the hydrogens in 2-butene. One hydrogen is on each carbon involved in the double bond. Both of these hydrogens are in the same plane as the double-bonded carbons. If the hydrogens are on the same side of the double bond, they are said to be in the *cis*-form. When the hydrogens are on opposite sides of the bond, they are in the *trans*-form. The two geometric isomers of 2-butene have the following structures.

$$
\underset{\text{cis-2-butene}}{
\underset{\overset{|}{H}\;\;\overset{|}{H}\;\;\overset{|}{H}\;\;\overset{|}{H}}{
\overset{\overset{|}{H}\;\;\;\;\;\;\;\;\overset{|}{H}}{
H-C-C=C-C-H}}}
\qquad\qquad
\underset{\text{trans-2-butene}}{
\underset{\overset{|}{H}\;\;\overset{|}{H}\;\;\;\;\;\;\overset{|}{H}}{
\overset{\overset{|}{H}\;\;\;\;\overset{|}{H}\;\;\overset{|}{H}}{
H-C-C=C-C-H}}}
$$

The structural differences affect the physical properties, as is seen for the butenes in Table 19.4.

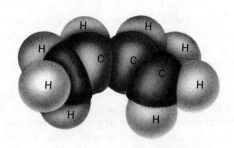

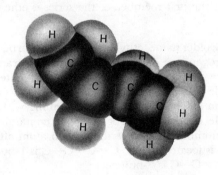

Fig. 19.5

Left: cis-2-butene. Right: trans-2-butene. Compare with Fig. 19.2.

Branched chain or substituted alkenes are named as the alkanes are, except that the numbering of the chain always begins at the end nearest the double bond. For example,

$$\underset{\begin{matrix}|\\C\end{matrix}}{C}-\underset{\begin{matrix}|\\C\end{matrix}}{C}-C=C-C$$

is 3,4-dimethyl-2-pentene. This structure is frequently written as $CH_3CH(CH_3)C(CH_3){=}CHCH_3$ for ease in typesetting and speed in writing.

As with the alkanes, the densities, boiling points, and melting points of the alkenes increase with molecular weight. Alkenes with less than five carbon atoms are gases at room temperature and pressure. Beginning with the pentenes, the alkenes are liquids at ordinary conditions up to about a 20-carbon chain. Above a 20-carbon chain, the melting point is above room temperature.

Table 19.4

Some Physical Properties of the Butenes

Name	Melting point	Boiling point	Density (25°C)
1-Butene	−185°C	−6.3°C	0.589
cis-2-Butene	−139°C	3.7	0.615
trans-2-Butene	−106°C	0.9	0.598

Alkenes are only slightly soluble in water. In general, they are very soluble in acetone, carbon tetrachloride, benzene, ether, and ethyl alcohol.

Chemically the double bond is very reactive. These are primarily addition reactions. Type reactions are shown in Table 19.5, where R and R' are generalized symbols for any radical or hydrogen. The correlation of organic reactions with structure is aided by the use of type reactions.

Table 19.5

Reactions of the Double Bond

	Remarks
$RCH{=}CHR' + H_2 \rightarrow$ RCH_2CH_2R' (alkane)	Catalyst needed
$RCH{=}CHR' + X_2 \rightarrow$ $RCHXCHXR'$ (alkyl dihalide)	$X_2 = Cl_2, Br_2, I_2.$ F_2 is too violent. Reaction rate decreases from Cl_2 to I_2.
$RCH{=}CHR' + HX \rightarrow$ $RCHXCH_2R'$ and RCH_2CHXR'	$HX = HI, HBr, HCl, HF.$ HI most easily added, HF hardest to add. Ratio of the two alkyl halides in product mixture depends upon reaction conditions.

It is possible to have more than one double bond in a compound. If there are two double bonds, the compound is a *-diene*. If there are three double bonds, it is a *-triene*, and so on. These compounds are known as alkapolyenes.

The number of carbons in the longest chain containing the double bonds is denoted by the appropriate root word on the suffix. The location of the double bonds is designated by the numbers of the carbon atoms after which the double bond appears. Thus

$$\begin{array}{cccc} H & H & H & H \\ | & | & | & | \\ C{=}C & - & C{=}C \\ | & & & | \\ H & & & H \end{array}$$

is 1,3-butadiene.

Alkynes

An alkyne has one triple bond in the carbon chain. The general formula for the alkynes is C_nH_{2n-2}. The first and most important member of the series is C_2H_2, ethyne or, more commonly, acetylene. The suffix *-yne* denotes the presence of the triple bond. Numbering and naming of substituents is the same as that for the alkenes.

The physical properties of the alkynes are similar to those of the alkanes and alkenes in that they are colorless and almost insoluble in water; the melting points, freezing points, and densities increase with molecular weight. Chemically the triple bond is very reactive, and addition occurs very easily. Halogens and hydrogen halides react readily with the triple bond.

Acetylene is prepared by the reaction of water and calcium carbide.

$$CaC_2 + H_2O \rightarrow Ca(OH)_2 + HC\equiv CH$$

This reaction is the basis of the acetylene lamps formerly worn by miners. Some acetylene welding units still generate acetylene by this reaction.

Benzene hydrocarbons

The discussion of aromatic hydrocarbons is limited to benzene and its homologs, which correspond to the formula C_nH_{2n-6}.

Some experimentally determined facts about benzene are that the molecular formula is C_6H_6, the nuclei of the twelve atoms are in a single plane, and the chemically identical carbon atoms form a ring with a single hydrogen attached to each carbon. The bonding in the molecule has been the subject of much discussion. Each carbon atom forms a bond with a hydrogen and two bonds with adjacent carbon atoms in the ring. One of the earliest satisfactory explanations for the fourth bond on each carbon atom was given by Friedrich Kekulé in 1865. The fourth bond is obtained in the Kekulé structure by alternating double bonds around the ring.

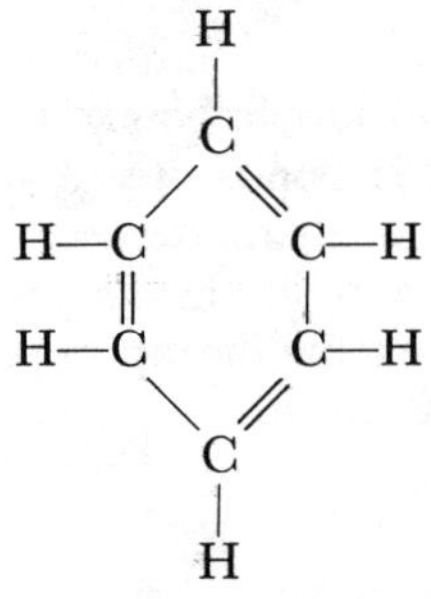

This structure does not totally explain all of the benzene reactions. One modification is the concept of resonance. The above structure is equivalent to

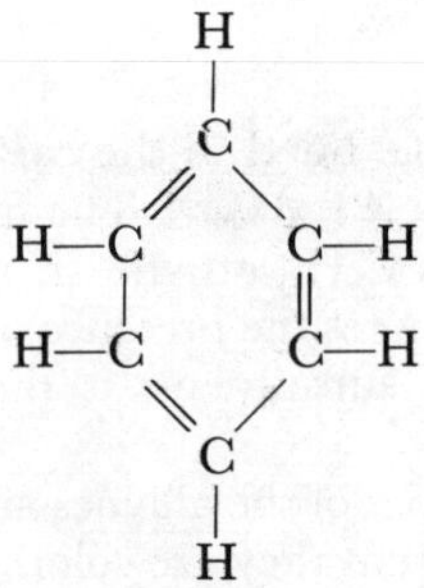

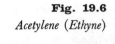

Fig. 19.6

Acetylene (Ethyne)

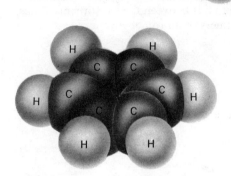

Fig. 19.7
Benzene

The resonance structure consists of equal parts of each structure. Benzene does not exist for a time as one structure and then as the other. The true structure is described in terms of these two structures and is a combination of the two.

Alternatively, in terms of hybridized orbitals, the carbons are bonded through planar sp^2 orbitals which are also involved in the C-H bond. The fourth electron of each carbon is in a non-localized molecular orbital above and below the plane of the molecule. This is thought of as a flow of charge and is represented by a circle within a ring of single bonded carbons.

Other bonding schemes have been advanced, but the resonance forms of the simple Kekulé structure appear to be the most satisfactory. Two of the many ways of representing the benzene ring in addition to the above diagram are

⬡ and ⌬

The benzene double bonds are very stable; addition to the ring is very difficult. Benzene does undergo many reactions, but they involve replacement of the hydrogens. For example, bromine in the presence of $FeBr_3$ reacts with benzene to form bromobenzene and HBr. Other derivatives of benzene are not too difficult to prepare. Some of the more common ones are given below.

⬡—Br   ⬡—NO₂   ⬡—OH

bromobenzene   nitrobenzene   phenol

⬡—NH₂   ⬡—C ⟨ O / OH

aniline   benzoic acid

Isomers are possible with disubstituted benzenes. If the substituted atoms are on adjacent carbon atoms, it is an *ortho* arrangement. In the *para* arrangement the atoms are on carbon atoms as far apart as possible or across the ring. The *meta* arrangement is intermediate; one carbon atom is between the substituents. Thus, there are three types or isomers of dibromobenzene.

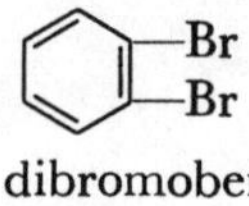

ortho dibromobenzene
or
1,2-dibromobenzene

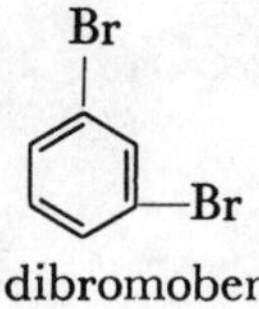

meta dibromobenzene
or
1,3-dibromobenzene

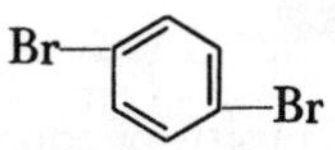

para dibromobenzene
or
1,4-dibromobenzene

In the preparation of disubstituted benzenes, a mixture of the *ortho*, *para*, and *meta* forms is obtained. The first substituent determines the favored disubstituted form. If a halide, a -CH$_3$ group, an -OH group, or an -OR group is added to the ring first, 80 to 90 per cent of the second substituent is in the *ortho* and *para* positions. These are called *ortho-para* directing groups. *Meta*-directing groups include -NO$_2$, -CN, -SO$_3$H, -COOH, and -COOR.

The benzene ring may be a substituent on an aliphatic chain (although the chain may be considered a substituent on the benzene ring), with C$_6$H$_5$ as the phenyl radical. Thus, there is

triphenyl methane H$_5$C$_6$—C—C$_6$H$_5$ and diphenyl

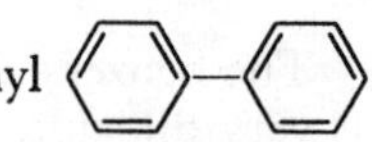

among others.

Monophenylmethane —CH$_3$ is more commonly known as toluene. It is very similar to benzene. Both are liquids at room temperature, although toluene has a higher boiling point and a lower melting point. They are mutually soluble in all proportions. Confusingly, the radical formed by the removal of the hydrogen from toluene is called the benzyl radical. Benzyl chloride is

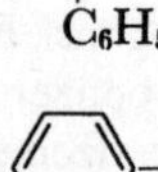

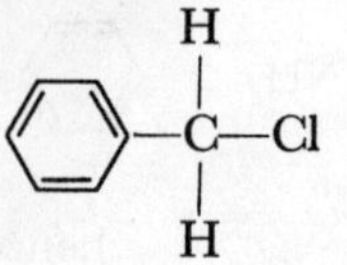

There are many compounds of commercial and biological importance which have two carbons common to two rings. This structure can continue through many rings. Each of these compounds may have several derivatives. The simplest of these is the two-ring compound naphthalene.

One common derivative of this is naphthol.

The three-ring compound is anthracene.

The build-up of rings is found in many biologically important systems.

Hydrocarbon derivatives

Hydrocarbon halides

A hydrocarbon halide is a hydrocarbon in which one or more hydrogens are replaced by a halogen. The IUPAC (International Union of Pure and Applied Chemistry) rule of nomenclature is to name the longest carbon chain and to treat the halogen as a substituent group. The *-ine* is dropped from the halogen name; then *-o* is added before the halogen is used in the name. Appropriate numbers are used to locate the halogen. For example, $CH_3CHBrCHBrCH_2C(CH_3)_2CH_2CH_3$ is 2,3-dibromo-5,5-dimethyl-heptane.

In the classical system of nomenclature, halide-substituted alkanes are treated as alkyl halides. Both IUPAC and classical names are encountered. CH_3I is methyl iodide in the classical system, iodomethane in the IUPAC system. The classical name for C_2H_5Br is ethyl bromide; the IUPAC name is bromoethane. The classical nomenclature becomes more difficult as the structures become more complex.

Multiple halide substitution is easily handled by IUPAC rules. For example, the two isomeric forms of C_2H_4Br are named

$$Br-\underset{\underset{H}{|}}{\overset{\overset{H}{|}}{C}}-\underset{\underset{H}{|}}{\overset{\overset{H}{|}}{C}}-Br \quad \text{1,2-dibromoethane}$$

$$H-C-C-Br \quad \text{1,1-dibromoethane}$$

with the structure showing:

H H on top, H and Br on bottom attached to the two carbons.

Trisubstituted methanes have common names composed of the halide name and the suffix *-form*. Trichloromethane, $CHCl_3$, more commonly is called chloroform. The common laboratory chemical, carbon tetrachloride, CCl_4, is tetrachloromethane in the IUPAC nomenclature. Due to its later commercial development, CF_4 is usually called tetrafluoromethane.

Alkyl halides can be prepared by the halogenation of an alkane with light of appropriate wave length or by addition of a hydrogen halide to an alkene (or alkyne). A good yield of alkyl halide is obtained from an alcohol and a hydrohalic acid in the presence of sulfuric acid. As in the case of the alkene addition, HI reacts more rapidly than HBr which in turn reacts more rapidly than HCl. The phosphorus halides may be used instead of the hydrohalic acid, in which case no sulfuric acid is needed.

The alkyl halides are quite reactive. Some type reactions include the following.

(a) Reaction with a base to form an alcohol

$$RX + OH^-(aq) \rightarrow ROH + X^-$$

(b) Reaction with sodium to form an alkane

$$2RX + 2Na \rightarrow R-R + 2NaX$$

If two alkyl halides are present, three alkanes can result

$$RX + 2Na + R'X \rightarrow \begin{Bmatrix} R-R \\ R'-R \\ R'-R' \end{Bmatrix} + 2NaX$$

(c) Reaction with ammonia to form amines

$$RX + 2NH_3 \xrightarrow[\text{pressure}]{\text{heat}} RNH_2 + NH_4X$$

Alcohols

Alcohols are characterized by the type formula, ROH, where R is an aliphatic radical. The OH group is not to be confused with a base. In the IUPAC system of nomenclature, the *e* is dropped from the alkane name and *-ol* is added to indicate the alcohol. Thus, C_2H_5OH is *ethanol*. In longer chain alcohols the location of the OH group is indicated by numbering the longest chain containing the carbon atom to which the OH group is attached. For example, $CH_3CHOHCH_3CH_3$ is 2-butanol. Other substituents are shown by the appropriate numbers.

$$CH_3CHBrC(CH_3)OHCH_3 \quad \text{2-methyl-3-bromo-2-butanol}$$

In the classical system of nomenclature the alkyl radical name is followed by the word *alcohol*. Thus, CH_3CH_2OH is ethyl alcohol.

It is necessary to distinguish between various types of alcohols in the classical system. The type is based upon the number of carbon atoms attached to the carbon with the OH group. The carbon to which the OH group is attached is at the end of a chain in a primary alcohol. If the alcohol carbon is attached to two other carbons, it is a secondary alcohol. If three carbons are attached to the alcohol carbon, it is a tertiary alcohol. This is shown diagrammatically.

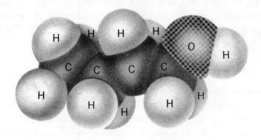

$$RCH_2OH \qquad\qquad R-\overset{\overset{\displaystyle R'}{|}}{C}HOH \qquad\qquad R-\overset{\overset{\displaystyle R'}{|}}{\underset{\underset{\displaystyle R''}{|}}{C}}OH$$

primary alcohol   secondary alcohol   tertiary alcohol

Alcohols are water soluble due to the presence of the OH group which introduces a polar character in the molecule. The long

Fig. 19.8

n-Butyl Alcohol (above) and tert-Butyl Alcohol (below)

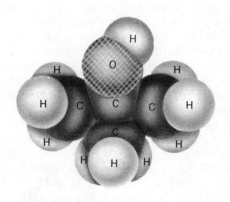

chain alcohols retain the alkane character of water insolubility. Methanol (CH_3OH) and ethanol (C_2H_5OH) have sufficient polar character to be water soluble in all proportions. Alcohols of less than twelve carbon atoms are liquids at room temperature. The others are solids.

Methanol is a by-product of the conversion of wood to charcoal. Consequently, it is known as wood alcohol. Most methanol is supplied by the catalytic combination of CO and H_2. Methanol is a very toxic substance. If consumed in substantial quantities, it can cause blindness. A large amount of methanol taken internally is lethal.

Ethanol (C_2H_5OH) is the best known of the alcohols. Usually the unmodified term *alcohol* refers to ethanol. Ethanol is the product of the fermentation of starch or sugar with yeast. Since the usual source of the starch for commercial alcohol is either the grains or molasses, ethanol is known as grain alcohol. Various alcoholic beverages have been prepared starting with many different sugars and starches. Each of these starting materials imparts an aroma and taste to the mixture.

Most of the alcohol used in the laboratory is 95% ethanol by volume. Water and alcohol form a constant boiling mixture at this concentration. A constant boiling mixture is characterized by a vapor of the same composition as the liquid. In order to break up this mixture, it is necessary to add a third component. In this case, benzene is added to obtain 100% absolute alcohol. Absolute alcohol is free from water but contains a trace of benzene which makes it quite toxic.

The U.S. Government levies a heavy tax on alcohol used as a beverage. Alcohol that has been denatured is free from tax. Denatured alcohol is prepared by adding methanol or some other toxic substance that cannot be easily separated from the ethanol. Usually some additional odor or color is added to warn potential users of the dangers. Some experiments require absolute or undenatured ethanol. Tax-free alcohol may be obtained if prescribed procedures of storage, dispensing, and record keeping are followed. The safest assumption in any chemical laboratory is that the alcohol is unfit for human consumption.

Ethanol is used in many chemical reactions. In addition, it finds widespread use as the solvent in tinctures, such as tincture of iodine. A 70% solution is widely used as a germicide. Rubbing alcohol may be 70% ethanol but is more likely to be a 2-propanol (isopropyl alcohol) solution. This alcohol, as well as the higher alcohols, is poisonous.

Some of the reactions of the alcohols include:

(a) Reaction of hydrohalic acid to form alkyl halides. (cf. hydrocarbon halides.)

(b) Reaction with active metals to produce the metal alkoxide

$$2ROH + 2M \rightarrow 2ROM + H_2$$
$$2CH_3OH + 2Na \rightarrow 2CH_3ONa + H_2$$

(sodium methoxide)

(c) Dehydration to form ethers

$$R\overline{OH} + H\overline{OR} \xrightarrow[\text{heat}]{H_2SO_4} ROR + H_2O$$

GLYCOLS AND GLYCEROL

Glycols contain an alcohol group on two carbon atoms. The simplest and most important glycol is ethylene glycol ($HOCH_2$-CH_2OH). Ethylene glycol is used as the base for permanent-type antifreeze. Due to the second OH group hydrogen bonding is increased, making the glycols rather viscous and high-boiling liquids.

Glycerol is an important three-carbon compound with an alcohol group on each carbon:

$$\begin{array}{ccc} H & H & H \\ HC\!\!-\!\!C\!\!-\!\!CH \\ O & O & O \\ H & H & H \end{array}$$

Glycerol, also known as glycerin, is a viscous, hydroscopic liquid, miscible with water in all proportions. Glycerol is obtained as a by-product of soap manufacturing.

Ethers

An *ether* is characterized by an oxygen linkage between two alkyl groups. Thus, the type formula is R—O—R', where R and R' may be the same or different alkyl radicals. The nomenclature for the ethers is very simple. The two alkyl radicals are named followed by the word *ether*. The most common ether is $C_2H_5OC_2H_5$ or diethyl ether. Diethyl ether is the one used as an anesthetic and is usually the one referred to when the non-chemist speaks of ether. Other examples of ethers include

$$C_2H_5\!\!-\!\!O\!\!-\!\!CH_3 \quad \text{methyl-ethyl-ether}$$

$$\begin{array}{cc} H_3C & CH_3 \\ | & | \\ HC\!\!-\!\!O\!\!-\!\!CH & \text{2-propyl-2-butyl-ether} \\ | & | \\ H_3C & CH_2 \\ & | \\ & CH_3 \end{array}$$

As indicated above, the most common method for the preparation of ethers is the dehydration of alcohols. A simple ether in which both radicals are the same is obviously prepared from the appropriate alcohol. The preparation of mixed ethers, where the two radicals are different, results in not only the mixed ether but the two simple ethers that come from the alcohols present, making it necessary to separate the three. The formation of the mixed ether may be favored by the use of appropriate reaction condi-

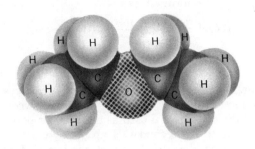

Fig. 19.9
Diethyl Ether

tions, but simple ether formation cannot be eliminated. In all ether synthesis reactions, there are other by-products, such as ethene and SO_2, which vary in amount as the reaction conditions are changed.

Ethers are somewhat less soluble in water than are alcohols. The alkane nature of the radicals becomes more apparent in the rather high solubility of ethers in hydrocarbon liquids. Diethyl ether is a liquid boiling at 35°C, substantially lower than ethyl alcohol. This reflects the fact that alcohols are capable of hydrogen bonding, while ethers are not.

Chemically, the ethers are much less reactive than the alcohols. When heated with hydriodic acid, the ether cleaves (breaks up) to form alcohols and alkyl iodides.

$$ROR' + HI \quad \begin{array}{c} \nearrow ROH + R'I \\ \\ \searrow R'OH + RI \end{array}$$

Aldehydes

Primary *al*cohols *dehy*drogenated by chemical processes yield *aldehydes*. The aldehyde group $\begin{array}{c} H \\ | \\ R{-}C{=}O \end{array}$ can appear only at the end of a carbon chain. Aldehydes are named by dropping the *-e* and adding *-al* to the alkane name for the longest carbon chain containing the -CHO group. The aldehyde carbon is always the number one carbon when naming substituted aldehydes. Common aldehyde names come from the traditional names for the corresponding acid, and the acid name is suffixed by *-aldehyde*. Substitution is shown by use of the letters of the Greek alphabet. The second carbon is the α position, the third is the β position, and so on. Some examples are given in Table 19.6.

Table 19.6

Common and IUPAC Names for Some Aldehydes

	IUPAC	Common
H | HC=O	methanal	formaldehyde
H H | | HC—C=O | H	ethanal	acetaldehyde

H₃C H H
  \ | |
    C—C=O
  /
H₃C
	2-methylpropanal	isobutyraldehyde

H H H H | | | | HC—C—C—C=O | | | H H Br	2-bromobutanal	α-bromo-butyraldehyde

Aldehydes are prepared by the oxidation of primary alcohols. A commonly used oxidizing agent is a dichromate–sulfuric acid solution. Care must be used to avoid continuation of oxidation to the formation of the acid. Usually it is possible to distill the aldehyde out of the mixture as fast as it is formed. Commercially, formaldehyde and acetaldehyde are prepared by passing methanol or ethanol vapor and air over heated copper gauze.

Aldehydes are somewhat polar molecules, and the short chain molecules are soluble in water as well as in alcohol and other organic solvents. Water solubility decreases rapidly as the chain length increases. Pentanal and higher aldehydes are only slightly soluble in water. Formaldehyde and acetaldehyde are gases at room temperature, the boiling point of acetaldehyde being 20°C.

Fig. 19.10

Acetaldehyde and Acetone

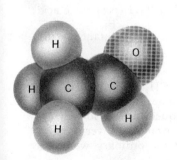 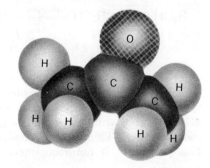

The higher aldehydes are liquids. Formaldehyde is commonly sold as a 37 to 40 per cent solution known as formalin.

Aldehydes are easily oxidized to acids. A common application of this oxidation is the formation of a silver mirror using Tollens' reagent. The reagent is prepared by adding NH_4OH to a $AgNO_3$ solution until the Ag_2O precipitate is dissolved. An aldehyde is oxidized to the acid, while the silver species is reduced to free silver. The silver adheres to a clean glass surface forming a mirror. A basic solution of a copper tartarate complex also is reduced to Cu_2O by an aldehyde.

Aldehydes are reduced to alcohols with sodium and moist ether or with sodium and ethyl alcohol. The presence of the aldehyde group makes the hydrogen on the α carbon more reactive.

Ketones

Ketones are very closely related to the aldehydes. The ketone

structure $R—\overset{\overset{\displaystyle O}{\|}}{C}—R'$ is found only within the carbon chain. The suffix *-one* is added to the alkane name of the longest carbon chain containing the ketone group. In the older nomenclature, the two alkyl radicals are named followed by the word *ketone*. Thus,

$$HC—C—C—C—CH$$

is 3-pentanone or diethyl ketone. Sub-stituted ketones are named as usual. $HC—C—C—CH$ is 3-chloro-2-butanone or α-chloro-ethyl-methyl-ketone.

The oxidation of ketones requires stronger oxidizing agents than those used for aldehyde oxidation. The products are the acids obtained by breaking the chain on either side of the ketone group. Thus, 3-hexanone yields three different acids.

$$CH_3CH_2\overset{\overset{\displaystyle O}{\|}}{C}CH_2CH_2CH_3 \xrightarrow{\text{oxidation}} \begin{cases} CH_3COOH \text{ (acetic acid)} \\ + \\ C_2H_5COOH \text{ (propanoic acid)} \\ + \\ C_3H_7COOH \text{ (butanoic acid)} \end{cases}$$

The most commonly used ketone is $CH_3\overset{\overset{\displaystyle O}{\|}}{C}CH_3$, propanone or dimethyl ketone, better known as acetone. Acetone is soluble in all proportions with water and is frequently used for drying a vessel rapidly. The acetone residue evaporates very rapidly. This procedure is not recommended for ordinary work since acetone is too costly to use needlessly, and it does leave a greasy film at times. Acetone also is used as a solvent for many organic materials not soluble in water.

Organic acids

The organic acid functional group is $R-C\diagarrow\begin{smallmatrix}O\\OH\end{smallmatrix}$. This is called a

carboxyl group which leads to the term, *carboxylic acids*. Most of the common acids have names that have developed through the years. The IUPAC system uses the suffix *-oic* on the appropriate alkane name followed by the word acid. The simplest acid is

$HC\diagarrow\begin{smallmatrix}O\\OH\end{smallmatrix}$, formic acid or methanoic acid. Formic acid derives its

name from the Latin word for ants, since it was obtained in the Middle Ages by the distillation of ants. When they bite, ants, bees, and several other insects inject a small amount of formic acid under the skin. The welt that appears is caused by the acid.

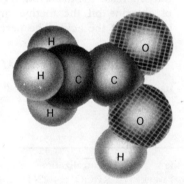

Fig. 19.11
Acetic Acid

The second member of the series is acetic acid (CH_3COOH) or more formally, ethanoic acid. Acetic acid is derived from the Latin for vinegar which is a dilute solution of acetic acid. Other organic acids, their IUPAC and common names, and their natural sources are given in Table 19.7.

The acids are obtained from natural sources or prepared by oxidation of appropriate alcohols. Formic acid may be prepared from CO and hot sodium hydroxide.

$$CO + NaOH \xrightarrow[\text{pressure}]{\text{heat}} HCOONa$$

The acid is recovered by adding HCl. Acetic acid may be prepared from acetylene, which combines with water in the presence

Table 19.7

Common Organic Acids

Formula	IUPAC name	Common name	Natural source
HCOOH	Methanoic	Formic	Ants
CH_3COOH	Ethanoic	Acetic	Vinegar
C_2H_5COOH	Propanoic	Propionic	————
C_3H_7COOH	Butanoic	Butyric	Rancid butter
$C_{15}H_{31}COOH$	Hexadecanoic	Steric	Palm oil
$C_{17}H_{35}COOH$	Octadecanoic	Palmitic	Tallow
$C_{17}H_{33}COOH$*	Octadecenoic	Oleic	Olive oil

*unsaturated

of $HgSO_4$ to form acetaldehyde. The acetaldehyde is air oxidized to acetic acid.

Organic acids undergo two major types of reactions indicated in Table 19.8. The unsubstituted hydrocarbon acids are weak acids, reacting with a hydroxide such as NaOH to produce salts which undergo hydrolysis. An active metal such as zinc liberates hydrogen from a solution of those acids which dissociate sufficiently. The addition of some substituent to the aliphatic chain may increase the dissociation of the acid. The successive addition of chlorine on the methyl group of acetic acid increases the strength of the acid. The percentage dissociation for this group of acids is

$1M$ CH_3COOH 0.54%, $1M$ $CH_2ClCOOH$ 3.7%,

$1M$ $CHCl_2COOH$ 21%, $1M$ CCl_3COOH 54%

Table 19.8

Type Reactions of Organic Acids

A. Properties of the H^+ ion (typical weak acid behavior)	(1) Neutralization $RCOOH + OH^- \rightarrow RCOO^- + H_2O$ $CH_3COOH + Na^+ + OH^- \rightarrow CH_3COO^- + Na^+ + H_2O$ acetic acid · · · · · · · · · · sodium acetate (2) Liberation of H_2 by active metal $2RCOOH + Zn \rightarrow 2RCOO^- + Zn^{++} + H_2\uparrow$
B. Properties of the (OH) group	(1) Esterification $RCOH + R'OH \rightarrow RCOOR' + H_2O$ acid · · · alcohol · · ester · · · · water $\qquad\qquad\qquad\qquad\qquad\overset{O}{\overset{\|}{}}$ $CH_3COOH + CH_3OH \rightarrow CH_3COCH_3 + H_2O$ acetic · · · · methyl · · · · methyl · · · water acid · · · · · · alcohol · · · · acetate

Esters. The -OH group of the organic acids reacts with alcohols to form an ester in a process called esterification. An ester is characterized by the $$R—\overset{\overset{\textstyle O}{\textstyle \|}}{C}—O—R'$$ linkage. Esterification reactions, unlike neutralization reactions, proceed slowly and have equilibrium constants of intermediate values. Another point of difference is that in the esterification reaction, the -OH group is lost by the acid, and an H comes from the alcohol to form the water. Esterification often is carried out in the presence of sulfuric acid for the catalytic effect of the hydrogen ion and the removal of water by the H_2SO_4.

Fats are esters of glycerol and long-chain aliphatic acids called fatty acids. In general, there are twelve or more carbon atoms in the fatty acid chain. When a fat reacts with NaOH (or KOH), glycerol and soap are formed. The reaction is called saponification.

$$
\begin{array}{l}
\text{H} \quad\quad \text{O} \\
| \quad\quad\; \| \\
\text{H—C—O—C—R} \\
| \\
\quad\quad\;\; \text{O} \\
\quad\quad\;\; \| \\
\text{H—C—O—C—R} \;+\; 3\text{OH}^- \;\rightarrow \\
| \\
\quad\quad\;\; \text{O} \\
\quad\quad\;\; \| \\
\text{H—C—O—C—R} \\
| \\
\text{H}
\end{array}
\qquad
\begin{array}{l}
\text{H} \\
| \\
\text{H—C—OH} \\
| \\
\text{H—C—OH} \;+\; 3\text{R—}\overset{\overset{\textstyle O}{\textstyle \|}}{\text{C}}\text{—ONa} \\
| \\
\text{H—C—OH} \\
| \\
\text{H}
\end{array}
$$

$$\text{fat} \qquad\qquad\qquad \text{glycerol} \qquad\qquad \text{soap}$$

R is a long carbon chain and varies from fat to fat. Solid animal fats and butter contain fats with R = $C_{15}H_{31}$, $C_{17}H_{35}$, and $C_{17}H_{33}$. ($C_{17}H_{33}$ has a single double bond.) Corn and cottonseed oils contain the same radicals plus $C_{17}H_{31}$, which has two double bonds. Olive and peanut oils consist primarily of R = $C_{17}H_{33}$, with some R = $C_{15}H_{31}$. If R is short or contains double bonds, the ester usually is a liquid and is termed an oil. By adding hydrogen (hydrogenation) to the double bond, the oil is solidified. Hydrogenated vegetable oils are used extensively as oleomargarine and shortening.

A *soap* is the sodium salt of a fatty acid formed in the saponification process. Commercial soaps do not contain the excess lye (NaOH) of the older homemade product. Rather, they may contain Na_2CO_3 or Na_3PO_4 as "soap builders." These additives increase the cleaning power by forming basic solutions upon hydrolysis. The base then saponifies the grease that is present.

When soap is placed in water, the -COO⁻ portion tends to dissolve in water, while the long hydrocarbon radical is insoluble. The soap forms a film around the dirt particles and holds them in suspension. The use of soap in hard water is limited by the insolubility of the calcium and magnesium salts of the fatty acids. Detergents have been developed to overcome the problem of a precipitate forming in hard water. A detergent has a sulfonate

$$\text{group } -\overset{\overset{\displaystyle O}{\|}}{\underset{\underset{\displaystyle O}{\|}}{S}}-O^- \text{ in place of the carboxyl group } -\overset{\overset{\displaystyle O}{\|}}{C}-O^- \text{ of a}$$

soap. The calcium and magnesium salts of the detergent are soluble. Most synthetic detergents contain additives to improve their cleaning power.

Amides, amines, amino acids

$$\text{The amide group is } \overset{\overset{\displaystyle O}{\|}}{\underset{}{R-C-NH}}\!\!\!\text{H} \text{ and is named by dropping the}$$

e from the alkane name and adding *-amide*. Thus

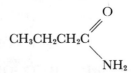

$$CH_3CH_2CH_2C\overset{\displaystyle O}{\underset{\displaystyle NH_2}{}}$$

is butanamide.

The amines are substituted ammonias. Thus, there may be one, two, or three radicals on the nitrogen corresponding to primary, secondary, and tertiary amines. The type formulas are

$$R-NH_2 \text{ for a primary amine, } \overset{R-NH}{\underset{R}{|}} \text{ for a secondary amine,}$$

$$\text{and } \overset{R}{\underset{R-N-R}{|}} \text{ for a tertiary amine.}$$

The common method of naming the amines is to follow the alkyl radical name by *-amine*. The prefix *amino-* is used in the IUPAC method along with a number to designate the location of the amine group. Some examples include

$$H_3C-NH_2 \qquad \text{methylamine (aminomethane)}$$

Fig. 19.12

Ethyl Amine. Compare this structure with that of ammonia (page 141).

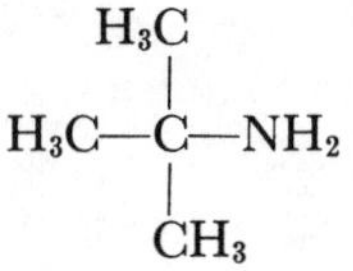

$$H_3C$$
$$|$$
$$H_3C—C—NH_2 \quad \text{2-amino-2-methylpropane}$$
$$|$$
$$CH_3$$

The lone-pair electrons of the amine nitrogen may enter into the formation of electron-pair bonds in a manner analogous to that of the OH⁻ in aqueous inorganic chemistry.

$$H:\overset{..}{\underset{..}{O}}:^- \quad + H^+ \rightarrow H:\overset{..}{\underset{..}{O}}:H$$

hydroxide ion   water

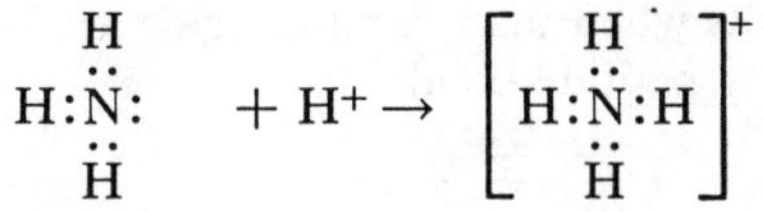

$$\overset{H}{\underset{H}{H:\overset{..}{N}:}} \quad + H^+ \rightarrow \left[\overset{H}{\underset{H}{H:\overset{..}{N}:H}} \right]^+$$

ammonia   ammonium ion

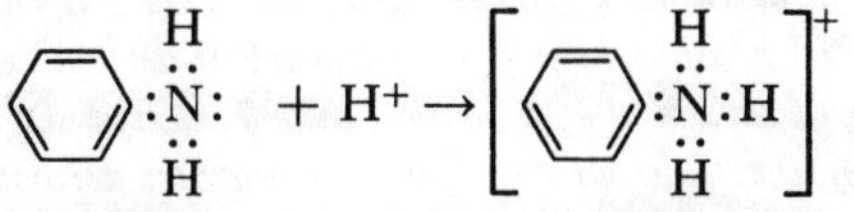

aniline   anilinium ion

In this respect, the amines are considered to be bases. Basic behavior is not limited to the reaction with H⁺ ions but may occur with any molecule or ion which can accept an electron pair (Chapter XX).

If the amino group and a carboxyl group occur in the same molecule, the result is an *amino acid,* some of which are considered in the next chapter. If the amino group is on the carbon next to the carboxyl (acid) group, it is an alpha amino acid,

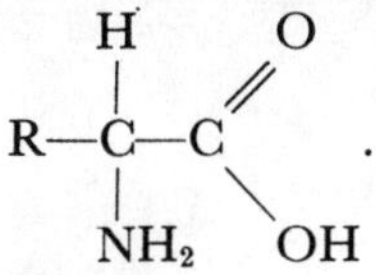

$$\overset{H}{\underset{NH_2}{R—C—}}\overset{O}{\underset{OH}{C}}$$

. A beta amino acid is one in which the amino group is on the second carbon from the acid group,

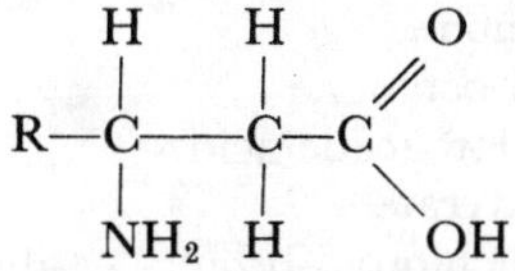

$$\overset{H}{\underset{NH_2}{R—C—}}\overset{H}{\underset{H}{C—}}\overset{O}{\underset{OH}{C}}$$

If the basic amine group of one amino acid reacts with the acidic carboxyl group of another amino acid, the amino acids

become bonded through a peptide linkage, $$—\overset{}{\underset{\|}{C}}—\overset{H}{\underset{}{N}}—.$$
$$\quad\quad\quad\quad\quad\quad\quad O$$

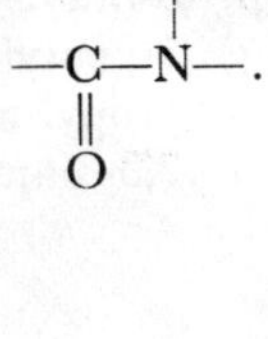

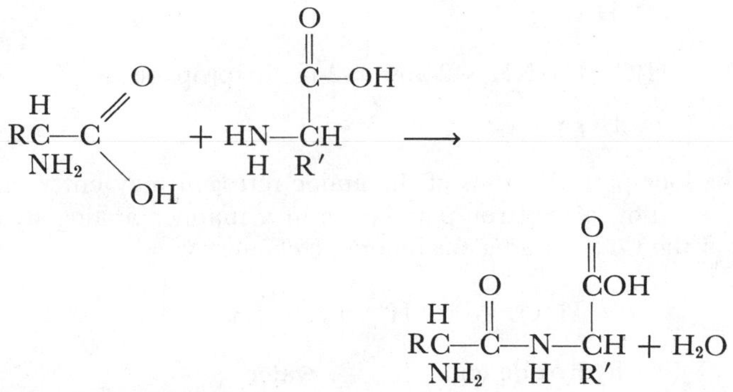

$$
\begin{array}{c}
\text{H} \quad\quad \text{O} \\
\text{RC—C} \overset{\displaystyle /\!\!/}{} \quad\quad\quad \text{O}=\!\!\overset{\displaystyle C—OH}{} \\
\text{NH}_2 \quad \diagdown \quad\quad + \text{HN—CH} \longrightarrow \\
\quad\quad\quad \text{OH} \quad\quad \text{H} \quad \text{R}'
\end{array}
$$

$$
\begin{array}{c}
\quad\quad \text{O} \quad\quad \text{COH} \\
\text{H} \;\|\quad\quad\| \\
\text{RC—C—N—CH} + \text{H}_2\text{O} \\
\text{NH}_2 \quad \text{H} \quad \text{R}'
\end{array}
$$

A protein results when many amino acids are linked together in one molecule by peptide bonds.

SIGNIFICANT TERMS AND CONCEPTS IN CHAPTER XIX:

Hydrocarbon, functional groups, aliphatic, IUPAC rules of nomenclature for the hydrocarbons and hydrocarbon derivatives, root words and number of carbon atoms, alkane, alkene, alkyne, isomer, chemical properties of the hydrocarbons and hydrocarbon derivatives, benzene structure and properties, type formulas, halides, alcohols, glycol, glycerol, ether, aldehyde, ketone, acid, ester, fats, saponification, soap, detergent, amine, basic character of the amines, amino acids.

Review questions

19.1. Write the structural formulas for the five isomers of the alkane with the formula C_6H_{14}. Name each.

19.2. Write structural formulas for the following.
  (a) 2-methyl-4-ethyl-hexane
  (b) 4-ethyl-6-methyl-nonane
  (c) 3,3,4-trimethyl-heptane
  (d) 3-chloro-4-methyl-2-pentene
  (e) 1,3-dipentyl-ether
  (f) octanal
  (g) 3-methyl-3-bromo-hexanal
  (h) 2-pentanone
  (i) 1-iodo-4-octanone
  (j) monochloroacetic acid
  (k) ethyl butyrate
  (l) *cis*-6,6-dichloro-5-bromo-3,4-dimethyl-3-octene
  (m) 3-propyl-1-heptyne
  (n) 1,3-dichloro-1,4-hexadiene
  (o) 2-methyl-2-pentanol
  (p) 6-butyl-4-decanol
  (q) 1-pentyl-3-hexyl-ether
  (r) propyl formate
  (s) 2,3-diamino-butane

(t) methyl-ethyl-amine
(u) 2-methyl-pentanamide
(v) 3-benzyl-2-phenyl-pentane

19.3. Name the following.
(a) $CH_3(CH_2)_4CH_3$

(b) $CH_3CH_2CCH_3$

(c) $CH_3CH_2CHClCH_2CH_2Cl$

(d) $CH_3CHCH_2CH_2CHO$
    |
    CH_3

(e) $CH_3CH_2OCH_2CH_2CH_3$

(f) $CH_3COOCH_2CH_2CH_2CH_3$

19.4. Give structural formulas for the following.
(a) 1,3,5-trinitrobenzene   (d) propyl-benzene
(b) 1-bromo-2-nitrobenzene   (e) ethyl benzoate
(c) 2,4-cyano-toluene

19.5. Write equations for the following.
(a) Combustion of pentane
(b) Chlorine and ethane irradiated with light
(c) Bromine + 3-heptene
(d) HI + 3-hexene
(e) 1-chloro-propane + NaOH
(f) 2-bromo-butane + sodium
(g) Chlorine + benzene
(h) Propanoic acid + butanol

(i)

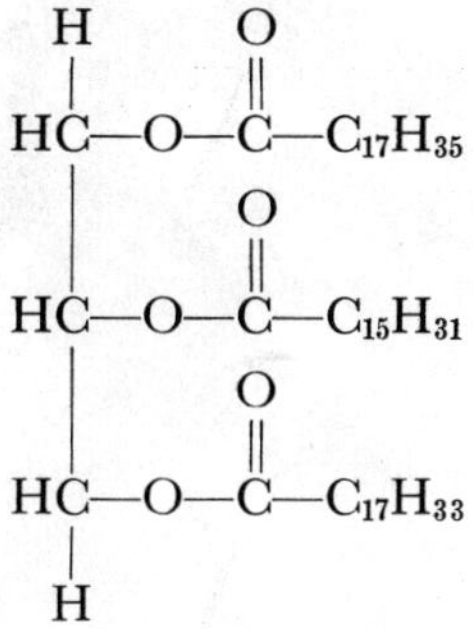

$$\begin{array}{c} H \quad\quad O \\ | \quad\quad || \\ HC\!-\!O\!-\!C\!-\!C_{17}H_{35} \\ | \quad\quad O \\ | \quad\quad || \\ HC\!-\!O\!-\!C\!-\!C_{15}H_{31} \quad + \text{ sodium hydroxide} \\ | \quad\quad O \\ | \quad\quad || \\ HC\!-\!O\!-\!C\!-\!C_{17}H_{33} \\ | \\ H \end{array}$$

twenty

biochemistry

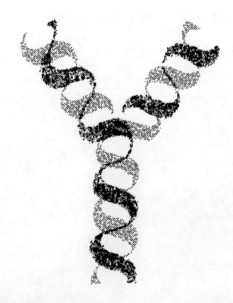

Approximately 4000 kilocalories are liberated as heat when one gram of sugar (sucrose) is burned to produce CO_2 and H_2O. Outside a living organism, the burning process proceeds at temperatures that are fatal to the organism. Yet many grams of sugar are burned·(oxidized) in a living animal each day at a carefully controlled rate so that the energy is made available as needed for work and maintenance of body temperature. The following introduction to the chemistry of biological systems is concerned chiefly with the process of conversion of foodstuffs into energy and other useful products of oxidation. The body synthesizes the proteins, carbohydrates, lipids, and other constituents of the body from many of these oxidation products. The energy required for synthesis is supplied by the oxidation process. The major classes of foodstuffs involved in the oxidation processes are the carbohydrates and lipids. Enzymes, vitamins, and certain other compounds play important roles in the conversion processes.

The complexity of biological systems makes the study of the whole system difficult until the behavior of the many interacting parts is known. The fundamental processes within a living organism are rather simple. The complexities arise from the interaction of the parts. For example, many of the molecules encountered are large and complex structures. Frequently, only a portion of such a molecule is directly involved in a given reaction. Therefore, functional group representations are used to describe the reactions. In other situations, it is convenient to use letters to represent the various groupings. The goal of this chapter is to present the underlying principles without becoming overly involved in structural details.

Biochemical materials

Carbohydrates

The term, *carbohydrate*, and its synonym, *saccharide*, refer to a group of aldehydes or ketones which have hydroxy (OH) groups on the other carbon atoms in the chain and to compounds which yield these products when hydrolyzed. Carbohydrates are classified according to the number of simple units obtained upon hydrolysis. A *monosaccharide* is a carbohydrate which does not undergo hydrolysis. A *disaccharide* is one that produces two molecules of monosaccharide upon hydrolysis. A *polysaccharide* is one that yields more than two molecules of one or more monosaccharides upon hydrolysis.

The three-dimensional structural details have a pronounced effect upon the biological processes. Many reactions within an organism are very specific for a certain structure. In writing the chemical formulas it is often useful to number the carbon atoms and to speak of reactions involving a given carbon atom. The aldehyde carbon or the carbon at the end of the chain nearest the ketone structure is the number one carbon.

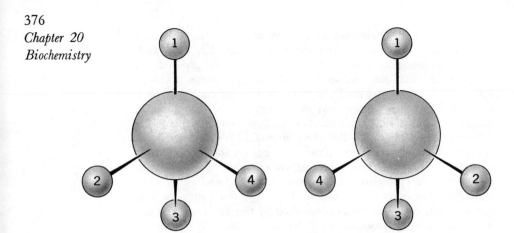

Fig. 20.1

Asymmetric Carbon Atom. Structure (b) cannot be superimposed on structure (a). They are mirror images of each other.

Optical isomers are of great structural importance. Optical isomers not only have the same molecular composition and weight but have the same ordering of functional groups on the carbon chain. Optical isomers arise from the presence of asymmetric carbon atoms in the chain. An asymmetric carbon atom is one which has four different groups attached to it. It is possible to arrange these four groups about the carbon atom in two forms that cannot be superimposed no matter how the structures are rotated. These mirror-image forms are called optical isomers.

One property of optical isomers is the rotation of the plane of polarized light. Polarized light vibrates only in one plane, while ordinary light vibrates in all planes perpendicular to its travel path. If the polarized light is rotated clockwise when it passes through a solution of an optical isomer, the isomer is said to be the *dextro*-form. If the rotation is counterclockwise, the isomer is said to be the *levo*-form. These are indicated by a (+) before the name of the sugar to indicate the *dextro*-form and a (−) for the *levo*-form.

The prefixes D- and L- refer to the arrangement of groups on the asymmetric carbon atom farthest from the aldehyde or ketone group. For the sugars, this is the next to the last carbon atom in the chain. The prefixes refer to the arrangement as compared to the two isomers of glyceraldehyde. Conventionally, the OH group on the middle carbon is written on the right-hand side of the chain to represent the D-form and on the left-hand side to represent the L-form. This same convention is used to show the relationship of the structure of other optical isomers to these two forms of glyceraldehyde. The terms D- and L- have no relationship to the direction of rotation of polarized light by the isomer.

The monosaccharides and disaccharides are often called sugars, the names of which are characterized by an -*ose* ending. Sucrose, which is cane or beet sugar, is a disaccharide which hydrolyzes to the two monosaccharides, glucose and fructose. Glucose is an aldehyde with several hydroxy (OH) groups on the carbon chain (i.e., it is a polyhydroxy-aldehyde), while fructose is a polyhydroxy-ketone.

$$
\begin{array}{cc}
\text{H---}^1\text{C}\!=\!\text{O} & \text{H---}^1\text{C---OH} \\
\text{H---}^2\text{C---OH} & ^2\text{C}\!=\!\text{O} \\
\text{HO---}^3\text{C---H} & \text{HO---}^3\text{C---H} \\
\text{H---}^4\text{C---OH} & \text{H---}^4\text{C---OH} \\
\text{H---}^5\text{C---OH} & \text{H---}^5\text{C---OH} \\
\text{H---}^6\text{C---OH} & \text{H---}^6\text{C---OH} \\
\text{H} & \text{H} \\
\text{D-glucose} & \text{D-fructose}
\end{array}
$$

The linear projection structures introduced by Emil Fischer may be converted to the ring structures proposed by W. H. Haworth

Fig. 20.2

Optical Isomers of Glyceraldehyde. L-glyceraldehyde is the mirror image of D-glyceraldehyde. The usual representation of the L-form is obtained from the mirrored form by rotating the –CH₂OH group 60° and the –CHO group 120°.

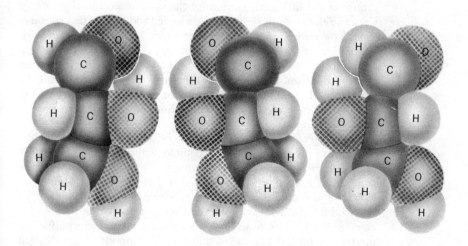

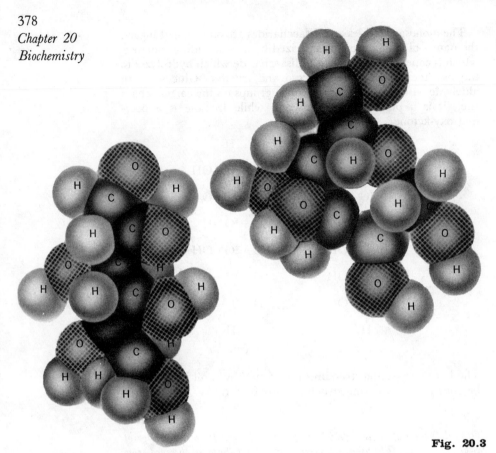

Fig. 20.3

Left: D-glucose, linear representation. Right: D-glucose, cyclic representation.

by an interaction of the aldehyde or ketone group with the OH group on the fifth carbon atom of the same molecule (Fig. 20.4). Certain relationships between the Fischer and Haworth structures should be noted. The Haworth structure is always written with the oxygen at the top or back of the ring. The aldehyde or ketone carbon is written on the right side of the ring. Thus, in the process of changing from the linear to cyclic structures the groups on the right side of the Fischer structure are represented as projecting below the plane of the ring, while those on the left side appear above the ring.

The projection of the OH group on the number one carbon atom plays an important role in biological processes. If the OH group of the D-form projects below the plane of the ring, the compound is said to be in the α-form. If it projects above the ring, the molecule is in the β-form. The α and β terminology is reversed for the L-forms. When either pure α- or pure β-D-glucose is dissolved in water, there soon develops an equilibrium mixture of both cyclic forms and a small amount of the straight chain species.

There are many optical isomers of a molecule like glucose because of the many possible structural arrangements. The rules for writing the structures of each form must be followed to maintain consistency, but it should be remembered that each form is a representation of the spatial arrangement of the atoms.

The sucrose molecule is formed by the linkage of an α-D-glucose molecule and a β-D-fructose molecule with the elimination of a water molecule (Fig. 20.5). The C-O-C linkage between the glucose and fructose units is broken easily. Thus hydrolysis takes place readily in dilute acid or by enzymatic action.

Starch, glycogen, and cellulose are other examples of the polysaccharides. Starch which is found in many plant materials constitutes a large portion of the carbohydrate intake in most diets. The starch molecule is a complex structure consisting of two components. One component consists of long chains of α-D-glucose units, while the other is a highly branched structure of α-D-glucose units. Glucose is the product when starch is

Fig. 20.4

Cyclic Forms of Glucose and Fructose

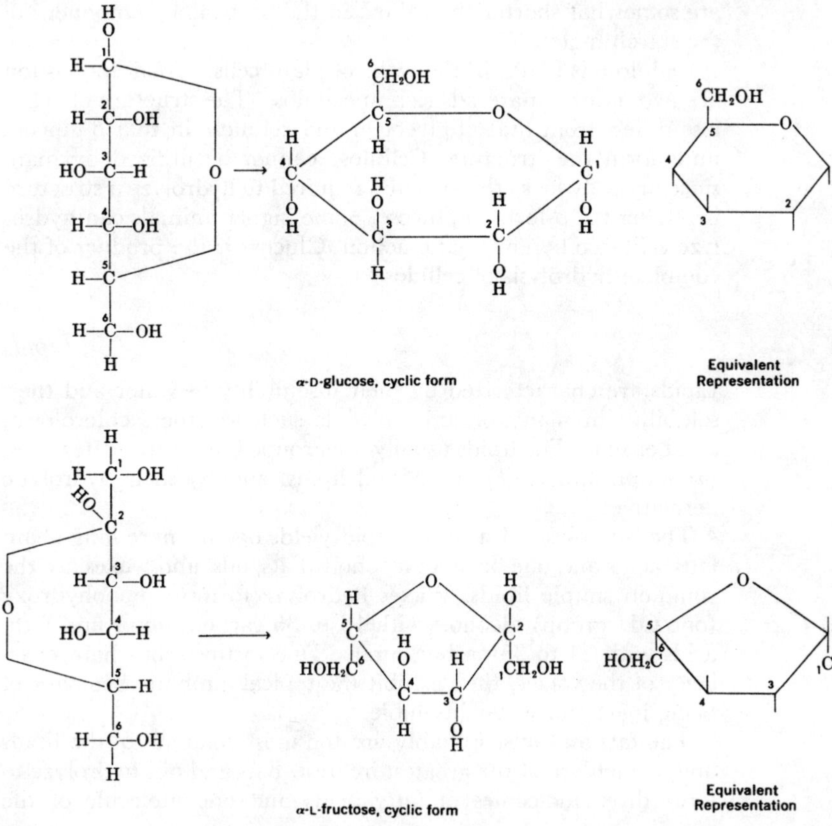

α-D-glucose, cyclic form

Equivalent Representation

α-L-fructose, cyclic form

Equivalent Representation

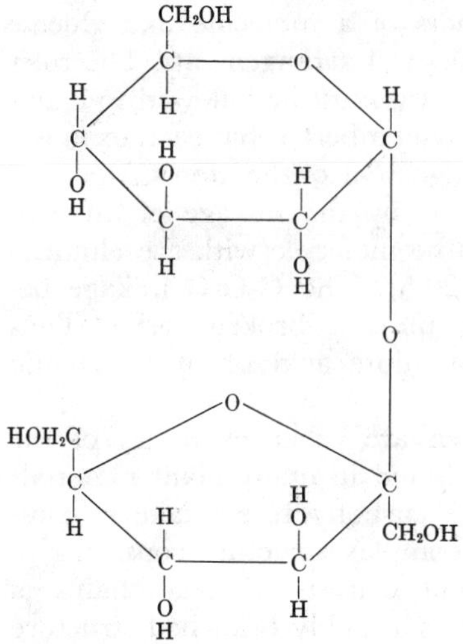

Fig. 20.5

The Sucrose Molecule

hydrolyzed completely. The general formula for starch is $(C_6H_{10}O_5)_n$.

The human body stores glucose in the form of glycogen. It is a highly branched structure of α-D-glucose units. The branches are somewhat shorter than those in the branching component of the starch molecule.

Cellulose is found in the walls of plant cells. Wood and cotton are two natural materials rich in cellulose. The structure of cellulose differs from that of glycogen and cellulose in that β-glucose units form the structure. Cellulose cannot be utilized by man, since his body lacks the enzymes required to hydrolyze a structure involving the β-form of glucose. Some higher animals can hydrolyze cellulose by enzymatic action. Glucose is the product of the complete hydrolysis of cellulose.

Lipids

Lipids are characterized by their insolubility in water and their solubility in many organic solvents such as ether, chloroform, and benzene. The lipids usually are grouped into three categories, (*a*) simple lipids, (*b*) compound lipids, and (*c*) their hydrolytic derivatives.

The hydrolysis of a simple lipid yields one or more long-chain fatty acids and one or more alcohols. Fats, oils, and waxes are the common simple lipids. Waxes hydrolyze to form monohydroxy (one OH group) alcohols with 16 to 36 carbon atoms and fatty acids with 24 to 36 carbon atoms. Due to this long-chain character of the waxes, they exhibit the typical aliphatic behavior of being inert and water insoluble.

The fats and oils probably are the most common of the lipids and as such are of the greatest interest. Fats and oils hydrolyze to form three molecules of fatty acids and one molecule of the trihydroxy alcohol, glycerol (page 361). The major distinguishing characteristic between fats and oils is the arbitrary assignment of the term *oil* to those simple lipids that are liquids at 20°C; the term *fat* is applied to those that are solids at this temperature.

The body stores foodstuffs not needed for immediate energy requirements in the form of fat or, to a very limited extent, as glycogen. The body synthesizes fats for storage from the products of glucose oxidation. Dietary fats are converted to the appropriate storage form by the body. The fats and glycogen are then readily available to the cells to meet the demands for energy.

The widely distributed phospholipids (or phosphatides) are examples of compound lipids. These compounds contain phosphate and in most cases glycerol, two fatty acids, and a nitrogenous base which is similar in behavior to the amines. The phospholipids probably are present in all plant and animal tissue; an especially high concentration occurs in brain tissues and cell membranes.

It is not possible to saponify the steroids, some of the vitamins, and some of the hormones, although these are classed as lipids. These substances exist in the body tissues in free (hydrolyzed) form as well as in the form of esters.

Proteins

Proteins are high molecular weight molecules which yield amino acids upon hydrolysis. The naturally occurring proteins consist of

$$\alpha\text{-amino acid} \left[\begin{array}{c} H \quad\quad O \\ | \quad\quad\quad \nearrow\!\!\!/ \\ R\!-\!C\!-\!C \\ | \quad\quad \backslash \\ NH_2 \quad OH \end{array} \right] \text{residues held together by a}$$

peptide linkage (p. 371).

Only 25 amino acids have been found in natural proteins. Twenty of the most common amino acids are listed in Table 20.1. These 25 building blocks are present in varying numbers and combinations in a large variety of proteins of all types.

The simplest of the amino acids is glycine, in which the R-group of the general amino acid formula is a hydrogen. Since there is no asymmetric carbon in glycine, no optical isomers are possible. D- and L-optical isomers are possible for the other amino acids. Laboratory synthesis of the amino acids results in a mixture of D- and L-forms. However, the biological catalysts in nature are specific for the formation of the L-amino acids.

The protein molecule does not consist only of straight chain linkages of the amino acids. Branching may occur along the chain. Some of the branches form peptide linkages with other chains. The breakage of these cross linkages is called *denaturation*. It occurs when the protein is exposed to various chemicals such as acids, bases, and various organic solvents, or is subjected to physical stresses such as high temperatures, high energy radiation,

Table 20.1

*Some of the Amino Acids Commonly Found
as Constituents of Proteins*

Name	Formula	Symbol
Glycine	NH_2-CH_2-COOH	gly
L-alanine	$CH_3-\overset{\displaystyle NH_2}{\underset{\displaystyle |}{CH}}-COOH$	ala
L-valine	$CH_3-\underset{\displaystyle \underset{\displaystyle CH_3}{|}}{CH}-\overset{\displaystyle NH_2}{\underset{\displaystyle |}{CH}}-COOH$	val
L-leucine	$CH_3-\underset{\displaystyle \underset{\displaystyle CH_3}{|}}{CH}-CH_2-\overset{\displaystyle NH_2}{\underset{\displaystyle |}{CH}}-COOH$	leu
L-isoleucine	$CH_3-CH_2-\underset{\displaystyle \underset{\displaystyle CH_3}{|}}{CH}-\overset{\displaystyle NH_2}{\underset{\displaystyle |}{CH}}-COOH$	ile
L-serine	$HO-CH_3-\overset{\displaystyle NH_2}{\underset{\displaystyle |}{CH}}-COOH$	ser
L-threonine	$CH_3-\underset{\displaystyle \underset{\displaystyle OH}{|}}{CH}-\overset{\displaystyle NH_2}{\underset{\displaystyle |}{CH}}-COOH$	thr
L-cysteine	$HS-CH_2-\overset{\displaystyle NH_2}{\underset{\displaystyle |}{CH}}-COOH$	CySH
L-cystine	$HOOC-\overset{\displaystyle NH_2}{\underset{\displaystyle |}{CH}}-CH_2-S-S-CH_2-\overset{\displaystyle NH_2}{\underset{\displaystyle |}{CH}}-COOH$	CyS-SCy

(*Note the dimeric character of L-cystine as compared to L-cysteine.*)

Name	Formula	Symbol
L-methionine	$CH_3-S-CH_2-CH_2-\overset{\displaystyle NH_2}{\underset{\displaystyle |}{CH}}-COOH$	met
L-glutamic acid	$HOOC-CH_2-CH_2-\overset{\displaystyle NH_2}{\underset{\displaystyle |}{CH}}-COOH$	glu
L-aspartic acid	$HOOC-CH_2-\overset{\displaystyle NH_2}{\underset{\displaystyle |}{CH}}-COOH$	asp

Name	Formula	Symbol
L-lysine	$NH_2-CH_2-CH_2-CH_2-CH_2-\overset{\displaystyle NH_2}{\underset{\displaystyle \vert}{C}}H-COOH$	lys
L-arginine	$HN=\overset{\displaystyle NH_2}{\underset{\displaystyle \vert}{C}}-NH-CH_2-CH_2-CH_2-\overset{\displaystyle NH_2}{\underset{\displaystyle \vert}{C}}H-COOH$	arg
L-histidine	$HC=\overset{\displaystyle}{C}-CH_2-\overset{\displaystyle NH_2}{\underset{\displaystyle \vert}{C}}H-COOH$ (imidazole ring with N, NH, C, H)	—
L-phenylalanine	(benzene ring)$-CH_2-\overset{\displaystyle NH_2}{\underset{\displaystyle \vert}{C}}H-COOH$	phe
L-tyrosine	$HO-$(benzene ring)$-CH_2-\overset{\displaystyle NH_2}{\underset{\displaystyle \vert}{C}}H-COOH$	tyr
L-tryptophan	(indole ring)$-C-CH_2-\overset{\displaystyle NH_2}{\underset{\displaystyle \vert}{C}}H-COOH$	trp
L-proline*	(pyrrolidine ring) $CH-COOH$	pro
L-hydroxyproline*	(hydroxy-pyrrolidine ring) $CH-COOH$	—

*The prolines are not true α-amino acids but closely related compounds and are included for that reason.

or high pressure. The hydrolysis products of a denatured protein differ from those of the undenatured protein.

Enzymes, vitamins, and hormones

Enzymes are the catalysts of chemical reactions in the living cell. They are proteins synthesized within the cell itself. Some enzymes are highly specific, catalyzing only one reaction in the organism. Others catalyze reactions involving a specific functional group, such as the hydrolysis of phosphate esters. The large number of known enzymes is indicative of the large number of chemical reactions which take place in living organisms.

Some enzymatically controlled reactions require the participation of another substance, a coenzyme. A *coenzyme* is a small organic molecule which readily dissociates from the enzyme during the course of the reaction. Vitamins are a part of the coenzyme structures. Unlike enzymes, vitamins are not synthesized in the human body but must be obtained from the diet. The body does not store large amounts of most vitamins. Thus, it is necessary to have a constant supply in the diet to maintain enzyme activity.

Certain metal ions are necessary in trace quantities for good nutrition. Their function is similar to that of the vitamins in that some metal ions activate some enzymes and some are components of enzymes or coenzymes. Other metal ions such as Na^+ and Ca^{++} are required in much larger quantities for proper body functioning.

Hormones, unlike vitamins and enzymes, are produced by various glands within the body. The hormones are carried from the glands to the cells by the bloodstream and by the lymph system. The precise mechanism of hormone activity in the body is not fully understood. The hormones appear to be regulators and coordinators of body activity.

ATP and ADP

Energy is required constantly by the body to maintain body temperature and to do work. When a mole of glucose reacts directly with oxygen to form CO_2 and H_2O, about 673 kilocalories are produced. If this energy were to be released suddenly, the temperature of the cell would rise to the point where it would be destroyed. The body utilizes glucose not in a single step but in a series of reactions. This permits the storage of energy in a chemical bond while a modest amount is released to meet the cell's immediate requirements. The same total energy is available as a result of these intermediate reactions as in the single step of combustion. The energy released during the oxidation of foodstuffs is used to form phosphate bonds. This trapped energy is utilized directly in the synthesis reactions of the cells. The most commonly used of the phosphate bonds is that in adenosine triphosphate (ATP).

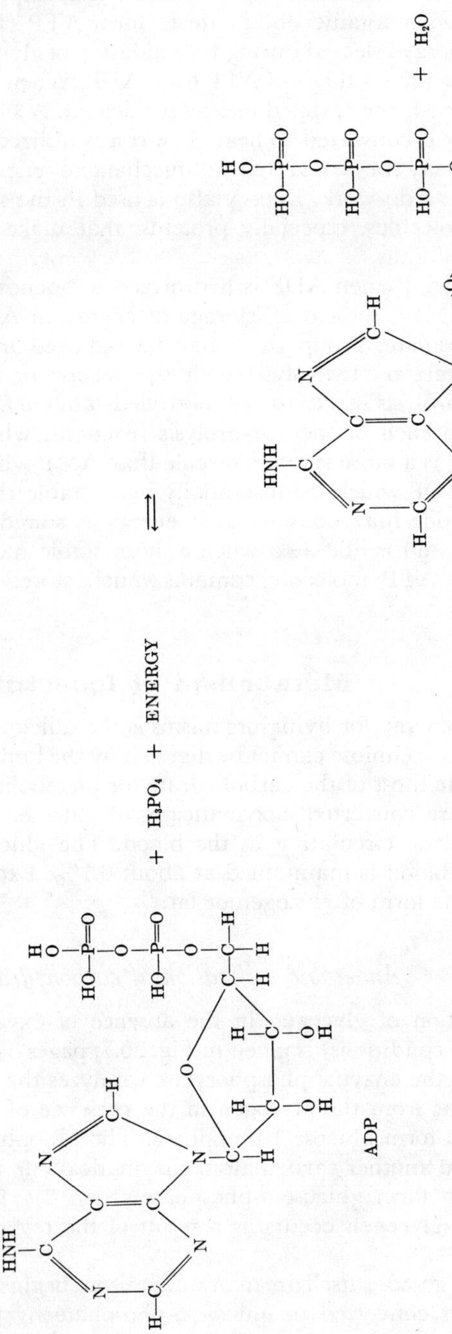

Fig. 20.6
The Formation of ATP from ADP

In the course of the utilization of glucose, adenosine diphosphate (ADP) takes on inorganic phosphate to form ATP (Fig. 20.6). Much of the energy released during the oxidation of glucose in the body is used for the synthesis of ATP from ADP. When the reaction is later reversed, the trapped energy is released. A small portion of this energy is converted to heat. The rest is utilized in other ways. Some may be converted to mechanical energy, enabling the muscles to do work. Energy also is used in the synthesis of complex molecules, especially proteins, that make up the body tissues and organs.

Energy is also released when ADP is hydrolyzed to adenosine (mono)phosphate (AMP), indicating storage of energy in ADP bonds. The last phosphate group then may be removed from the adenosine molecule by hydrolysis with the release of less energy. All of the hydrolysis reactions are controlled catalytically. Energy is released in each of these hydrolysis reactions, which means that adenosine is a more stable molecule than AMP which is more stable than ADP which is substantially more stable than ATP. Alternatively, one may consider that energy is stored in the phosphate bonds and is liberated when a more stable molecule is formed. The ATP molecule contains much stored or trapped energy.

Metabolism of foodstuffs

The major source of energy for living organisms is the utilization of carbohydrates. Since cellulose cannot be digested by the human body, starches provide most of the carbohydrate for metabolism. The carbohydrates are converted enzymatically to glucose, the primary monosaccharide circulating in the blood. The glucose concentration in the blood is maintained at about 0.1%. Excess glucose is stored in the form of glycogen or fat.

Anaerobic utilization of carbohydrates

The stepwise utilization of glycogen in the absence of oxygen (i.e., under anaerobic conditions) is given in Fig. 20.7, pages 388–389. In the first step, the enzyme phosphorylase catalyzes the removal of glucose units from the glycogen in the presence of inorganic phosphate to form glucose-1-phosphate. The phosphate group is transferred to another carbon atom enzymatically in the presence of Mg^{++} to form glucose-6-phosphate (Step 2). The storage of glucose as glycogen occurs as a result of the reversal of Steps 1 and 2.

The utilization of glucose itself in many organisms begins at this point. Glucose is converted to glucose-6-phosphate by the enzymatic transfer of phosphate from ATP.

$$\text{glucose} + \text{ATP} \rightleftarrows \text{glucose-6-phosphate} + \text{ADP}$$

An estimated 5000 calories are liberated by this reaction, since the phosphate bonds in glucose-6-phosphate and ADP are substantially more stable than those in ATP and glucose.

Glucose-6-phosphate is converted to its isomer, fructose-6-phosphate, in Step 3 by a reaction specific enzyme. Another enzyme then catalyzes the transfer of a second phosphate group from ATP to form fructose-1-6-diphosphate. Again the relative bond strengths are such that energy is released in this reaction (Step 4).

In Step 5 the fructose-1-6-diphosphate is split enzymatically into two three-carbon sugars, dihydroxyacetone phosphate and glyceraldehyde-3-phosphate. These two isomeric molecules exist in equilibrium; the dihydroxyacetone phosphate form is substantially favored. However, glyceraldehyde-3-phosphate is the form utilized in Step 6. The acetone form is then converted to the aldehyde form due to the shift in equilibrium brought about by the utilization of glyceraldehyde-3-phosphate.

Inorganic phosphate is introduced into the molecule as glyceraldehyde-3-phosphate is converted to an acid in Step 6. In addition to the enzyme, a coenzyme, nicotinamide-adenine-dinucleotide (NAD^+), must be present for this reaction to occur. NAD^+ is a coenzyme for redox reactions and is itself oxidized and reduced.

As glyceraldehyde-3-phosphate is converted enzymatically to 1-3-diphosphoglyceric acid in Step 6, energy is released. Some of the energy is used in the formation of the second phosphate bond. When this phosphate group is transferred to the ADP molecule to form ATP in Step 7, some of the energy trapped in the 1-3-diphosphoglyceric acid is transferred to the ATP molecule. Thus, some of the energy released by the oxidation of the three-carbon aldehyde in Step 6 is trapped in the ATP molecule where it is available for use in synthesis reactions or for muscular activity.

In Step 8 there is a redistribution of the energy in the molecule, making the phosphate bond a high energy bond (i.e., energy is trapped in it) in the phosphoenolpyruvic acid. This phosphate and much of its trapped energy is transferred to an ADP molecule in Step 9 to form ATP and pyruvic acid. Again, energy is trapped in the ATP molecule for other uses. The fate of pyruvic acid is dependent upon whether degradation is carried out in the cells of a higher animal or in the fermentation process by yeast cells.

The pyruvic acid is converted by the enzymes present in the fermentation broth to acetaldehyde and carbon dioxide in Step 10. In the last step (Step 11), the enzyme, alcohol dehydrogenase, converts the aldehyde to alcohol in the presence of NADH. This step results in the regeneration of NAD^+ which was used in Step 6.

When a muscle contracts under anaerobic conditions, lactic acid is produced and accumulates until the muscle is fatigued. Thus, lactic acid is the terminal product of the utilization of carbohydrates in higher animals under anaerobic conditions. The lactic acid can be converted further under aerobic conditions (the Krebs cycle, pages 392–393).

388

$(C_6H_{12}O_6)_n$ $n = 12$ to 18
(glycogen)   Step 1

$+ H_3PO_4$
($+$ phosphorylase)

glucose-1-phosphate   Step 2

Mg^{2+}
(enzymatic)

$\rightleftharpoons$ Glucose $+$ ATP

glucose-6-phosphate   Step 3

(enzymatic)

fructose-6-phosphate

Step 4

Mg^{2+}
(enzymatic)
$+$ ATP

Step 5

(enzymatic)

fructose-1-6-diphosphate

$+$ ADP

glyceraldehyde-3-phosphate

dihydroxyacetone phosphate

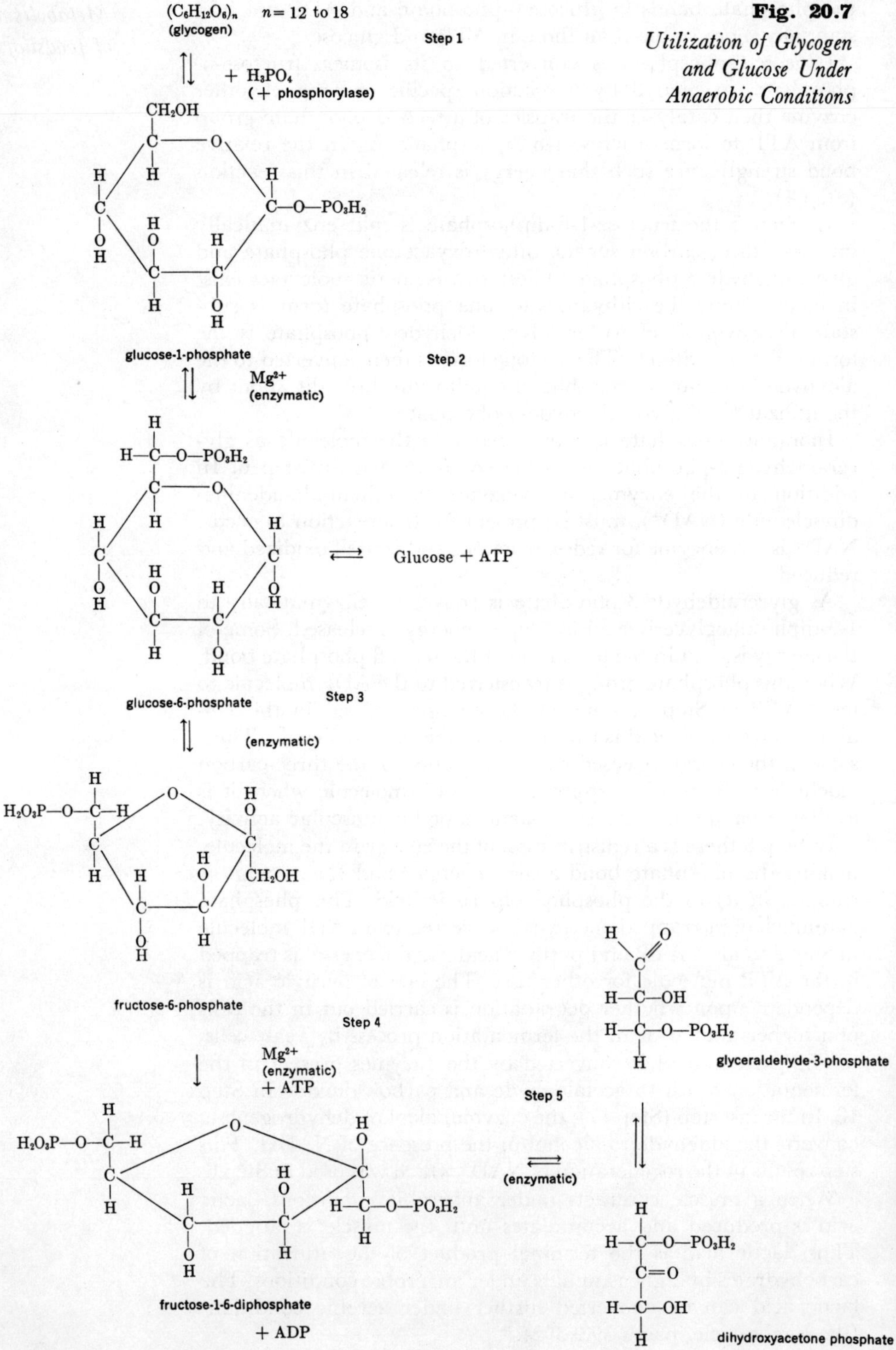

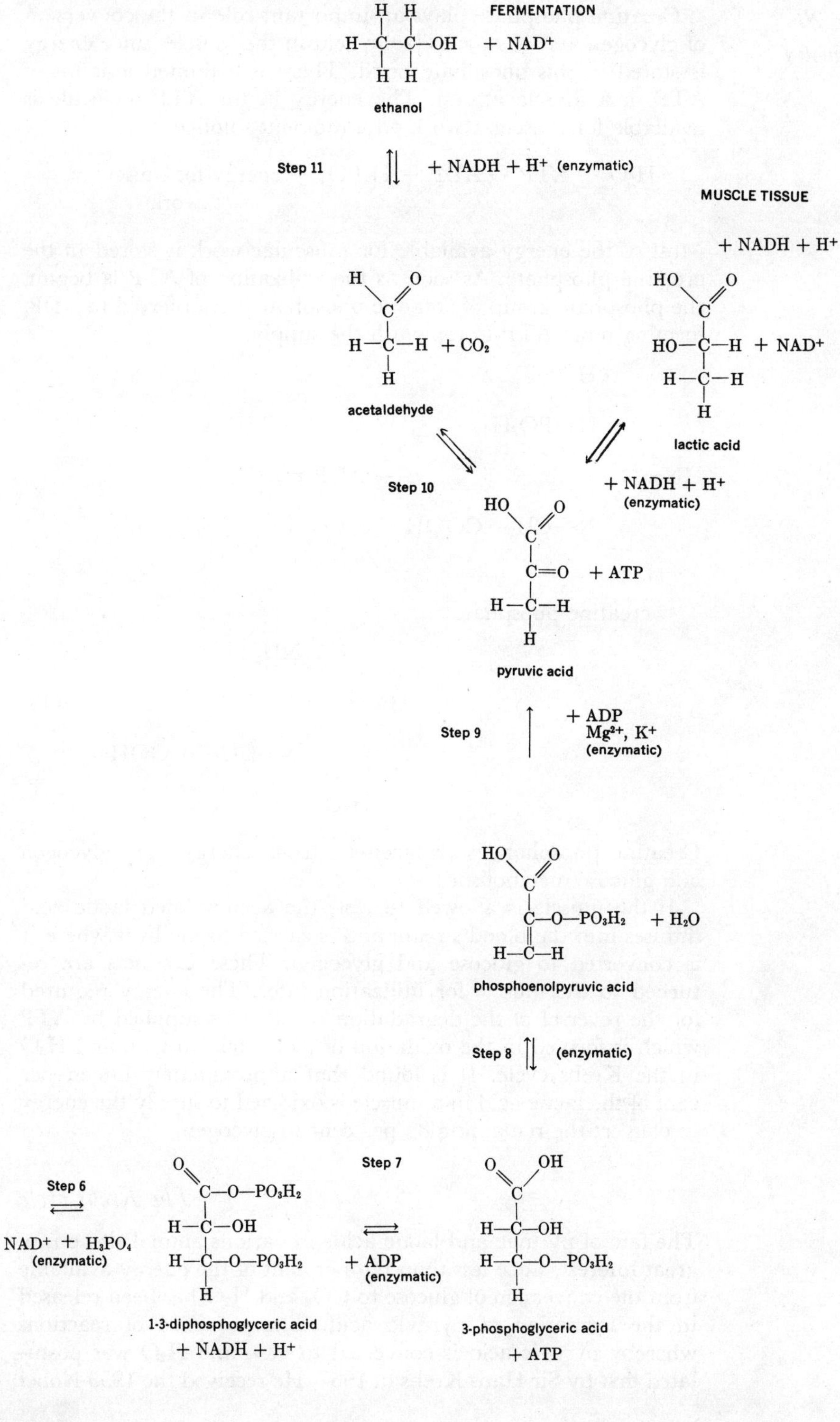

FERMENTATION

$$H-\overset{\overset{\displaystyle H}{|}}{\underset{\underset{\displaystyle H}{|}}{C}}-\overset{\overset{\displaystyle H}{|}}{\underset{\underset{\displaystyle H}{|}}{C}}-OH \quad + NAD^+$$

ethanol

Step 11 ⇅ + NADH + H⁺ (enzymatic)

MUSCLE TISSUE

+ NADH + H⁺

$$H-\overset{\displaystyle O}{\overset{\|}{C}}$$
$$H-\overset{\overset{\displaystyle}{|}}{\underset{\underset{\displaystyle H}{|}}{C}}-H \quad + CO_2$$

acetaldehyde

$$HO-\overset{\displaystyle O}{\overset{\|}{C}}$$
$$HO-\overset{|}{\underset{|}{C}}-H \quad + NAD^+$$
$$H-\overset{|}{\underset{\underset{\displaystyle H}{|}}{C}}-H$$

lactic acid

Step 10

+ NADH + H⁺
(enzymatic)

$$HO-\overset{\displaystyle O}{\overset{\|}{C}}$$
$$\overset{|}{C}=O \quad + ATP$$
$$H-\overset{|}{\underset{\underset{\displaystyle H}{|}}{C}}-H$$

pyruvic acid

Step 9 ↑ + ADP
Mg²⁺, K⁺
(enzymatic)

$$HO-\overset{\displaystyle O}{\overset{\|}{C}}$$
$$\overset{|}{C}-O-PO_3H_2 \quad + H_2O$$
$$H-\overset{|}{\underset{}{C}}-H$$

phosphoenolpyruvic acid

Step 8 ⇅ (enzymatic)

Step 6
⇌

NAD⁺ + H₃PO₄
(enzymatic)

$$\overset{\displaystyle O}{\overset{\|}{C}}-O-PO_3H_2$$
$$H-\overset{|}{\underset{|}{C}}-OH$$
$$H-\overset{|}{\underset{\underset{\displaystyle H}{|}}{C}}-O-PO_3H_2$$

1-3-diphosphoglyceric acid
+ NADH + H⁺

Step 7
⇌

+ ADP
(enzymatic)

$$\overset{\displaystyle O}{\overset{\|}{C}}\overset{\displaystyle OH}{}$$
$$H-\overset{|}{\underset{|}{C}}-OH$$
$$H-\overset{|}{\underset{\underset{\displaystyle H}{|}}{C}}-O-PO_3H_2$$

3-phosphoglyceric acid
+ ATP

Creatine phosphate plays an important role in the conversion of glycogen and glucose to lactic acid in the muscle, since energy is stored in this phosphate bond. There is a limited amount of ATP in a muscle at rest. The energy in the ATP molecule is available for muscular work on a moment's notice.

$$H_2O + ATP \rightarrow ADP + H_3PO_4 + \text{energy for muscular work}$$

Most of the energy available for muscular work is stored in the creatine phosphate. As soon as the utilization of ATP is begun, the phosphate group of creatine phosphate is transferred to ADP, forming more ATP to replenish the supply.

creatine phosphate

Creatine phosphate is replaced by using energy from glycogen and glucose metabolism.

If the muscle is allowed to rest, the accumulated lactic acid diffuses into the blood stream and is carried to the liver where it is converted to glucose and glycogen. These products are returned to the muscle for utilization later. The energy required for the reversal of the degradation reactions is supplied by ATP which is formed in the oxidation of lactic acid to CO_2 and H_2O in the Krebs cycle. It is found that approximately fifteen per cent of the lactic acid in a muscle is oxidized to supply the energy to convert the remaining 85 per cent to glycogen.

The Krebs cycle

The fate of pyruvic and lactic acids in various animal tissue is of great interest, since less than ten per cent of the energy available from the conversion of glucose to CO_2 and H_2O has been released in the formation of pyruvic acid. The sequence of reactions whereby pyruvic acid is converted to CO_2 and H_2O was postulated first by Sir Hans Krebs in 1937. He received the 1953 Nobel prize for his contribution to what he calls the tricarboxylic acid cycle or what many others call the Krebs cycle.

The Krebs cycle shown in Fig. 20.8 does not begin with pyruvic acid but with an acetyl $\left(\begin{array}{c} H_3C{-}C{-} \\ \| \\ O \end{array}\right)$ derivative of coenzyme-A, called acetyl-CoA. The pyruvic acid is converted to acetyl-CoA in a very complex, enzymatically controlled, irreversible reaction which may be represented in a simplified form as

$$
\begin{array}{ccc}
H & O & O \\
| & \| & \| \\
H{-}C{-}C{-}C{-}OH & + & CoA{-}SH & + NAD^+ \rightarrow \\
| \\
H
\end{array}
$$

pyruvic acid   coenzyme-A

$$
\begin{array}{cc}
H & O \\
| & \| \\
H{-}C{-}C{-}S{-}CoA & + NADH + H^+ + CO_2 \\
| \\
H
\end{array}
$$

acetyl-CoA

In Step 1 of the Krebs cycle acetyl-CoA reacts with oxalacetic acid under enzymatic influence to form citric acid and to re-generate coenzyme-A. Oxalacetic acid is regenerated in the previous step of this cyclic process.

In the presence of an enzyme activated by ferrous ions, citric acid is converted to the isomer, isocitric acid, for Step 2. In Step 3 isocitric acid is oxidized to α-ketoglutaric acid in the presence of the coenzyme, NADP$^+$, and the isocitric enzyme.

In Step 4, succinyl-CoA is formed by a reaction very similar (except for the enzyme) to the one that resulted in the formation of acetyl-CoA from pyruvic acid. This is the only irreversible step in the cycle.

Succinyl-CoA reacts with guanosine-5'-diphosphate (GDP) in the presence of phosphoric acid to form the guanosine-5'-triphosphate (GTP), the coenzyme, and succinic acid (Step 5). Very little energy is released in this step since the energy is trapped in the phosphate bond of GTP. This energy is transferred to the ATP molecule when the GDP is re-formed by the reaction of ADP + GTP.

$$ GTP + ADP \rightleftarrows GDP + ATP $$

In Step 6 two hydrogen atoms are enzymatically removed from the succinic acid to form fumaric acid which then reacts with water (Step 7) to form L-malic acid.

In the eighth step L-malic acid is oxidized to oxalacetic acid which is utilized in Step 1 to continue the Krebs cycle with an-

Fig. 20.8

The Krebs Cycle

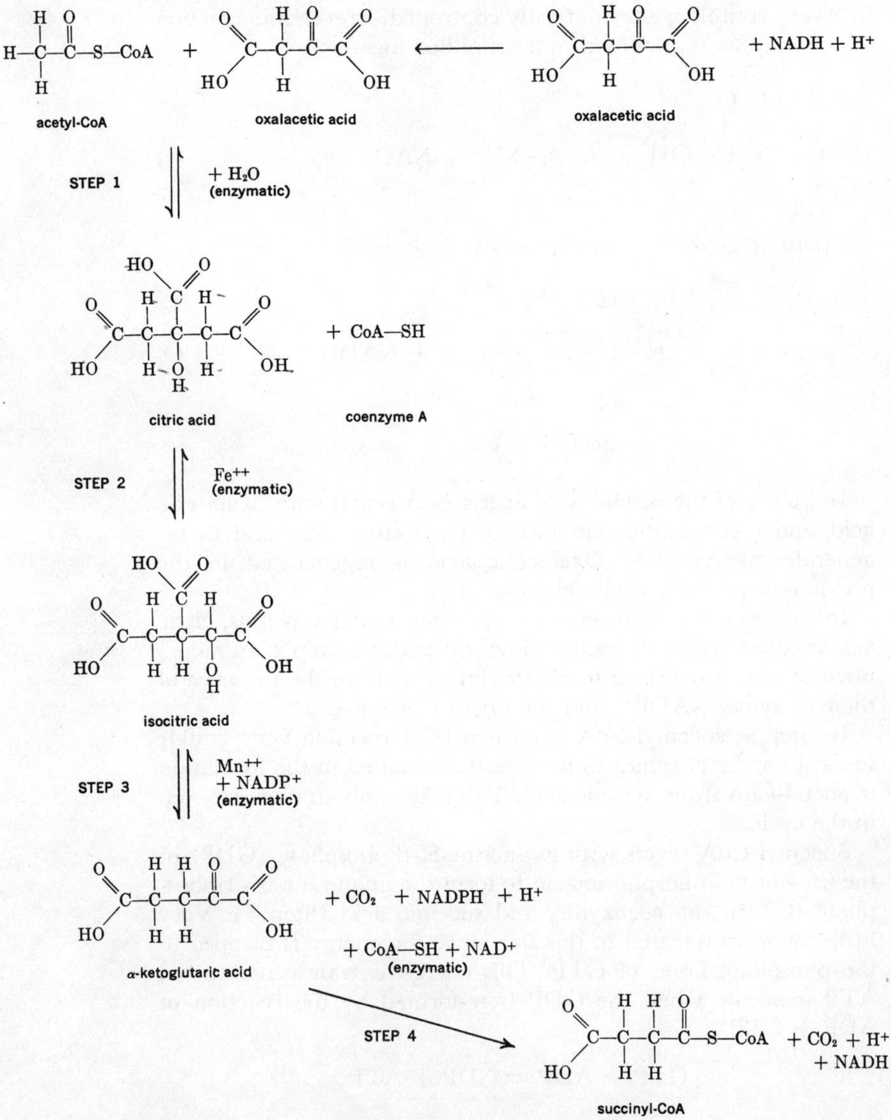

STEP 1 $+ H_2O$ (enzymatic)

STEP 2 Fe^{++} (enzymatic)

STEP 3 Mn^{++} $+ NADP^+$ (enzymatic)

STEP 4

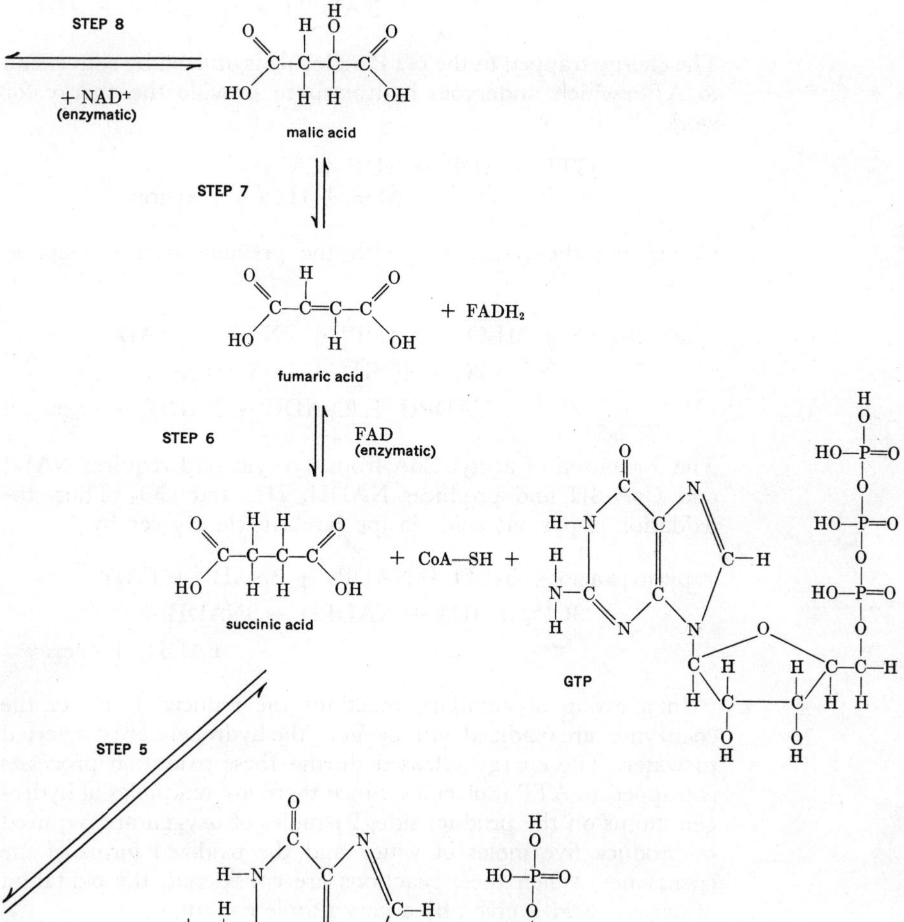

STEP 8

+ NAD⁺
(enzymatic)

malic acid

STEP 7

+ FADH₂

fumaric acid

STEP 6   FAD
(enzymatic)

+ CoA—SH +

succinic acid

GTP

STEP 5

+

GDP   + H₃PO₄

other molecule of acetyl-CoA. The overall reaction of the Krebs cycle (Fig. 20.7) is

$$\text{acetyl-CoA} + 2H_2O + H_3PO_4 + GDP + NADP^+ +$$
$$2NAD^+ + FAD \longrightarrow 2CO_2 + 3H^+ + GTP + CoA\text{-}SH +$$
$$NADPH + 2NADH + FADH_2$$

The energy trapped in the GTP molecule is utilized by conversion to ATP which undergoes hydrolysis to provide the energy for work.

$$GTP + ADP \rightarrow GDP + ATP$$
$$ATP + H_2O \rightarrow ADP + H_3PO_4 + \text{energy}$$

Combining these reactions with the previous overall reaction gives

$$\text{acetyl-CoA} + 3H_2O + NADP^+ + 2NAD^+ + FAD$$
$$\longrightarrow 2CO_2 + 3H^+ + CoA\text{-}SH +$$
$$NADPH + 2NADH + FADH_2 + \text{energy}$$

The formation of acetyl-CoA from pyruvic acid requires NAD^+ and CoA-SH and produces NADH, H^+, and CO_2. Thus, the oxidation of pyruvic acid via the Krebs cycle is given by

$$\text{pyruvic acid} + 3H_2O + NADP^+ + 3NAD^+ + FAD \rightarrow$$
$$3CO_2 + 4H^+ + NADPH + 3NADH +$$
$$FADH_2 + \text{energy}$$

In a group of auxillary reactions the reduced forms of the coenzymes are oxidized with oxygen; the hydrogens are converted to water. The energy released during these oxidation processes is trapped in ATP molecules. Since there are ten moles of hydrogen atoms on the product side, $2\frac{1}{2}$ moles of oxygen are required to produce five moles of water and the oxidized forms of the coenzymes. When these reactions are considered, the oxidation of pyruvic acid is given by a very simple equation.

$$CH_3COCOOH + 2\tfrac{1}{2}O_2 \rightarrow 3CO_2 + 2H_2O + \text{energy}$$

In the anaerobic metabolism of glucose, one mole of glucose yields two moles of pyruvic acid and two moles of water. Thus, the complete oxidation of a mole of glucose produces six moles of CO_2 and six moles of H_2O, as well as energy in various forms.

Many of the intermediates in Krebs cycle serve as starting materials for the synthesis of other substances in the body. For example, acetyl-CoA is converted enzymatically to various fatty acids in several steps. The energy required for the formation of the fatty acid molecule is supplied by a reaction with ATP in one of the steps.

Pentose pathway for glucose oxidation

The predominant pathway for the oxidation of glucose derived from starch is that discussed in the last two sections. Glucose undergoes oxidation in some tissues by the loss of a carbon atom from six molecules, forming six five-carbon sugars (pentoses), CO_2, H_2O, and energy. The six pentose molecules undergo a series of rearrangements to form five molecules of six-carbon sugars. This oxidation loss of a carbon atom from six glucose molecules and subsequent rearrangement of the pentoses produces energy equivalent to oxidation of one glucose molecule.

Lipid metabolism

In the first step of lipid utilization glycerol and fatty acids are formed by hydrolysis. One mode for the oxidation of glycerol is the stepwise conversion to glyceraldehyde-3-phosphate which is metabolized in the manner discussed above. The fatty acids form a fatty acid–coenzyme-A compound in the presence of ATP and appropriate enzymes. The product undergoes a series of reactions, forming a molecule of acetyl-CoA and a molecule of a new fatty acid–coenzyme-A compound with two less carbon atoms than the original fatty acid. The process is repeated until the entire fatty acid is converted to acetyl-CoA which is utilized in the Krebs cycle.

$$\underset{\text{fatty acid}}{R\text{—COOH}} + (CoA\text{—SH}) \xrightarrow[\text{enzyme}]{\text{ATP}} R\text{—}\overset{\overset{\textstyle O}{\|}}{C}\text{—S—CoA} \underset{}{\overset{\text{4 steps}}{\rightleftharpoons}}$$

$$R'\text{—}\overset{\overset{\textstyle O}{\|}}{C}\text{—S—CoA} + \underset{\text{acetyl-CoA}}{CH_3\text{—}\overset{\overset{\textstyle O}{\|}}{C}\text{—S—CoA}}$$

(R′ = radical with two less carbon atoms than R)

Only one molecule of ATP is required to activate a molecule of fatty acid for the complete conversion to acetyl-CoA.

Protein metabolism

Proteins are hydrolyzed to the component amino acids in the digestive process. The amino acids are used to form the proteins and other nitrogen-containing compounds needed by the body. About one half of the amino acids required for the proteins are synthesized in the body. The other amino acids must be obtained from the diet. If the intake of amino acids is greater than that required by the body for protein synthesis, the excess is metabolized. The carbon portions are converted to some component of the Krebs cycle such as acetyl-CoA, oxalocetic acid, and α-ketoglutaric acid, and utilized in that sequence of reactions.

The nitrogen cycle

The atmosphere provides an essentially unlimited reservoir of free nitrogen which cannot be utilized until it is converted into nitrogen-containing molecules by a process called nitrogen fixation. The usual form of fixed nitrogen is either as the highly oxidized nitrate state which can be utilized only by plants and some microorganisms, or the highly reduced ammonia state. The non-biological nitrogen fixation processes are discussed in Chapter XV.

Nitrogen fixation

Biological fixation of nitrogen is accomplished either by microorganisms that live within the soil or by certain bacteria that live in the nodules on the roots of the legumes (clover, alfalfa, soybeans) and several species of shrubs and trees (the alder). The process whereby the bacteria in the nodules fix the nitrogen is not well understood. One of the early intermediate products of the fixation process is thought to be ammonia, which is transformed rapidly to amino acids and amides. In turn, these are converted to proteins by enzymes in the cells. The ammonia concentration must be kept on a minute level because of its great toxicity. When bacteria or higher plants die, the amino acids and proteins decompose and ammonia is returned to the soil.

Although ammonia, or the ammonium ion, is the usual form for the addition of nitrogen to the soil, very little of it is found there. It is oxidized very readily by the soil bacteria to the nitrite ion (NO_2^-) or the nitrate ion (NO_3^-). Plants utilize nitrate after enzymatically reducing it to the ammonium ion, then incorporating the nitrogen into amino acids. A few plants accumulate nitrate ions in the tissues and as a result are toxic to livestock.

Nitrogen utilization

Animals depend upon plants for their nitrogen supply. Higher animals hydrolyze the complex molecules found in the plants into smaller molecules by the process called digestion. Small molecules are absorbed readily and utilized by the body tissues. The digestive process in man begins in the mouth where starch is hydrolyzed. This process is seldom completed, since food is retained in the mouth for only a short period. In the acid conditions of the stomach (pH of 1 to 2), the enzyme pepsin causes the rupture of many peptide bonds in the proteins. Digestion is completed in the small intestine where the conditions are sufficiently alkaline to neutralize the material entering from the stomach. The pancreas secretes several enzymes which catalyze the hydrolysis of all of the major complex molecules. The process is completed by enzyme catalyzed reactions in the lining of the intestine. Absorption of the amino acids and simple sugar molecules (e.g., glucose) takes place through the walls of the small intestine. The blood carries these materials to the cells throughout the body for metabolism of the sugars and for synthesis of proteins and nitrogen-containing compounds from the amino acids.

During metabolism the body converts the carbon atoms to CO_2, the hydrogen atoms to H_2O, and nitrogen atoms to urea. Amino groups are released (or removed) during the oxidation of amino acids and converted to urea.

There are three major modes of nitrogen excretion by animals. Marine animals generally excrete nitrogen wastes directly as ammonia, since there is sufficient water available to dilute the toxic ammonia very rapidly. Land animals no longer have sufficient water available to dilute the ammonia. Since ammonia is toxic, it cannot be accumulated in the tissues but must be converted to some non-toxic form. Animals whose embryos develop in close contact with the circulatory system of the mother convert

$$H_2N-\underset{\underset{O}{\|}}{C}-NH_2$$

the ammonia into urea, . The rather soluble urea is removed from the embryo by the mother's circulatory system. The urea is removed from the blood by the kidneys and excreted in the urine. It is not possible for an embryo that develops in a hard shell egg to excrete the urea from the system and its concentration would become fatal. Such animals, as well as land-dwelling reptiles, convert ammonia to uric acid.

$$
\begin{array}{c}
\overset{O}{\underset{\|}{}} \quad \overset{H}{\underset{|}{}} \\
C \qquad N \\
\diagup \quad \diagdown \quad \diagup \quad \diagdown \\
H-N \qquad C \qquad \quad C{=}O \\
| \qquad \quad \| \qquad \diagup \\
O{=}C \qquad C \\
\diagdown \qquad \diagup \\
N \qquad N \\
| \qquad | \\
H \qquad H
\end{array}
$$

The insoluble uric acid precipitates, thereby avoiding the toxicity of either ammonia or urea. Adult animals continue to use this mode of excretion.

Photosynthesis

Living organisms obtain their energy by converting foodstuffs to more stable, lower energy compounds. The supply of food and energy would have been exhausted long ago if it were not for the process of photosynthesis.

The overall photosynthesis process is essentially the reverse of the oxidation of foodstuffs. This conversion of CO_2 and H_2O to the carbohydrates requires the addition of energy. The sun is the source of this energy. Photosynthesis is carried out in plant tissues where light is absorbed by the chlorophyll pigments in the leaves. These pigments are capable of converting light energy into chemical energy. It appears that upon absorption of light, electrons in the chlorophyll molecules are excited to some higher energy level. The excited molecules have the capability to reduce substances such as NAD^+ and $NADP^+$ in the presence of water.

$$2NADP^+ + 2H_2O \xrightarrow[\text{chlorophyll}]{\text{light}} 2NADPH + 2H^+ + O_2$$

Hydrogen in the reduced form of the coenzyme is available for the reduction steps in the various synthesis reactions in the plant. The energy released by this oxidation is trapped in ATP molecules. This trapped energy is available to drive the synthesis reactions. Although there are several intermediate compounds between CO_2 and the carbohydrate products, the overall photosynthesis reaction often is written as

$$CO_2 + H_2O \xrightarrow{\text{light}} C(H_2O) + O_2$$

where $C(H_2O)$ represents the carbohydrate.

DNA and RNA

The synthesis of a large protein molecule in which there must be an exact sequence of hundreds of L-amino acid components requires some mechanism whereby each amino acid is placed in a specific position in the protein chain. The code for the amino

Fig. 20.9
Structure of Chlorophyll-a

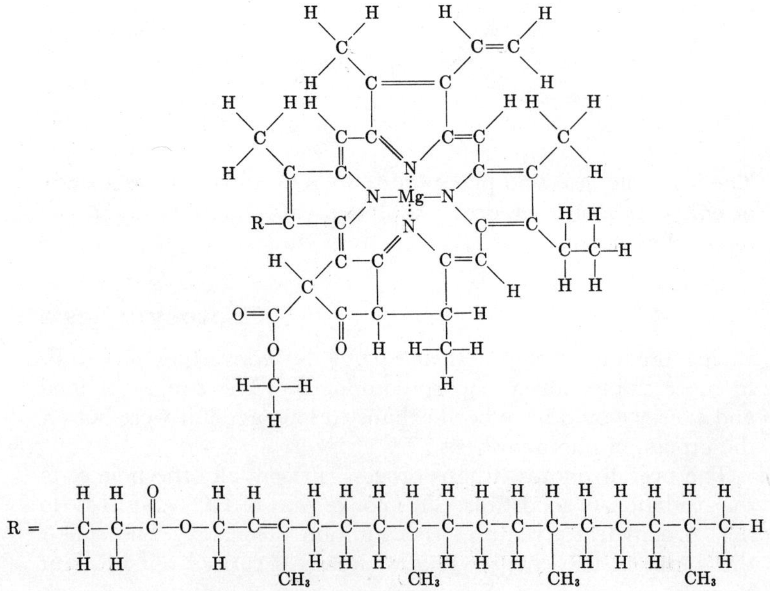

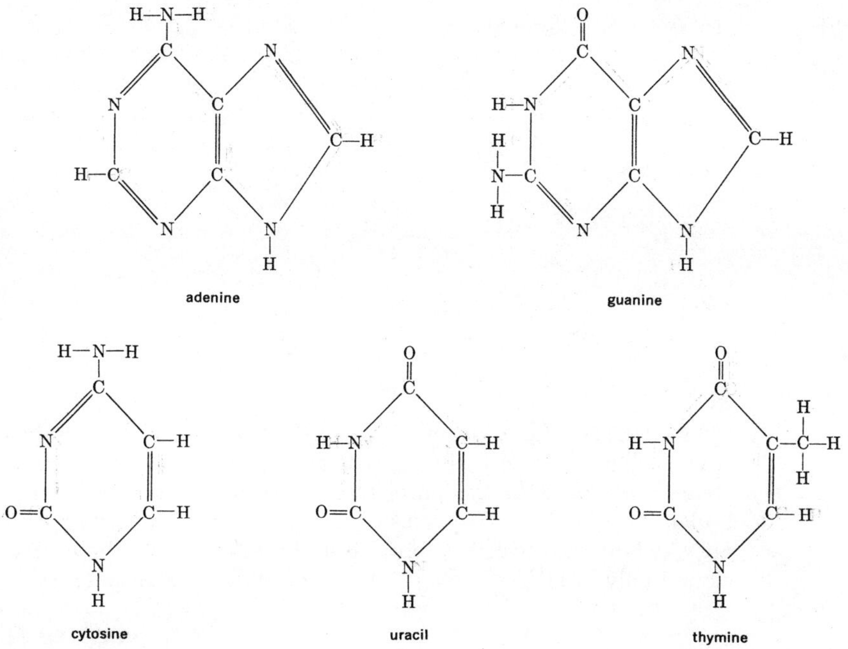

Fig. 20.10

Structure of the Nitrogenous Bases Found in Nucleic Acids

acid sequence in the proteins is carried by the deoxyribonucleic acids (DNA).

Nucleic acids are long chain molecules consisting of sugar residues connected by phosphate bridges. Attached to each sugar residue is a nitrogenous organic base. The five major base components are adenine, guanine, cytosine, thymine, and uracil (Fig. 20.10).

There are two types of nucleic acids, the deoxyribonucleic acids (DNA) and the ribonucleic acids (RNA). The two types have different sugar residues and base groups. The sugar residue in RNA is the cyclic form of D-ribose.

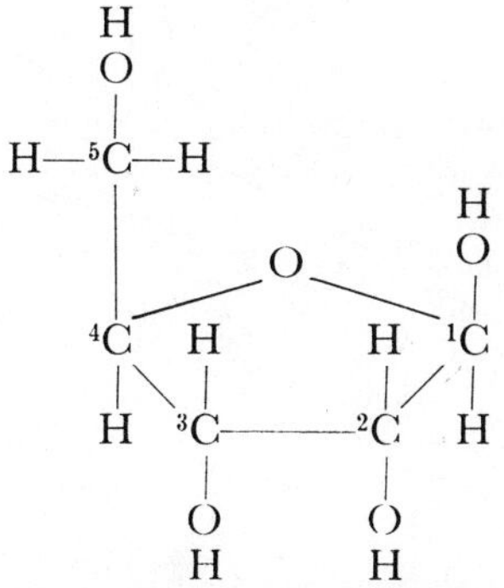

In DNA, it is 2-deoxyribose.

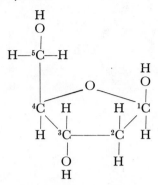

These sugars differ only in that an OH group is on the number two carbon atom in D-ribose; it is absent in 2-deoxyribose. The base is attached to the number one carbon atom of the ring. Adenine, guanine, and cytosine are found in both DNA and RNA; however, uracil is found only in RNA, while thymine is found only in DNA. The only structural difference between these

Fig. 20.11

Structure of DNA

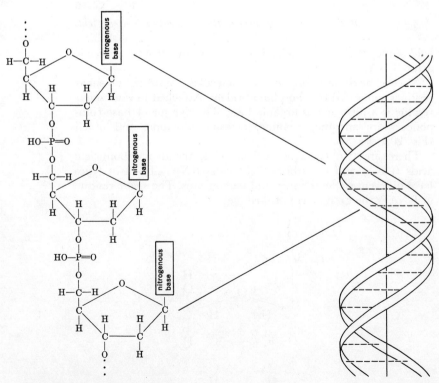

The structural units that make up the DNA helix

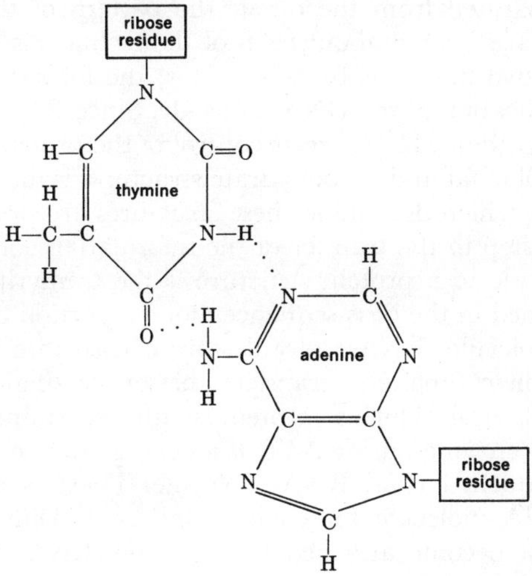

Fig. 20.12

Hydrogen Bonding Between Thymine and Adenine in DNA

two compounds is the presence of a methyl group in thymine which is not found in uracil.

DNA molecules consist of two parallel chains wound around each other in the form of a helix (Fig. 20.11). The sugar-phosphate chain is outside; the base groups are inside. The two chains are held together by hydrogen bonds between the base groups across the axis of the double helix. The base-to-base bonding is very specific. Thus, the thymine structures on one chain form a pair of hydrogen bonds only with adenine structures on the other chain (Fig. 20.12). Similarly, only the cytosine and guanine structures on the two chains form hydrogen bonds (Fig. 20.13).

Thus, the sequence of the nitrogenous bases on one DNA chain fixes the sequences of these structures on the other chain. If one

Fig. 20.13

Hydrogen Bonding Between Guanine and Cytosine in DNA

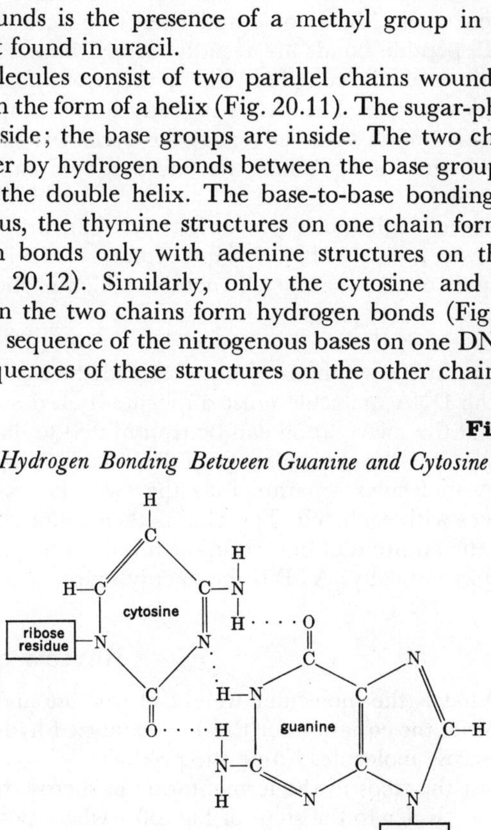

chain is separated from the other, the pattern of the two new chains that are formed about each of these chains is fixed. DNA carries out two functions by this means, the formation of RNA and the replication of the DNA molecule. Since RNA is involved in protein synthesis, DNA exerts control of the protein structures. DNA control of fat and carbohydrate structures is indirect in that the enzymes which determine these structures are proteins.

The first step in the transfer of the information contained in a DNA molecule to a protein structure is the transcription of the code contained in the base sequence along a portion of a DNA to an RNA molecule. RNA molecules are classed into four groups based on their function: transfer, messenger, high molecular weight, and viral. During protein synthesis, amino acids are activated by enzymes, using ATP as an energy source. The amino acids are attached to a *t*RNA molecule. There is at least one unique *t*RNA molecule for each amino acid. Different amino acids do not become attached to the same *t*RNA. The *t*RNA-amino acid complex moves to the surface of the ribosomes, a portion of the cell. Here *m*RNA, which has moved away from its DNA template, causes *t*RNA-amino acid complexes to line up in the order coded into it by the DNA structure. In the presence of enzymes, Mg^{++} ions, and energy sources such as ATP and GTP, peptide bonds are rapidly formed between the amino acid portions of the complex. Then, the newly formed protein and *t*RNA separate. The *t*RNA is ready to be complexed again with specific amino acids to repeat the cycle. New *m*RNA must be formed, since *m*RNA loses its informational capability after one synthesis.

The role of high molecular weight RNA in protein synthesis is not known; it is probably very important, since it is found as an integral part of all ribosomes, structures which participate in the synthesis of cellular protein.

In addition to the information coded into the DNA molecule that results in the synthesis of proteins and their subsequent behavior, the DNA molecule must duplicate itself during cell division so that the information can be transmitted to daughter cells. DNA is found in the chromosomes of the cells. During cell division the DNA molecules separate into the two chains. One set of chains goes with each cell. The chains then re-form DNA molecules by the addition of one group at a time. The process is controlled enzymatically; ATP is the energy source.

Review questions

20.1. What is the molecular weight of fructose and of glucose?

20.2. Write the equation for the acid catalyzed hydrolysis of the sucrose molecule. Name the products.

20.3. List the steps in the fermentation of sucrose to form alcohol. (Refer to the steps of Fig. 20.7 where possible.)

20.4. How many moles of CO_2 and ethanol are produced from

SIGNIFICANT TERMS AND CONCEPTS IN CHAPTER XX:
Carbohydrate, saccharide, optical isomerism, D- *and* L-*forms, glucose, fructose, Fischer and Haworth structures, starch, glycogen, cellulose, lipids, proteins, enzyme, vitamin, hormone, coenzyme, ATP, ADP, the role of ATP in the utilization of energy; anaerobic metabolism, creatine phosphate, Krebs cycle, GTP, lipid metabolism; nitrogen cycle, nitrogen excretion, photosynthesis; DNA, RNA, role of RNA and DNA in protein synthesis.*

the fermentation of one mole of glucose?

20.5. How many moles of ATP are used as a reactant in the fermentation of one mole of glucose? How many moles of ATP are produced?

20.6. How many moles of NAD^+ and NADH are formed in the fermentation of one mole of glucose? How many moles of each are used?

20.7. Write the overall equation for the conversion of glucose to lactic acid.

20.8. How many moles of ATP are used as reactants in the formation of lactic acid from one mole of glucose? How many moles are produced?

20.9. One technique for the determination of balance in biochemical reactions is to count carbon atoms. With reference to the Krebs cycle (Fig. 20.8):
   (a) How many carbon atoms are involved in Step 1?
   (b) How many carbon atoms are produced in Step 8?
   (c) At what point and in what form are the carbon atoms lost?

20.10. Write the overall equation for the complete metabolism of glycine in man and in a typical fish.

20.11. What is the molecular weight of the following compounds?
   (a) ATP
   (b) D-ribose
   (c) Adenine
   (d) Uric acid
   (e) Oxalacetic acid

20.12. What structural features distinguish between the compounds in each of the following pairs?
   (a) D-ribose and 2-deoxyribose
   (b) D-ribose and cyclic β-fructose
   (c) ATP and GTP
   (d) Adenine and guanine
   (e) Uracil and uric acid
   (f) Adenine and uric acid
   (g) Uracil and cytosine
   (h) Cyclic α-D-glucose and cyclic β-fructose
   (i) Succinyl-CoA and acetyl-CoA

   answer: (a) D-ribose has an OH group on carbon atom number 2, while 2-deoxyribose has an H atom.

20.13. Most of the complex molecules encountered in this chapter are composed of portions (residues) of simpler substances. What residues make up the following molecules?

(a) ATP   (b) GDP   (c) DNA   (d) RNA

answer: (d) D-ribose, phosphate, adenine, guanine, cytosine, uracil.

20.14. If the bases along one strand of DNA are arranged adenine-guanine-cytosine-thymine, what is the arrangement of the bases in the complementary stand?

appendices

Appendix I
A review of mathematical principles
Factor-unit method

The factor-unit approach to problem solving eliminates reliance on memorizing formulas, and on a purely mechanical approach to problem solving. There are two prerequisites to the solution of any problem with the factor-unit method. One is the ability to read and understand the question. The other is a knowledge of the principles to be applied. Many students attempt to use every item of information given in the problem, an approach that often proves fallacious. Other fallacies include the tendency to try one formula or equation when two or three steps are needed, and failure to recall relationships set forth in the text material (often in a previous chapter). If the arithmetic procedures are carried out using the units as well as the numbers, the necessary conversion factors will be determined by a little logic, and often an erroneous final answer will be discovered. For example, if length is called for in the problem, the answer should have units of centimeters rather than something such as ml/sec.

Example I: (Problem 1.7 j) 2.5 ft = _____ mm.

Very few people remember the number of millimeters in a foot. More likely, the relationship, 1 in = 2.54 cm, is the one committed to memory. Thus, one converts feet to inches, then to centimeters, and finally to millimeters. The question of multiplication or division by the conversion factors is answered by the cancellation of units.

$$mm = (2.5\,ft)\left(\frac{12\ in}{1\ ft}\right)\left(\frac{2.54\ cm}{1\ in}\right)\left(\frac{10\ mm}{1\ cm}\right)$$

$$= 762\ mm = 7.6 \times 10^2\ mm.$$

Other examples of the use of the factor-unit method are found in the examples worked in the text.

Exponential numbers

Arithmetical operations are simplified by the use of exponential numbers. Since our number system is based on the use of the ten digits (0,1,2,3,4,5,6,7,8,9), any number can be expressed conveniently as a power of 10. Thus, 100 is expressed as 10^2 since $10 \times 10 = 100$.

Likewise,

$$1000 = 10 \times 10 \times 10 = 10^3$$
$$1,000,000,000 = 10^9$$
$$10^5 = 100,000$$
$$10^1 = 10.$$

Note that the exponent represents the number of zeros in the number. Thus, $10^0 = 1$.

The value of a number between 0 and 1 is expressed as a negative power of 10. For example, $0.1 = 1/10^1 = 10^{-1}$. A negative exponent indicates that 10 raised to the same (positive) power is in the denominator. Thus,

$$10^{-2} = 1/10^2 = 1/100 = 0.01$$
$$10^{-3} = 1/10^3 = 1/1000 = 0.001$$
$$10^{-6} = 1/10^6 = 1/1,000,000 = 0.000\ 001.$$

An exponential number is a number multiplied by 10 raised to some power. For example,

$$328 = 3.28 \times 100 \quad = 3.28 \times 10^2$$
$$1440 = 1.44 \times 1000 = 1.44 \times 10^3$$
$$12.8 = 1.28 \times 10 \quad = 1.28 \times 10^1$$
$$6.11 = 6.11 \times 1 \quad = 6.11 \times 10^0.$$

The exponent of 10 indicates the number of places the decimal point has been moved to the left in expressing the exponential form. A negative exponent indicates that the decimal point has been moved to the right.

$$0.0032 = 3.2 \times 0.001 = 3.2 \times (1/1000) = 3.2 \times 10^{-3.}$$
$$0.0265 = 2.65 \times 0.01 = 2.65 \times (1/100) = 2.65 \times 10^{-2}$$
$$0.000\ 000\ 005\ 2 = 5.2 \times 10^{-9}.$$

When adding or subtracting exponential numbers, all of the terms must be converted to the same power of 10. The digits are added or subtracted as usual. The uniform power of 10 is used in the answer. In the sum

$$(4.2 \times 10^2) + (3.501 \times 10^4) + (5.11 \times 10^3)$$

several choices for the power of 10 are possible. If 10^3 is chosen as the exponential form, the terms are rewritten as follows.

$$4.2 \quad \times 10^2 = \quad 0.42 \times 10^3$$
$$3.501 \times 10^4 = 35.01 \times 10^3$$
$$5.11 \quad \times 10^3 = \quad 5.11 \times 10^3$$

The sum is $40.54 \times 10^3 = 4.054 \times 10^4.$

Alternatively, 10^4 may be chosen as the exponential form.

$$4.2 \quad \times 10^2 = 0.042 \times 10^4$$
$$3.501 \times 10^4 = 3.501 \times 10^4$$
$$5.11 \quad \times 10^3 = 0.511 \times 10^4$$
$$4.054 \times 10^4$$

In the subtraction of 2.2×10^{-3} from 6.75×10^{-2} a conversion to 10^{-2} or 10^{-3} may be made.

$$6.75 \times 10^{-2} = \quad 6.75 \times 10^{-2} = \quad 67.5 \times 10^{-3}$$
$$-2.2 \times 10^{-3} = -0.22 \times 10^{-2} = \quad -2.2 \times 10^{-3}$$

The difference is $\quad 6.53 \times 10^{-2} = \quad 65.3 \times 10^{-3}$

When multiplying exponentials the digits are multiplied as usual and the powers of 10 are added.

$$(2 \times 10^2)(4 \times 10^6) = (2)(4) \times 10^{2+6} = 8 \times 10^8.$$
$$(1.6 \times 10^2)(8.3 \times 10^3)(2.2 \times 10^1) = (1.6)(8.3)(2.2) \times 10^{2+3+1}$$
$$= 29 \times 10^6 = 2.9 \times 10^7.$$
$$(7.2 \times 10^{-1})(2.5 \times 10^{-3})(6.0 \times 10^2) = (7.2)(2.5)(6.0) \times 10^{-1-3+2}$$
$$= 108 \times 10^{-2} = 1.08.$$

When division is carried out, the digits are divided conventionally; while the power of 10 of the divisor (denominator) is subtracted from the power of 10 of the dividend (numerator).

$$\frac{2 \times 10^2}{4 \times 10^6} = \frac{2}{4} \times 10^{2-6} = 0.5 \times 10^{-4} = 5 \times 10^{-5}.$$

$$\frac{1.8 \times 10^{-3}}{4.5 \times 10^5} = \frac{1.8}{4.5} \times 10^{-3-5} = 0.40 \times 10^{-8} = 4.0 \times 10^{-9}.$$

$$\frac{4.8 \times 10^2}{4.0 \times 10^{-3}} = 1.2 \times 10^{2-(-3)} = 1.2 \times 10^5.$$

Significant figures

Meaningless digits are often produced while carrying out mathematical operations. The number of significant digits in an answer is determined by the least precise number used in making the calculations. The last digit written down from an experimental measurement is the one in which there is some uncertainty unless a greater uncertainty is indicated. E.g., when using a balance capable of weighing to 0.1 mg, a sample weight of 0.6253 g represents an actual weight between 0.62525 g and 0.62535 g. A fifth digit, as in 0.62532 g, is not significant in this case, since there is already a degree of uncertainty in the fourth digit.

The significance of a zero depends upon its placement with respect to the decimal point. A zero placed after some other digit to the right of the decimal point is significant. For example, there are 5 significant figures in each of the numbers: 0.62530, 625.30, and 6253.0. Zeros placed between the decimal point and the first digit in a number smaller than one are never significant but serve only to locate the decimal point. Thus, there are only two significant figures in 0.10, 0.010, and 0.00000010. Zeros to the left of the decimal point may or may not be significant in numbers greater than 10. If digits appear to the right of the decimal point when expressing a number greater than one, all of the digits, including the zeros, are significant.

It is possible to indicate clearly the number of significant digits in an expression such as 7500 by the use of the exponential notation. Two significant figures are indicated by 7.5×10^3 or 75×10^2; three significant figures by 7.50×10^3 or 75.0×10^2; and four significant figures by 7.500×10^3, 75.00×10^2, or 750.0×10^1.

There are two significant digits in the expressions 0.0024 and 0.25; three in the expressions 02.01, 0.0610, 6.02×10^{23}, and 602×10^{21}; and five in the expressions 2630.0, 100.00, and 1.0000×10^{-8}.

The following rules are to be observed with respect to the number of significant digits when carrying out mathematical operations:

(a) In multiplication or division there are no more significant figures in the product or quotient than in the term with the smallest number of significant figures.

e.g.: $(6526)(26)(388) = 6.6 \times 10^7$. (Only two figures are significant.)

(b) In addition or subtraction there are no more decimal places in the sum or difference than there are in the term with the smallest number of decimal places. All terms must be expressed in the same power of 10.

e.g.: $12.46 + 0.0085 + 161. = 173.$

Example II: (Problem 1.12a) A 400 mg film of metal measuring 3.52 cm by 9.25 cm has a thickness of 5×10^{-3} mm.

(a) What is the volume of the film in cubic centimeters?

$$V. = 3.52 \text{ cm} \times 9.25 \text{ cm} \times (5 \times 10^{-3} \text{ mm})\left(\frac{100 \text{ cm}}{1000 \text{ mm}}\right)$$

$$= 163 \times 10^{-4} = 2 \times 10^{-2} \text{ cm}^3.$$

There is only one significant digit in the answer, since the thickness is measured to only one digit.

Common logarithms of numbers

The quantitative expression of many properties of matter is in terms of a logarithmic function. Also, it is often easier to use logarithms of numbers to carry out arithmetical operations such as multiplication, division, and the extraction of a root of a number, than it is to calculate with the original numbers.

A common logarithm is that power of 10 which expresses a particular number. A number that is an integral power of 10 such as 100 is easy to represent in logarithmic form. Since 100 is 10 raised to the 2nd power, $\log 100 = 2.0000$. Similarly, $\log 1000 = 3.0000$ and $\log 0.01 = -2.0000$.

It is necessary to utilize a table of logarithms to represent the log of a number between integral powers of 10. Such a table is given inside the back cover. The value of the logarithm depends only upon the sequence of the digits in the number. This is easily seen from a property of logarithms and from the use of the exponential notation. The number 725 may be expressed as 7.25×10^2. The logarithm of this number becomes

$$\log (7.25 \times 10^2) = \log 7.25 + \log 10^2.$$

The value of the log 7.25 is independent of the value of the exponent of 10. To find the value of log 7.25 from the table follow the left-hand column down to 72 and then go into the body of the table to the column headed by 5. At this point, one should find the number 8603. Since 7.25 is between 1 and 10, the value of the log must be between 0 and 1, or 0.8603. Thus,

$$\log 7.25 = \log 7.25 + \log 10^2 = 0.8603 + 2.0000 = 2.8603.$$

Likewise,

$$\log (8.72 \times 10^5) = 5.9405,$$
$$\log 2970 = 3.4728,$$
$$\log 297{,}000 = 5.4728.$$

A logarithm is made up of two parts: the *characteristic*, the number to the left of the decimal point, and the *mantissa*, the number to the right of the decimal point. In the above case, where log 725 = 2.8603, the characteristic is 2 and the mantissa is 8603. The log table lists only those mantissa values which depend solely upon the order of the digits. The characteristic may be obtained by taking one less than the number of digits to the left of the decimal point.

The same principles may be applied to logarithms of numbers less than one. For example, log 0.075 is

$$\log (7.25 \times 10^{-2}) = \log 7.25 + \log 10^{-2}$$
$$= 0.8603 + (-2) = -1.1397.$$

Also,

$$\log (8.53 \times 10^{-4}) = -3.0691,$$
$$\log (8.00 \times 10^{-7}) = -6.0969,$$
$$\log 0.00046 \quad = -3.3372.$$

The logarithm of a four-digit number is obtained by adding a proportional part of the difference between the logarithms of the first three digits and the next higher three-digit number to the logarithm of the smaller three-digit number. For example,

$$\log 7.256 = \log 7.25 + 0.6 \, (\log 7.26 - \log 7.25)$$
$$= 0.8603 + 0.6 \, (0.8609 - 0.8603)$$
$$= 0.8603 + 0.6 \, (0.0006)$$
$$= 0.8603 + 0.00036$$
$$= 0.8607.$$

Similarly,

$$\log 1.168 = 0.0675,$$
$$\log (8.314 \times 10^3) = 3.9198,$$
$$\log (8.314 \times 10^{-3}) = -2.0802,$$
$$\log (1.993 \times 10^{-5}) = -4.7004.$$

Usually, a four-place table is not used to determine logarithms of numbers with more than four digits.

Antilogarithms

An antilogarithm is the number for which the logarithm is given. The antilog value is determined in a procedure that is the reverse of that used in the determination of the log value. The mantissa value is found in the body of the log table. If the exact value is not found, the value nearest it is used unless a four-digit antilog is desired. In the latter case, the fourth digit is equal to the proportional part of the difference in mantissa values. The first two digits of the antilog are found in the far left column. The third digit is at the top of the column. A decimal point is placed between the first and second digit and the number is multiplied by 10 to the power equal to the value of the characteristic. As an example, consider the antilog of 3.8603. In the log table 8603 is found in the column headed "5" and in the line at "72." The decimal point is placed between 7 and 2 to obtain the antilog value of 7.25×10^3. Similarly,

$$\text{antilog } 2.6865 = 4.86 \times 10^2,$$
$$\text{antilog } 8.9211 = 8.34 \times 10^8,$$
$$\text{antilog } 1.6105 = 4.08 \times 10^1 = 40.8,$$
$$\text{antilog } 0.0508 = 1.12 \times 10^0 = 1.12.$$

Since only positive values of the mantissa are found in the log table, a slightly different procedure must be followed for determining the antilog of a negative logarithm. Recall that a negative log value is obtained by the addition of the positive log of a number to a negative exponent of 10. This process is reversed in the determination of the antilog of a negative number. First, the mantissa is subtracted from 1.0000 to obtain a positive mantissa value for use with the log table. After determining the appropriate set of digits, place the decimal point between the first and second digits and multiply by a power of 10 that is one less than the value of the characteristic. The procedure is illustrated by the evaluation of the antilog of -4.2854.

Step 1: Subtract 0.2854 from 1.0000. (1.0000 − 0.2854 = 0.7146.)

Step 2: Find the antilog of 0.7146 from the log table. (antilog 0.7146 = 518.)

Step 3: Place the decimal point between the first and second digits. (5.18.)

Step 4: Multiply by a power of 10 one less than the characteristic. (characteristic = −4. Multiply by 10^{-5}.)

The answer is: antilog $-4.2854 = 5.18 \times 10^{-5}$.

Repeating these steps for the antilog of -1.2816,

$$1.0000 - 0.2816 = 0.7184,$$
$$\text{antilog } 0.7184 = 5.23,$$
$$\text{multiply by } 10^{-1-1} = 10^{-2}.$$

Answer: antilog $-1.2816 = 5.23 \times 10^{-2}$.

Similarly,
$$\text{antilog } -2.1654 = 6.83 \times 10^{-3},$$
$$\text{antilog } -8.2968 = 5.05 \times 10^{-9},$$
$$\text{antilog } -1.9548 = 1.11 \times 10^{-2},$$
$$\text{antilog } -0.8211 = 0.151.$$

Applications of logarithms and antilogarithms

Logarithms are particularly useful in the multiplication and division of numbers. When two numbers are multiplied, their logarithms are added to obtain the logarithm of the product. When two numbers are to be divided, the logarithm of the divisor is subtracted from the logarithm of the dividend for the logarithm of the quotient.

The product $(2.303)(6.28)(1.987)$ is obtained by taking the sum of the logarithms of each term.

$$\begin{aligned} \log \text{ product} &= \log 2.303 + \log 6.28 + \log 1.987 \\ &= 0.3623 + 0.7980 + 0.2983 \\ &= 1.4586. \\ \text{product} &= \text{antilog } 1.4586 = 2.87 \times 10^1 = 28.7. \end{aligned}$$

The product $(28.9)(2.95 \times 10^5)(4.28 \times 10^{-3})$ is evaluated in the same way.

$$\begin{aligned} \log \text{ product} &= \log 28.9 + \log (2.95 \times 10^5) + \log (4.28 \times 10^{-3}) \\ &= 1.4609 + 5.4698 + (-2.3686) \\ &= 4.5621. \\ \text{product} &= \text{antilog } 4.5621 = 3.65 \times 10^4. \end{aligned}$$

To evaluate $(4.26 \times 10^2)/3.29$, $\log 3.29$ is subtracted from $\log (4.26 \times 10^2)$.

$$\begin{aligned} \log \text{ quotient} &= \log (4.26 \times 10^2) - \log 3.29 \\ &= 2.6294 - (0.5172) \\ &= 2.1122. \\ \text{quotient} &= \text{antilog } 2.1122 = 1.29 \times 10^2. \end{aligned}$$

Similarly, the evaluation of $(8.52 \times 10^{-5})/(5.20 \times 10^{-8})$ is

$$\begin{aligned} \log \text{ quotient} &= \log (8.52 \times 10^{-5}) - \log (5.20 \times 10^{-8}) \\ &= -4.0696 - (-7.2840) \\ &= 3.2144. \\ \text{quotient} &= \text{antilog } 3.2144 = 1.64 \times 10^3. \end{aligned}$$

Multiplication and division are combined in

$$(6.21)(4.75 \times 10^5)/(7.21 \times 10^{-3}).$$

$$\begin{aligned} \log \text{ answer} &= \log 6.21 + \log (4.75 \times 10^5) - \log (7.21 \times 10^{-3}) \\ &= 0.7931 + 5.6767 - (-2.1421) \\ &= 8.6119. \\ \text{answer} &= \text{antilog } 8.6119 = 4.09 \times 10^8. \end{aligned}$$

Logarithms also are used in the taking of roots of numbers and in the raising of numbers to a given power. The raising of a number to a power is the repeated multiplication of the number by itself. Thus, $(6.75)^4$ represents $(6.75)(6.75)(6.75)(6.75)$. The arithmetic operations are carried out by the multiplication of the logarithm of the number by the power to which it is being raised. In this example,

$$\log (6.75)^4 = 4 \times \log 6.75$$

$$= 4 \times (0.8293)$$
$$= 3.3172.$$
$$(6.75)^4 = \text{antilog } 3.3172 = 2.08 \times 10^3.$$

The taking of a root of a number may be expressed in two ways. For example, the fourth root of 6.75 is represented as $\sqrt[4]{6.75}$ or $(6.75)^{1/4}$. The second form indicates an analogy to the raising of a number to a power. The fourth root of 6.75 is determined in a similar manner.

$$\log (6.75)^{1/4} = \tfrac{1}{4}(\log 6.75)$$
$$= \tfrac{1}{4}(0.8293)$$
$$= 0.2073.$$
$$\sqrt[4]{6.75} = \text{antilog } 0.2073 = 1.61$$

The square root of 0.00275 is obtained as follows.

$$\log (0.00275)^{1/2} = \tfrac{1}{2}(\log 0.00275)$$
$$= \tfrac{1}{2}(-2.5607)$$
$$= -1.2803.$$
$$\sqrt{0.00275} = \text{antilog } -1.2803 = 5.24 \times 10^{-2}.$$

Example III: (Problem 3.21) What volume will be occupied by 0.76 grams of F_2 gas at 800°C and 570 torr?

$$V = \frac{(0.76\ g)\left(\dfrac{1\ \text{mole}}{38\ g}\right)\left(0.0820\ \dfrac{l\text{-atm}}{\text{mole-deg}}\right)(1073°\ K)}{(570\ \text{torr})\left(\dfrac{1\ \text{atm}}{760\ \text{torr}}\right)}$$

$$\log V = \log 0.76 - \log 38 + \log 0.0820 +$$
$$\log 1073 - (\log 570 - \log 760)$$

$$= (-0.1192) - (1.5798) + (-1.0862) +$$
$$(3.0306) - (2.7559 - 2.8808)$$

$$= 0.3703.$$
$$V = \text{antilog } 0.3703 = 2.35 = 2.3 \text{ liters.}$$

(Note that only two digits are significant.)

Example IV: (Problem 11.26a) What is the pH . . . in . . . 0.002 N H_2SO_4?

$$pH = -\log [H^+].$$
$$[H^+] = 0.002\ N = 2 \times 10^{-3} \text{ moles per liter.}$$
$$pH = -\log (2 \times 10^{-3}) = -(-2.6990) = 2.7.$$

The following problems provide an opportunity to practice the principles discussed in this appendix.

Problem exercises

I. Express the following numbers in exponential form.

(a) 100	(d) 18500	(g) 6,050,000
(b) 12.0	(e) 235	(h) 0.00765
(c) 0.12	(f) 100200	(i) 0.00000054

II. Express the following as numbers.
(a) 7.45 × 10⁻²   (d) 9.98 × 10⁻³   (g) 9.45 × 10¹
(b) 6.01 × 10⁵   (e) 5.54 × 10⁻¹   (h) 81.1 × 10²
(c) 8.01 × 10¹   (f) 6.28 × 10⁰   (i) 95.2 × 10⁻³

III. Determine the following.
(a) log 90,000   (h) log 90,090   (o) antilog −5.8915
(b) log 0.0008   (i) log 0.001139   (p) antilog −7.0750
(c) log 1.68 × 10⁻²   (j) log 5,322   (q) antilog 0.3008
(d) log 7.89 × 10³   (k) antilog 2.3856   (r) antilog −0.9727
(e) log 0.619   (l) antilog 2.1461   (s) antilog 7.8862
(f) log 9,081,000   (m) antilog 0.1553   (t) antilog −5.7861
(g) log 1.233 × 10⁻⁴   (n) antilog −1.4389

IV. Solve the following problems using logarithms.
(a) (21.57)(0.673)
(b) (825)(3.19 × 10⁻⁴)
(c) (2.63 × 10⁴)(1.54 × 10⁻³)(1.467 × 10⁻¹)
(d) (1.39 × 10¹)(2.359)(4.3 × 10⁻⁴)
(e) (582)/(13.2)
(f) (6.288 × 10²)/(8.95 × 10⁴)
(g) (7.63 × 10⁻²)/(0.833)
(h) 1/(3.03 × 10⁶)
(i) (16.9)(0.263)/(89)(0.0175)
(j) (6.70)(2.94)(4.5 × 10⁻⁴)/(1.73 × 10²)(2.69 × 10³)
(k) (0.759)⁵
(l) (3.70 × 10⁻²)³
(m) (1.937)⁶
(n) (1.83 × 10³)³
(o) (1.07)^(1/2)
(p) (8.20 × 10⁻⁴)^(1/3)
(q) (1 × 10⁻⁴)^(1/6)
(r) (2.109)⁵
(s) (45.8)(4.216)²/(21.5)(42.18)^(1/2)
(t) [(8.46 × 10⁶)/(158)(0.635)²]^(1/3)
(u) [(17.9)(1.03)⁴/(4647)(2.6 × 10³)^(1/4)]⁵
(v) (2.50)^(0.6)
(w) (0.836)^(0.47)(0.0321)^(0.53)

Answers:
I.   (a) 1 × 10², (b) 1.20 × 10¹, (c) 1.2 × 10⁻¹, (d) 1.85 × 10⁴,
      (e) 2.35 × 10², (f) 1.002 × 10⁵, (g) 6.05 × 10⁶, (h) 7.65 ×
      10⁻³, (i) 5.4 × 10⁻⁷.

II.   (a) 0.0745, (b) 601,000, (c) 80.1, (d) 0.00998, (e) 0.554,
      (f) 6.28, (g) 94.5, (h) 8110, (i) 0.0952.

III. (a) 4.9542, (b) −3.0969, (c) −1.7747, (d) 3.8971, (e)
      −0.2083, (f) 6.9581, (g) −3.9091, (h) 4.9546, (i) −2.9435,
      (j) 3.7261, (k) 2.43 × 10², (l) 1.40 × 10², (m) 1.43, (n)
      3.64 × 10⁻², (o) 1.28 × 10⁻⁶, (p) 8.41 × 10⁻⁸, (q) 2.00,
      (r) 0.106, (s) 7.70 × 10⁷, (t) 1.64 × 10⁻⁶.

IV. (a) $1.45 \times 10^1 = 14.5$, (b) $2.63 \times 10^{-1} = 0.263$, (c) $5.94 \times 10^0 = 5.94$, (d) 1.4×10^{-2}, (e) $4.41 \times 10^1 = 44.1$, (f) 7.03×10^{-3}, (g) 9.16×10^{-2}, (h) 3.30×10^{-7}, (i) $2.8 \times 10^0 = 2.8$, (j) 1.9×10^{-8}, (k) 2.52×10^{-1}, (l) 5.06×10^{-5}, (m) $5.280 \times 10^1 = 52.80$, (n) 6.13×10^9, (o) $1.03 \times 10^0 = 1.03$, (p) 9.36×10^{-2}, (q) 2.15×10^{-1}, (r) 4.169×10^1, (s) $5.83 \times 10^0 = 5.83$, (t) $5.10 \times 10^1 = 51.0$, (u) 8.2×10^{-17}, (v) 1.73, (w) $1.49 \times 10^{-1} = 0.149$.

Appendix II
Conversion factors for the metric and
U.S. systems of weights and measures

LENGTH

1 inch (in) = 2.54 centimeters (cm)
1 foot (ft) = 0.3048 meter (m)
1 yard (yd) = 0.9144 meter (m)
1 mile (mi) = 1.6094 kilometers (km)

1 centimeter (cm) = 0.394 inch (in)
1 meter (m) = 39.37 inches (in)
1 kilometer (km) = 0.6214 mile (mi)

1 Angstrom (Å) = 1×10^{-8} centimeter (cm)
1 micron (μ) = 1×10^{-6} meter (m)
1 micron (μ) = 1×10^{-4} centimeter (cm)

MASS

1 ounce (oz) = 28.35 grams (g)
1 troy ounce = 31.10 grams (g)
1 pound (lb) = 453.59 grams (g)
1 short ton = 907 kilograms (kg)

1 gram (g) = 0.0353 ounce (oz)
1 kilogram (kg) = 2.205 pounds (lb)

VOLUME

1 cubic inch (in³) = 16.39 milliliters (ml)
1 gallon (gal) = 3.785 liters (l)
1 ounce (fluid) (fl oz) = 29.57 milliliters (ml)
1 quart (liquid) (qt) = 0.9464 liter (l)
1 tablespoon (Tbs) = 14.79 milliliters (ml)

1 milliliter (ml) = 0.03382 ounce (fluid) (fl oz)
1 liter (l) = 1.0567 quarts (liquid) (qt)

1 milliliter (ml) = 1 cubic centimeter (cc, cm³)

ENERGY

1 British Thermal Unit (Btu) = 252 calories (cal)
1 calorie (cal) = 3.97×10^{-3}
                            British thermal unit (Btu)
1 electron volt (eV) = 3.83×10^{-20} calorie (cal)
1 electron volt (eV) = 23.06 kilocalories per mole
                            (kcal/mole)

PRESSURE

1 atmosphere (atm) =   14.70 pounds per square inch (psi)

1 atmosphere (atm) =   29.92 inches of mercury (in Hg)

1 atmosphere (atm) = 406.8 inches of water (in H_2O)

1 atmosphere (atm) = 760 torr

1 atmosphere (atm) = 1.01×10^7 dynes per square centimeter (dynes/cm²)

1 torr   = 1.32×10^{-3} atmosphere (atm)

Appendix III
Vapor pressure of water

Temperature (°C)	Vapor Pressure (torr)
0	4.6
5	6.5
10	9.2
15	12.8
20	17.5
21	18.6
22	19.8
23	21.1
24	22.4
25	23.8
26	25.2
27	26.7
28	28.4
29	30.0
30	31.8
35	42.2
40	55.3
45	71.9
50	92.5
60	149.4
70	233.7
80	355.1
90	525.8
95	633.9
96	657.6
97	682.1
98	707.3
99	733.2
100	760.0

See Back off Book

Appendix IV
Alphabetical listing of the elements

ELEMENT	SYMBOL	ATOMIC NUMBER	ATOMIC WEIGHT
Actinium	Ac	89	(227)
Aluminum	Al	13	27
Americium	Am	95	(243)
Antimony (Stibium)	Sb	51	122
Argon	Ar	18	40
Arsenic	As	33	75
Astatine	At	85	(210)
Barium	Ba	56	137
Berkelium	Bk	97	(249)
Beryllium	Be	4	9
Bismuth	Bi	83	209
Boron	B	5	10.8
Bromine	Br	35	80
Cadmium	Cd	48	112
Calcium	Ca	20	40
Californium	Cf	98	(251)
Carbon	C	6	12
Cerium	Ce	58	140
Cesium	Cs	55	133
Chlorine	Cl	17	35.5
Chromium	Cr	24	52
Cobalt	Co	27	59
Copper (Cuprum)	Cu	29	63.5
Curium	Cm	96	(247)
Dysprosium	Dy	66	162.5
Einsteinium	Es	99	(254)
Erbium	Er	68	167
Europium	Eu	63	152
Fermium	Fm	100	(253)
Fluorine	F	9	19
Francium	Fr	87	(223)
Gadolinium	Gd	64	157
Gallium	Ga	31	70
Germanium	Ge	32	72.6
Gold (Aurum)	Au	79	197
Hafnium	Hf	72	178.5
Helium	He	2	4
Holmium	Ho	67	165
Hydrogen	H	1	1.008
Indium	In	49	115
Iodine	I	53	127
Iridium	Ir	77	192
Iron (Ferrum)	Fe	26	56
Krypton	Kr	36	84
Lanthanum	La	57	139
Lawrencium	Lw	103	(257)

ELEMENT	SYMBOL	ATOMIC NUMBER	ATOMIC WEIGHT
Lead (Plumbum)	Pb	82	207
Lithium	Li	3	7
Lutetium	Lu	71	175
Magnesium	Mg	12	24
Manganese	Mn	25	55
Mendelevium	Md	101	(256)
Mercury (Hydrargyrum)	Hg	80	200
Molybdenum	Mo	42	96
Neodymium	Nd	60	144
Neon	Ne	10	20
Neptunium	Np	93	(237)
Nickel	Ni	28	59
Niobium	Nb	41	93
Nitrogen	N	7	14
Nobelium	No	102	(254)
Osmium	Os	76	190
Oxygen	O	8	16
Palladium	Pd	46	106
Phosphorus	P	15	31
Platinum	Pt	78	195
Plutonium	Pu	94	(242)
Polonium	Po	84	(210)
Potassium (Kalium)	K	19	39
Praseodymium	Pr	59	141
Promethium	Pm	61	(145)
Protactinium	Pa	91	231
Radium	Ra	88	226
Radon	Rn	86	(222)
Rhenium	Re	75	186
Rhodium	Rh	45	103
Rubidium	Rb	37	85.5
Ruthenium	Ru	44	101
Samarium	Sm	62	150
Scandium	Sc	21	45
Selenium	Se	34	79
Silicon	Si	14	28
Silver (Argentum)	Ag	47	108
Sodium (Natrium)	Na	11	23
Strontium	Sr	38	88
Sulfur	S	16	32
Tantalum	Ta	73	181
Technetium	Tc	43	(99)
Tellurium	Te	52	128
Terbium	Tb	65	159
Thallium	Tl	81	204
Thorium	Th	90	232
Thulium	Tm	69	169
Tin (Stannum)	Sn	50	119

ELEMENT	SYMBOL	ATOMIC NUMBER	ATOMIC WEIGHT
Titanium	Ti	22	48
Tungsten (Wolfram)	W	74	184
Uranium	U	92	238
Vanadium	V	23	51
Xenon	Xe	54	131
Ytterbium	Yb	70	173
Yttrium	Y	39	89
Zinc	Zn	30	65.4
Zirconium	Zr	40	91

index

See P-420

Symbol	Atomic Number	Name	Abundance (Weight %)
Ac	89	Actinium	3×10^{-14}
Ag	47	Silver	1×10^{-5}
Al	13	Aluminum	7.73
Am	95	Americium	
Ar	18	Argon	3.6×10^{-4}
As	33	Arsenic	5×10^{-4}
At	85	Astatine	(4×10^{-23})
Au	79	Gold	5×10^{-7}
B	5	Boron	0.001
Ba	56	Barium	0.040
Be	4	Beryllium	6×10^{-4}
Bi	83	Bismuth	2×10^{-5}
Bk	97	Berkelium	
Br	35	Bromine	2.5×10^{-4}
C	6	Carbon	0.087
Ca	20	Calcium	3.45
Cd	48	Cadmium	1.8×10^{-5}
Ce	58	Cerium	0.004
Cf	98	Californium	
Cl	17	Chlorine	0.14
Cm	96	Curium	
Co	27	Cobalt	0.004
Cr	24	Chromium	0.018
Cs	55	Cesium	3.2×10^{-4}
Cu	29	Copper	0.007
Dy	66	Dysprosium	4.5×10^{-4}
Er	68	Erbium	2.5×10^{-4}
Es	99	Einsteinium	
Eu	63	Europium	1×10^{-4}
F	9	Fluorine	0.072
Fe	26	Iron	4.75
Fm	100	Fermium	
Fr	87	Francium	(7×10^{-23})
Ga	31	Gallium	0.0015
Gd	64	Gadolinium	6.5×10^{-4}
Ge	32	Germanium	7×10^{-4}
H	1	Hydrogen	0.76
He	2	Helium	3×10^{-7}
Hf	72	Hafnium	4.5×10^{-4}
Hg	80	Mercury	5×10^{-5}
Ho	67	Holmium	1.1×10^{-4}
I	53	Iodine	3×10^{-5}
In	49	Indium	1×10^{-5}
Ir	77	Iridium	1×10^{-7}
K	19	Potassium	2.47
Kr	36	Krypton	2×10^{-8}
La	57	Lanthanum	0.0018
Li	3	Lithium	0.0065
Lu	71	Lutetium	7.5×10^{-5}
Lw	103	Lawrencium	
Md	101	Mendelevium	
Mg	12	Magnesium	2.00
Mn	25	Manganese	0.085
Mo	42	Molybdenum	7.5×10^{-4}
N	7	Nitrogen	0.30
Na	11	Sodium	2.74
Nb	41	Niobium	0.002
Nd	60	Neodymium	0.0024
Ne	10	Neon	5×10^{-7}
Ni	28	Nickel	0.010
No	102	Nobelium	
Np	93	Neptunium	(4×10^{-17})
O	8	Oxygen	48.6
Os	76	Osmium	1×10^{-7}
P	15	Phosphorus	0.11
Pa	91	Protactinium	8×10^{-11}
Pb	82	Lead	0.0016
Pd	46	Palladium	1×10^{-6}
Pm	61	Promethium	
Po	84	Polonium	3×10^{-14}
Pr	59	Praseodymium	5.5×10^{-4}
Pt	78	Platinum	5×10^{-7}
Pu	94	Plutonium	(2×10^{-19})
Ra	88	Radium	1.3×10^{-10}
Rb	37	Rubidium	0.028
Re	75	Rhenium	1×10^{-7}
Rh	45	Rhodium	1×10^{-7}
Rn	86	Radon	6×10^{-16}
Ru	44	Ruthenium	1×10^{-7}
S	16	Sulfur	0.048
Sb	51	Antimony	1×10^{-4}
Sc	21	Scandium	5×10^{-4}
Se	34	Selenium	9×10^{-6}
Si	14	Silicon	26.3
Sm	62	Samarium	6.5×10^{-4}
Sn	50	Tin	0.004
Sr	38	Strontium	0.015
Ta	73	Tantalum	2×10^{-4}
Tb	65	Terbium	9×10^{-5}
Tc	43	Technetium	
Te	52	Tellurium	2×10^{-7}
Th	90	Thorium	0.0015
Ti	22	Titanium	0.42
Tl	81	Thallium	3×10^{-5}
Tm	69	Thulium	2×10^{-5}
U	92	Uranium	4×10^{-4}
V	23	Vanadium	0.015
W	74	Tungsten	0.001
Xe	54	Xenon	2.4×10^{-9}
Y	39	Yttrium	0.0028
Yb	70	Ytterbium	2.7×10^{-4}
Zn	30	Zinc	0.008
Zr	40	Zirconium	0.020